"Girls Write Now Unmuted is a powerful collection of truths expressed through the witness of girls of varied backgrounds and experiences. This anthology of writing gives us a glimpse into their stories. We would do ourselves a great service to listen."

    –KHRISTI LAUREN ADAMS, author of *Parable of the Brown Girl*

"To witness hearts and minds coming together to create art is always a magical, precious thing. Girls Write Now does the important work of fostering this creativity by bringing mentor and mentee together, and this beautiful anthology—a showcase of diverse and significant talent—is powerful proof that we need this incredibly important resource now more than ever."

    –KRISTEN ARNETT, author of *Mostly Dead Things* and *With Teeth*

"It's so important to nurture the gift of writing, particularly in young women who are still discovering their voice and place in the world. The stories inside *Girls Write Now Unmuted: The 2021 Anthology* are a chorus of women who have much to say, their collective voice painting a star map, enlarging our universe and lighting the way for others."

    –ADRIENNE BANKERT, national journalist and author of *Your Hidden Superpower: The Kindness That Makes You Unbeatable at Work and Connects You with Anyone*

"Girls Write Now is doing a remarkable service—teaching girls the importance of centering their own voices and stories in a world where so many forces want to see them relegated to the margins."

    –MAISY CARD, author of *These Ghosts Are Family*

"The stories of femme-presenting youth have often been dismissed, which is why Girls Write Now feels more vital than ever. This collection of essays reveals an intimate and important view of the world through the eyes of today's girls and gender-nonconforming youth that will empower the next generation of readers, thinkers, and individuals."

    –LORRAINE CINK, author of *Marvel: Powers of a Girl*

"Girls Write Now shines a light on voices that are too often silenced in our society. This collection is a treasure that grants its readers the honor of discovering unmuted stories of resilience from a generation of outstanding youth."

  –PHYLLISSA DEROZE, health humanities scholar

"*Girls Write Now Unmuted: The 2021 Anthology* is so empowering, I wish I could go back in time and hand a copy to my painfully awkward middle school self. Get a copy for yourself, and one for a young 'future' writer who is ready to drop the qualifier."

  –LAUREN DUCA, author of *How to Start a Revolution: Young People and the Future of American Politics*

"Beyond just creating better writers, Girls Write Now encourages young women to think deeply about themselves, their experiences, the strength and value of their voices. Personal mentorship, space to stretch and grow, this organization reminds us that while writing is a solitary act, the effects our words have on others matter, can make people who have felt invisible, feel less so."

  –JEAN KYOUNG FRAZIER, author of *Pizza Girl*

"In a year full of grief and despair, *Girls Write Now Unmuted: The 2021 Anthology* is a gift. It offers girls the chance to channel their feelings around the pandemic into art—and see other ways forward. For some writers, like Emma Kushnirsky and Robin Messing in 'Pandemic Letters: The Wind or a Leaf Stuck to the Sidewalk,' the project has been a way to process the loss of our old lives and find new reasons for hope. Or for writers such as Althea Collier in her essay 'Spring Sunday,' it's a means to escape to a brighter time and place. Readers will find their own ups and downs from this pandemic year reflected in the work of these talented young writers."

  –MALAKA GHARIB, author of *I Was Their American Dream*

"This anthology introduces writers whose careers I'll be eagerly following. It's filled with circuses, the stinging veracity of being alive and young today, and the gorgeousness of ginkgo trees and cities opening themselves wide to these writers' big imaginations. You'll leave this collection with hope for the future books to come."

  –MEGAN GIDDINGS, author of *Lakewood*

"Girls Write Now embodies my favorite superpower: finding our voices and sharing them with the world. I am so grateful for their work."

  –SARAH MARSHALL, host of *You're Wrong About*

"What a gift it is to have the space and safety to hone one's creative voice. Girls Write Now has kicked open both the doors and windows for girls and youth to continue that journey through the power of writing. *Girls Write Now Unmuted: The 2021 Anthology* is a powerful and significant bridge between creativity and possibility."
   –ALISON MALEE, author of *This Is the Journey*

"Girls Write Now gives me hope for our future and gives young writers what we all would have given our younger selves—space to grow, generous guidance, and the opportunity to flourish unfettered."
   –MIA MERCADO, author of *Weird but Normal*

"Encouraging young women to speak genuinely of their experience is the first step in reminding the world that adolescent girls are pioneers in truth and awareness. Offering mentorship is crucial for reminding the girls of this as well. *Girls Write Now Unmuted: The 2021 Anthology* shows how inspiring this effort is and then delivers."
   –SUSAN MINOT, author of *Why I Don't Write: And Other Stories*

"I wish I was part of Girls Write Now when I was younger, and now I'm so happy to be part of the family, because this is just such an invaluable tool and resource. Thank you for keeping this space for creativity."
   –SEPIDEH MOAFI, actor, singer, writer, producer, humanitarian

"Thank you to Girls Write Now for cultivating these incredible and necessary new voices. This anthology is a breathtaking preview of the next generation of female and nonbinary writers."
   –ALISSA NUTTING, author of *Made for Love*

"The breath of possibility and extraordinary insight of the young voices in this anthology fill me with hope for our future. There is nothing more beautiful—and nothing more crucial—than a young writer given the encouragement of a page and a pen to make room for herself in the world."
   –SAFIYA SINCLAIR, author of the forthcoming memoir *How to Say Babylon*

"At a time when so much feels uncertain about the future, *Girls Write Now Unmuted* is a surge of light and hope. In empowering the next generations' voices, Girls Write Now helps us all imagine being in a world worthy of young people's hopes, dreams, and ambitions."
   –NATALIA SYLVESTER, author of *Running*

GIRLS WRITE NOW UNMUTED

The 2021 Anthology

Girls Write Now
UNMUTED

The 2021 Anthology

Foreword by
ABI DARÉ

Introduction by
ROBYN CRAWFORD

GIRLS WRITE NOW UNMUTED
The 2021 Anthology

Ayooluwa Akintayo was my mentee in the Girls Write Now Digital Media Mentorship Program—a tech-savvy space for the next generation of content creators. In the spring we met at Washington Square; it was the perfect place to practice the art of being unmuted. When she wasn't reading her award-winning poetry out loud, I read her my freewrites about culture and New York City. Initially, I leaned in to hear her read tightly woven verses over the sounds of splashing fountain water, flirtatious college chatter, and saxophones blaring from the opposite end of the park, but it didn't take long for her voice to dominate the outdoor orchestra.

Growing up bookish and Black had its challenges twenty years ago, but I knew one day I'd find a tribe eager to embrace me for reading at parties and writing at the dinner table. I was happy to find that Girls Write Now offers a community for young writers to create truthful and inventive work. Today's bookish girls face the challenge of confronting a charged political climate and the labyrinth of young adulthood in an enormous and confined online world. That's no small feat and that's what *Unmuted* is all about. It's inconvenient outspokenness. It's bold talk at one of the most crucial times in history. It's taking ownership of your voice rather than waiting your turn to speak. To be unmuted right now requires a new brand of bravery and these writers show us how it's done. They have traversed fear, silence, and ego to gift us vivid reflections on contemporary humanity.

The current class of Girls Write Now mentees have served up originality in prose, poetry, essay, and craft for a collection that is powerful and vulnerable. These boundless coming-of-age stories summon the voices of Fran Ross, Octavia E. Butler, and Ann Petry as they uniquely mirror this moment with imagination and detail. *Girls Write Now Unmuted* is a louder, brighter social post with all of the heart and self-expression we desperately need and deserve. Enjoy.

NADIA DeLANE is a writer, storyteller, and multimedia designer. She is cofounder of Visual Muze—a narrative arts residency on Governors Island. DeLane is also a Girls Write Now mentor alum and co-chair of the Girls Write Now anthology committee.

ANTHOLOGY EDITORIAL COMMITTEE

EDITOR

Molly MacDermot

PRINT EDITORIAL ANTHOLOGY COMMITTEE CO-CHAIRS

Rosalind Black
Nadia DeLane
Spencer George

Jisu Kim
Maya Millett

PRINT EDITORIAL ANTHOLOGY COMMITTEE

Grace Aneiza Ali
Nan Bauer-Maglin
Annie Bryan
Meg Charlton
Jordan Cowell
Erica Drennan
Morayo Faleyimu
Amy Flyntz
Kristen Gaerlan
Sophia F. Gottfried
Catherine Greenman
Donna Hill
Becca James

Jinnie Lee
Melissa Milich
Sepideh Moafi
Livia Nelson
Alyssa Nittolo
Carol Paik
Nikki Palumbo
Jennifer Rowe
Charis Satchell
Hannah Sheldon-Dean
Marissa Silverman
Maryellen Tighe
Liza Wyles

PROMOTIONS AND DISTRIBUTION SUB-COMMITTEE CO-CHAIRS

Jisu Kim
Jinnie Lee
Livia Nelson

CONTENTS

FOREWORD

ABI DARÉ

As a young girl, I was terrified to say what was on my mind. I lived in a muted bubble and sealed it tight with fear. *What would people think?* I would wonder, before frantically swallowing the words I wanted to say. But this silence, this shoving down of opinions and thoughts and feelings for fear of judgment or of being laughed at, made me miserable.

I must have been five or six when I discovered my love for writing. I desecrated our family photo album by giving each image speech balloons and lots of effusive dialogue punctuated by too many exclamation marks. It annoyed my mother, but I was secretly thrilled. I had finally found a way to capture and convey my feelings without opening my mouth. I had found my voice. I embraced writing from then on: I wrote on scraps of paper I found lying around, then glued them together to make a book solely for my own reading pleasure. I wrote in the back of exercise books, creating characters that both terrified and delighted me in equal measure. In secondary school, I wrote terrible plays and forced my friends to act in them while I directed and produced.

After I left Nigeria, as I struggled to find my place in a society where I looked different, and where my ability to speak "good English" surprised an astounding number of people, I found myself trying to make my writing fit into the expectations that society had created for me. I wrote about characters who had blue eyes and blond hair and who played lacrosse and attended boarding school in the Scottish Isles even though I had no idea what lacrosse was at that time. The fairy tales I loved also did not feature any characters who looked like me, and so as I wrote my own stories, I subconsciously erased my own existence out of my own narrative. It was torturous, and it wasn't until I began to read books filled with characters who braided their hair or wore it in an afro, and who lived in Lagos or Ibadan and ate jollof rice and yams and spoke Yoruba and Hausa as well as they could speak English, that I realized that I could, and should, write the stories my soul wants to write, about people who looked like me. It was then that I began to emerge gloriously liberated from the process.

It gives me immense pleasure to present this anthology, and to share work from girls who are more courageous and inspiring than I was at their age. Girls who have decided to use their voices to tell stories that are relevant and undiluted and authentic, each word constructed with care and urgency, as if to say: *This is my story, told in my own way—Listen!*

And I hope you will listen.

I hope you will experience every remarkable piece, each one written from a particular point of view no one else has, by writers from myriad backgrounds and perspectives, whether in the stanzas of poetry that deserve to be memorized and recited or in prose that is stunning in its beauty. I hope you will hear these unmuted and unafraid voices and that they will inspire and move you, and as you turn the last page, I hope you will emerge transformed by the journey, and with your heart imprinted with the power of the unforgettable voices in this book.

Enjoy every moment.

ABI DARÉ is the *New York Times*–bestselling author of *The Girl with the Louding Voice* and a Girls Write Now honoree. She lives in Essex, England, with her husband and two daughters, who inspired her to write her debut novel.

INTRODUCTION

ROBYN CRAWFORD

For many years I was asked, encouraged, and even solicited to tell my story and the story of my longtime friendship with Whitney Houston.

I did not want to talk, share, or open myself up. Talking about my life felt like going backward at a time when I was on a mission to better myself and build a future. Other than examining my life in therapy, I found comfort in my silence.

But over time, after regularly hearing, reading, and sometimes watching untrue things about me, slowly I began to reconsider. I was no longer content being quiet. I felt the need to speak up in truth and honesty, to set things straight. I wondered what would happen if I exposed myself? Would it be fair to those I loved? What would I say? Would I reveal too much? But at the same time, something in me was confident, ready to take ownership of my story, realizing that putting the words on paper would require me to relive the past and that doing so would be an emotional roller coaster.

Before moving forward, I discussed the possibility with those closest to me. Though apprehensive, my wife was supportive, believing that I had not truly processed the letdowns and losses in my life. She thought that writing a memoir would force me to confront the feelings that had been packed away for so long. As a child I'd had an adultlike response to my parents' constant fights and ultimately failed marriage. AIDS claimed the lives of my only brother and my loving mother, both gone within three years of each other. Later, there was the tragic loss of my dearest friend, with whom I'd dreamed, planned, and fulfilled so many goals. Making up my mind took some time, as I understood that once I opened up, my story would no longer be mine alone.

I clearly recall how intimidated I felt the first day I sat down to write. Before long, I was overwhelmed by a surging mass of feelings that I had been running from for decades and had to force myself to acknowledge. The details that can be evoked when you reside in your memories for a while are amazing, bringing with them moments of profound joy and deep pain.

As I persevered, slowly I let go of the trepidation. I came to understand that my life has been such a gift, and that sharing it might be freeing not only for me, but for others.

And now, here we are. Our experiences and collective stories have brought us together. To the bold and beautiful young women of Girls Write Now: I know how it feels to have secret, sacred stories and fears swirling around in your head, thoughts that awaken you in the night. Instead of picking up the phone, pick up a pad and pencil and jot down the ideas ping-ponging back and forth in your brain. The words will be by your bedside when you awaken, and in the days that follow, the process of writing them into sentences and paragraphs may release you. Sometimes it will come easily, and at times it will be frustrating and laborious, but you must keep going, because in the end you will get to where you are meant to be.

In this great big world, there is only one you. My hope is that each of you will have a full life, great adventures, and deep loves, and that one day you will share those stories—if you choose to do so. Surely, the one who lives it is the one who owns it, but in sharing your truth with the world, you have an opportunity to motivate women like you—and not like you—to generously pass on their own stories. Imagine that.

After a long career in the music industry, ROBYN CRAWFORD, who is a Girls Write Now honoree, is now focused on mental and physical wellness and writing. In 2019, Robyn released *A Song for You: My Life with Whitney Houston*. She lives in New Jersey with her wife and children.

GIRLS WRITE NOW UNMUTED

The 2021 Anthology

OBENEWA ADU

YEARS AS MENTEE: 2

GRADE: Senior

BORN: New Haven, CT

LIVES: Stamford, CT

MENTEE'S ANECDOTE:

Tracy and I meet weekly via Zoom, and although I miss our weekly meets at Starbucks, lately we've been finding ways to stay interested and to cope with everything that's going on now. I find that Tracy and I agree on many topics but experience them differently. Journaling and chatting about current events with Tracy are often the highlight of my week. COVID has undeniably affected the world as a whole, which is why I knew I wanted to do a collaborative piece with Tracy, to share both of our experiences and to reflect on our year together.

TRACY MILLER

YEARS AS MENTOR: 5

OCCUPATION: Director of Digital Communications

BORN: Columbus, OH

LIVES: Queens, NY

MENTOR'S ANECDOTE:

Obenewa and I both gravitate toward using current events as a basis for our writing—to record, and also to reflect. We started off our year by taking a journalistic approach, conducting interviews for a podcast about the life changes people experienced in 2020. For our pair project, we decided to turn inward to focus on our personal experiences. Although the past year was challenging in many ways, we both felt strongly about creating a personal history of this time to help us understand what we lived through, so we can continue to learn from it.

Stages of Isolation

OBENEWA ADU AND TRACY MILLER

This cowritten poem reflects our journaled memories of the year 2020, as well as our conversations with each other about our lives in lockdown.

I lazily rolled out of bed at any time I pleased.
> **I slept in late, too, and let my MetroCard expire.**

Just to make my daily walk to the kitchen, where I taught myself to
brew homemade iced coffee.
> **I opened up my laptop, where my entire world lives now.**

I brushed my teeth, showered, sat down, and mindlessly scrolled on
social media, traveling from app to app.
> **I waited anxiously for my contact-free deliveries.**

I reminisced over what life used to be.
> **To be honest, I didn't always miss it.**

I completed some work, joined some Zooms, sent some emails, ate
until I was full.
> **Memorized the reflection of my face on a webcam.**

Sat and watched the news in awe.
> **I'm so tired of living in interesting times.**

This rotation of events went on for month after month, all while I was
confined to my tiny apartment in Connecticut.
> **And I to my tiny apartment in Queens.**

As a student, at first, lockdown seemed like a well-needed break, a
relaxation period.

I worked from the safety of home, while others risked their lives.

Until those COVID statistics were no longer just statistics, but friends and family.

Until one friend got sick, then another, then another.

Until our two weeks of distance learning carried on to the end of the year.

Until I let go of every carefully made plan.

Until I feared trips to the grocery store and packages on my doorstep.

Until I feared seeing my family.

Until I was forced to watch injustices on the news.

Until it seemed like the world had shattered.

Until I lost track of what day it was or even how long it had been since I last went outside.

And when no one was around, I removed my mask to sneak just one breath of fresh air.

I could no longer see everyone's smiling faces. Instead I looked for squinted eyes.

I learned there's more than one way to smile.

No more handshakes and hugs; now we raise our masks and make sure to cover noses.

It's the least we can do for one another.

A basic sign of respect in 2020.

Because this year is happening to all of us.

Last March I walked around freely with no idea what was to come.

Two weeks turned into twelve months.

Since then I have battled staying motivated and hopeful.

A new year, a new vaccine, a new President.

Together we have grieved, we have grown, and we have felt all the stages of isolation.

YOSEIVY AGUILAR

YEARS AS MENTEE: 1

GRADE: Senior

BORN: New York, NY

LIVES: Brooklyn, NY

MENTEE'S ANECDOTE:

This poem was written during one of my first meetings with my mentor, Molly. This is mainly for practice, but she told me I could submit this poem if I wanted to, since one of my goals was to improve in poetry.

MOLLY HORAN

YEARS AS MENTOR: 4

OCCUPATION: English Professor

BORN: New Britain, CT

LIVES: Queens, NY

MENTOR'S ANECDOTE:

It's been great working with Yoseivy. There have been times when we have to change our meetings because of Internet issues, but every meeting shows me that Yoseivy works hard to improve upon her skills and isn't afraid to ask for help.

The Ocean's Depths

YOSEIVY AGUILAR

Based off of my love for the ocean but fearing what is underneath the waves.

The ocean will never be fully explored
Just like our ever-growing universe
Never knowing what's underneath the waves
Maybe there are creatures
Some that went undiscovered for so long
Some that inspired so many myths and legends
Perhaps there's just nothing at all
Just water filling all of the cracks of the world

They say eyes are the windows to a person's soul
You can say the same for the Earth's water
At surface level, you see what it's like
Waves crashing onto shores
People having fun in the salty water
Fishes and crabs that dare to venture to the top
Wonderful and calm
Like meeting someone for the first time

By only looking
You can never truly see
You must build for what it really is
Venture into the depths
Fill with things no other person has ever seen

EMMANUELLA AGYEMANG

YEARS AS MENTEE: 2

GRADE: Junior

BORN: Bronx, NY

LIVES: Bronx, NY

PUBLICATIONS & RECOGNITIONS:
Bronx Community College
Spoken Word: Third Place

MENTEE'S ANECDOTE:

Grace has always been an individual to give me clear-cut feedback on my work. Without her, I am not sure where my writing would be now. Grace continues to challenge the way that I think about my writing. She has taught me that with each sentence, with each word, I need to be intentional. She allows me to look at both the big and small details within my writing. And, most important, she has always encouraged me to write from my heart.

GRACE ANEIZA ALI

YEARS AS MENTOR: 3

OCCUPATION: Professor

BORN: Georgetown, Guyana

LIVES: New York, NY

MENTOR'S ANECDOTE:

Emmanuella had a clear and brilliant vision for the character—the child soldier—in her short story "Deadly Militia." She knew she wanted to write about the complexity of what a young girl might face in a situation of being recruited by a rebel group. As we were writing through drafts, we kept going back to the importance of research when telling stories about real, lived experiences. Emmanuella was always committed to this part of the writing process—learning, exploring, researching—as a way to make her story stronger and insightful.

Deadly Militia

EMMANUELLA AGYEMANG

"Deadly Militia" is a short story that portrays the life of a young child soldier during the Congo War.

The gun's weight across my chest holds my body down as I lean my head against a tree trunk. My mind goes back to my recent combat. My eyes widen as I watch the episode unfold, causing the hairs on the back of my neck to stand up. I feel my lips curling into a sinister smile. My gun is a dusty black AK-47 paired with a camo strap. We have quite the history.

Whenever it is time for combat, I can easily piece the gun parts together. We have done things that I cannot let depart from my lips. I begin to blink at the sight of the sunrise, my eyes focusing on the forest as I adjust the camouflage-patterned hat on my short hair. Living with my family, just two years ago, was more than a faint memory; it was an actuality. It is now hard to concentrate on combat when I remember my mother soothing me with a gathering song she once sang every Saturday night. I can always hear my mother's faint voice singing, *"Tout le monde aime samedi soir."* I ease into her words. A few days have passed since we took over a village in the northern area of the city of Kananga. Soon it will be time to leave, since the Congolese government soldiers are looking to arrest rebel groups like us. Rebel groups are formed in the first place to fight for political change in the government. We are not the first and we will not be the last.

A vivid memory of my life is when I was initiated into Milice Mortelle, Deadly Militia. During my initiation, white powder was dusted onto my face, neck, and shoulders by the hands of a voodoo priest. The white powder by the same voodoo priest is applied before any combat. In doing so, I am protected by my ancestors and any spirit of death will keep away; I am invincible on the outside. But then again, I never signed up to be a child soldier. I never wanted to be invincible. A young and innocent girl is in here somewhere. I have been looked down upon, pushed around, and, worst of all, almost taken advantage of. I have realized that no one is coming to rescue me. I will never get married, have children, finish school, or even touch the cheekbones of my mother and hear her say, "I am glad I have a beautiful daughter like you."

My thoughts are soon interrupted by Commandant's stern voice. "Get up, we need to look for more food and ammunition." Commandant and the rest of the boys have already searched for more ammunition and food, but have come back with nothing. Commandant is a tall, imposing man from Kinshasa. Every time he takes his shirt off to do his daily push-ups I see a scar that travels from under his right pec to the bottom of his ribs. He is mysterious. I do not know Commandant's real name. It is not something that needs to be brought up. I want to ask him questions about the life he has lived. *Why do you have such a large scar? Why are you so ruthless?* Or even *What happened to your family?*

As I march behind Commandant, my gun now behind my back, a woman appears from behind a bush four feet away from us. Her face is flushed with fear and her colorful wrapper is stained in red. Commandant notices and steps toward her.

"Hey! What are you doing here?" His brown eyes examine her like a piece of raw meat; he is ready to pounce on her. That was his personality, he loved to pounce on any- and everything that moved like a woman. My arm automatically blocks Commandant from the woman. His eyes lower to mine as he rolls them in annoyance.

The woman's legs begin to shake as she steps back. She was getting ready to run, then she stopped abruptly and stood strangely still, eyeing me.

"Mireille," she spoke softly. "My girl," she said, with tears running down her face.

My eyes rise to meet hers. "Mother?"

DOHA AHMED

YEARS AS MENTEE: 1

GRADE: Junior

BORN: Queens, NY

LIVES: Queens, NY

MENTEE'S ANECDOTE:

Cynthia has been an amazing mentor and friend. She has always cared about how I feel and will listen to me speak about my emotions even if I can't find the right words to explain them. Despite the short time we've known each other, from the moment I met her I felt as though she was a trustworthy person whom you can always count on. She has not only helped me develop my writing skills, but life skills as well, and I am inspired by seeing her always going after what she is passionate about no matter the obstacles. I hope her light never stops shining because it helps so many people, including me. She may not realize it, but she is one of the most optimistic, confident, and kind women I have ever met, and what she brings to the table, especially what she has brought to mine, is something unforgettable.

CYNTHIA AMOAH

YEARS AS MENTOR: 1

OCCUPATION: Spoken Word Poet and Educator

BORN: Accra, Ghana

LIVES: Columbus, OH

PUBLICATIONS & RECOGNITIONS: Paul Violi Prize in Poetry: Honorable Mention; Excellence in Poetry by The New School; *OURS* magazine; *Nimrod; Crab Orchard Review*

MENTOR'S ANECDOTE:

Doha's name means "sunrise," after a prayer in Islam. I remember her telling me this in one of the very first meetings we had. So, I nudged her in another meeting. "Doha, you gotta get out and get some sun. Listen to the meaning of your name." But I quickly realized that she was more than the light that the sun offers, she is the very fire that it is consumed of. Doha is the most blazing and brilliant teenager I have ever met, more sure of herself than I ever was at that age. She is guided by the quiet confidence that is her religion, makes me laugh hysterically, and is a gentle reminder of how young people can be so fierce, so carefully created, so wildly kind.

The Side They Never See

DOHA AHMED

Captured in a moment of pain, this poem was a way for me to release my emotions onto the page. I hope to show anyone who encounters this piece that they are not alone.

I feel so invisible
to everyone and everything
I do not know what I have done to deserve it
but my phone now never rings
I held myself
in my worst moments but my heart can never sing
It's only a ringing in my ears with the biggest fear
of the worst occurring
I am trying to stop myself from breaking
but with all this pain it's as if my mind is shaking
You told me I don't matter and no one will understand
That this life is more than one stupid man
or everyone that has caused me pain
I cannot blame you, I put myself in the chains
I do not know how to go back, the path is unclear
Tell me to hold on a little longer
Tell me there is a chance hope will appear
Tell me I'm not just a deer in headlights waiting to get hit in
    the rear

As I stand in between the surface I am crushed between your lies
I realize you I don't despise it was me all along
Telling myself I am not strong enough to move on
No it is me I hate I do not fake
This love was made for something more than me
I am not enough so do not say I matter
Always climbing the ladder just to fall off
I cannot take this anymore my heart has gone soft
I do not laugh at your jokes
It's like one big propaganda
We're all just plain folks
Walking around with a smile on our face
I bet you used to love the way I made your heart race
and with no expression on my face
I sang the tune that had been replaying in my head
The voices said it's time to sing a little song
and even if your heart can't sing just try to go along
wth the lyrics in your head that say they want you dead

Lying on a bed I cannot get up from,
with my arms and legs that feel like boulders
Like bricks my heart said it was so heavy
It feels like it might drop to my stomach
Although it had been empty for days
begging to be fed
As if someone had to pull my body parts
together with a thread to fix the broken pieces
and as the hate for myself increases
I laid there still realizing the deer
had been shed of all its protective covering
Naked
It lost the race
and now you look for that deer in every place

and you fear that something is not right
Maybe someone will hold you tight
Tell you it's alright but for me it's over
You've proved me wrong
What you have been waiting for has come
I am gone

KETI AKHALBEDASHVILI

YEARS AS MENTEE: 1

GRADE: Senior

BORN: Tbilisi, Georgia

LIVES: Brooklyn, NY

MENTEE'S ANECDOTE:

In just a few months of working together, Liz has become more than a mentor to me. Her accomplishments have been an inspiration, encouraging me to step out of my comfort zone and start new and exciting projects. Liz pushes me to explore my interests and to look beyond the limits of what I thought I could create. With her support, I was able to gain confidence in my writing. Liz has become a dear friend who I can always count on to cheer me on in any future creative endeavors.

LIZ DONOVAN

YEARS AS MENTOR: 1

OCCUPATION: Journalist

BORN: Doylestown, PA

LIVES: New York, NY

MENTOR'S ANECDOTE:

Keti is seventeen years old and wise beyond her years. Her thoughtfulness and insight have taught me so much already in just six months of working together—sometimes it's easy to forget which one of us is the mentor and which is the mentee! I've seen her grow tremendously as she began to explore journalistic writing and oral history editing. She has so many talents, from languages and philosophy, to visual arts and filmmaking, to interviewing and boot-leather reporting. I am excited to see all she will accomplish in the very near future.

King of Kings

KETI AKHALBEDASHVILI

Who decides what a text means? And how much can be lost in translation?

უბრძანა: "ნუ სტირ, ასულო, ისმინე ჩემი თხრობილი:
დღეს შენ ხარ მეფე არაბეთს, ჩემგან ხელმწიფედ ხმობილი"

Then he said: "Weep not, my daughter, but hear what I'm about to say: You are a king, named by me a sovereign today."

−FROM *THE KNIGHT IN THE PANTHER'S SKIN,*
SHOTA RUSTAVELI (C. 12TH CENTURY)

I was only seven years old when I was gifted my first copy of the epic poem describing the coronation of Tamar, the powerful King of Georgia, who was a woman. Not being able to comprehend Medieval Georgian, I would quickly skip through the masterpiece that I then deemed boring, and land on an illustration of King Tamar. I studied the piece carefully in awe. Sitting on her marvelous throne, her dress illuminated by precious stones and fabrics, Tamar gazed down as the most respected men of the Georgian intelligentsia bowed down to her. Her ornate dress and intimidating gaze were enough for my seven-year-old self to be enthralled by the King, who was never really dethroned from being a subject of my fascination.

Years later, having learned to read Medieval Georgian, it was not the sparkly jewelry and vibrant dresses that caught my attention, but rather her title that read "მეფე"—a King. A title that tore down the walls of gender norms, broadening my idea of what I could achieve as a woman.

Without realizing it, I had grown up believing I could be anything, even a King.

In most modern languages, the title is associated with a male ruler, but the terminology was not so constricted in Medieval Georgian. In order to avoid puzzling readers, however, her title is often translated to *Queen* in English. Seeing this interpretation frustrates and saddens me. The meaning behind her title, along with the impact it had on my identity as an ambitious young woman, was lost. Its purpose was to signify the excellence of her reign, not only among female monarchs, but among monarchs in general. I mulled over the pitfalls of adapting cultural references into a different language. Who decides what a text means? And how much can be lost in translation?

During March of this year, deep into the hole of boredom and monotony from weeks in quarantine, I revisited books that I used to enjoy when I was younger. Particularly sensitive to nostalgia (considering I was deprived of any experience that required stepping out of my apartment), rereading the *Odyssey* brought up the same questions that bothered me when I first read the book.

I think of reading as a superpower. Stephen King describes the writer-reader relationship as telepathy. "We're having a meeting of the minds," he wrote in his memoir, *On Writing*. For this reason, I have always prided myself on being a sensitive reader. I admired the bittersweet intimacy between the writer and her audience—with the text providing a bridge, creating a silent conversation from one mind to another. Upon contemplation, I realized I hadn't experienced this intimacy when reading some of the ancient texts that held the most importance to me. I wasn't metaphorically present to Homer's telling of the adventures of Odysseus and Achilles, nor was I connected to Plato as he recited the wisdom shared in *The Symposium*. Instead, by reading the translator's interpretation of the works, I was seeing them through a filter.

I decided that learning to read Ancient Greek would be an advantageous use of my time, which I would otherwise spend scrolling through Twitter or rewatching *Parks and Recreation* for the second time that month. By the end of the year, the months of struggling to grasp the concept of declensions paid off, as I am now able to translate the myths I so deeply admire.

I have come to appreciate translation as a form of art itself, as it is the great conjunction of all that is important to understand a certain culture. The convoluted sentence structure of Ancient Greek that once seemed chaotic turned out to be my favorite, yet the most challenging, part to interpret. I noticed it highlighted the lyricism of the ancient language, something so hard to grasp in modern languages, which are constricted with grammar rules. I came to see this lack of structure as a reflection of their society, which valued freedom. I am finally able to grasp the concepts of Eros, Philia, and Pragma that would all be under the same label of *love* in English. Single words, such as *panaōrios*, that invoke an entire myth—these can never have the same significance in English.

Ancient linguistics serve as a map to ancient antiquity. Understanding a language opens a gate to a perception of the world that was vastly different from ours. It gives me access to the mind and soul of the storytellers. It gives a King her rightful title.

AMA ANWAR

YEARS AS MENTEE: 1

GRADE: Senior

BORN: Comilla, Bangladesh

LIVES: Bronx, NY

MENTEE'S ANECDOTE:

Macaela is a ray of sunshine; her optimism and positivity make our weekly meetings a joy. She's an awesome conversation starter and makes our casual book conversations delightful. Her insightful feedback, college advice, and organizational tips are some things I will never take for granted. I'm grateful for the time we spend together and the enthusiasm she radiates through my computer screen. I am inspired by how open-minded and thoughtful she is as a reader and writer. After the Girls Write Now program, I know we will continue to cheer each other on in our accomplishments.

MACAELA MacKENZIE

YEARS AS MENTOR: 1

OCCUPATION: Journalist

BORN: Rochester, MI

LIVES: Brooklyn, NY

PUBLICATIONS & RECOGNITIONS:
Glamour, Marie Claire, Forbes

MENTOR'S ANECDOTE:

I was impressed with Ama before I even met her. Not many high school students have Google search results, but before our first meeting I was already familiar with her work with Climate Speaks—my expectations were high. It's been an honor to get to know her in the months since. She's soft-spoken but full of sharp, inquisitive questions and has a genuine sense of curiosity for the world around her. I can't wait to see what she does next at Columbia University—I know she'll exceed all expectations.

High School Students Across the Country Start Projects During Quarantine

AMA ANWAR

The article centers on five high school students in the US who are pursuing their hobbies to create projects that are bringing people around the world together during the pandemic.

Working from home has its perks—one can work in the comfort of their room without having to worry about morning commutes and outfits, for starters. But more free time can also lead to the dreaded phenomenon: procrastination.

These high schoolers may be spending less time interacting with their peers and more time cooped up in their homes, but rather than grow stagnant, they're finding surprising and inspiring ways to share their passions. Here are the stories of five high school students who are creating passion-driven projects in quarantine.

Rajvi Umrigar, California

Rajvi Umrigar, a current senior at Homestead High School in California, began lockdown early in March 2020. This was the initial brainstorming stage for Inara, a nonprofit organization that pairs high school mentors with local middle school students in the San Jose area. Rajvi smiles as she elaborates on the meaning behind her project's name—*Inara* is an Arabic word that means "shining light." It's a fitting description for the immense help that students are receiving as they navigate remote learning.

As an immigrant, Rajvi says, she didn't have mentors to guide her. The educational system was foreign to her and she didn't know what Advanced Placement classes or standardized testing were, or what *GPA* meant. Along with one-on-one mentoring sessions, Inara also offers workshops and has attendees from twelve different countries. "It's something that keeps me going, knowing that I'm helping others," Rajvi says.

Swetha Tandri, Texas

Swetha Tandri, eighteen, a senior at Coppell High School in Texas, is an aspiring computer science major. At the beginning of the quarantine, she started Melodies for Math, a YouTube channel that explains math concepts through original songs. Attending a large competitive high school, with numerous tests and comparisons among peers, Swetha often felt like a number. "Melodies for Math is how I can express myself beyond numbers," she says.

Swetha wants to ensure that the word about Melodies for Math spreads in her local community. She has emailed test centers to tell them about the resource and researched YouTube marketing and search engine optimization. One of the project's milestones was reaching 7,500 views this year. Next she plans on monetizing her videos to financially compensate everyone on the team and donate to other educational nonprofits, such as Khan Academy.

The project has had a profound effect on her. "This project was a catalyst to me finding out what my overall purpose is," she says. "My purpose is to help other people find their creative energies, so they can change the world however they can."

Michelle Cao, New York

Michelle Cao, seventeen, attends Brooklyn Technical High School in New York City. In the summer, during a peak of COVID cases, she found it difficult to process the racial tensions within her own community and the rising Black Lives Matter movement. But as she learned more about social issues, she decided to start a club dedicated to raising cultural awareness within the Asian community where members can participate in conversations surrounding race and culture.

Her club is a small step in building a community that's antiracist. Michelle wants to explore topics such as the model-minority myth and the Asian take on the BLM movement, and share her personal experiences to create a space where everyone feels welcome. "It's grounded me knowing there's a community to turn to," Michelle says, "when there's hardship and hatred surrounding the world."

Alexandra Chu, New York

Alexandra Chu, sixteen, is a current sophomore at Scarsdale High School in New York. As an aspiring biology major, she founded Med-Create, dedicated to merging medicine and creativity. Its primary focus is on creative writing and art—she's built a community of fifty members from ten different countries.

In the past, members have put together works of art and written articles and poems, and the team is currently working on launching creative writing and art classes for kids, which they hope to implement in hospitals. "You should always have a passion project or something you love to do," she says.

Kristen Adams, New Jersey

Kristen Adams, seventeen, currently attends a STEM high school in New Jersey, but also harbors a passion for music. She started teaching piano lessons in her sophomore year, and at the end of 2019, she held a small music recital for her fifteen students at a local library. "My hard work and this dream I had was coming alive," she says. But when the pandemic forced her to pause lessons in March 2020, she decided to take her business online, kickstarting Music Generation and recruiting several teachers through Slack from Turkey, India, and Canada. "I'm a high school student by morning and entrepreneur by afternoon. I can't wait until college to expand the business," Kristen says and smiles.

She plans to continue her business after the pandemic by finding more teachers and students to create YouTube videos, and will expand her team to include graphic designers and coders to assist with the website. "My music journey wasn't perfect; it was rocky," she says. "What if I could share my experiences with music and learning the piano? What if I could help other kids?"

SHAYLA ASTUDILLO

YEARS AS MENTEE: 1

GRADE: Junior

BORN: Queens, NY

LIVES: Queens, NY

PUBLICATIONS & RECOGNITIONS:
Scholastic Art & Writing Awards:
Honorable Mention

MENTEE'S ANECDOTE:

When Danielle and I met I was instantly in a safe place. I knew my writing would only grow and prosper in our Zoom meetings. The first few minutes of our meetings begin with me talking about my week and where I am in life. She gives advice, laughter, and a sense of understanding. Our writing relationship continues to deepen as I write about the hardest moments of life. She writes comments on my work on how I can truly tell the reader what I feel. All in all, our writing relationship has taught me how to write for myself.

DANIELLE MAZZEO

YEARS AS MENTOR: 1

OCCUPATION: Federal Grant Writer

BORN: Staten Island, NY

LIVES: Brooklyn, NY

MENTOR'S ANECDOTE:

It's funny that Shayla and I have never met in person. Despite connecting only through our computer screens, Shayla has shared so much about themself and their writing. Shayla is a courageous writer. They turn their heart out to tell the whole story, to get something true and hard onto paper. Shayla offers authenticity, honesty, and accountability in their work; they write from their own life. I'm so excited for Shayla to continue to grow as a writer, to keep telling important stories about family, loss, becoming, and self, and I look forward to reading more and more new work!

You Are Found Guilty for Your Lies. Death Sentence from Truth Is Punishment.

SHAYLA ASTUDILLO

As a teenager grows into adulthood, they begin to understand the consequences of their words. They no longer have bliss, and the people around them continue to remind them of it.

There is ink on your hands:

Words typically come easy to me.

My hands usually aren't quick enough to capture all the words going through my head.

That is not the case when it comes to you.

Instead, I try to erase ink from my hands.

Ink has spilled all over, my tears wet the page, and once again I'm throwing out another piece of paper.

I try and try and try to take off the ink on my hands. But it resists.

My hands become red from the scrubbing and the sink is overflowing.

I slide down the wall next to the sink.

My clothes are wet and clinging to my body.

The ink is clear too clear for my liking.

My hands shake at the knowing that I can't get rid of your words and your pain on my hands.

I thought writing would finally rid me of you.

But now I am forced to consider the pain you have caused me over and over again.

Please, please, please just stop.

I scrub on my hands harder, why won't it hurry up and come off?
Soon there's banging on the door of the bathroom.
You're calling out my name.
Over and over and over again.
Please go away.
I don't want it to be over.
I thought writing stories, fairy tales, and my little lies would help me
    stay longer with you.
Or at least stop you from coming to say goodbye.
But, you are ending it now why?
I just want my fairy tale please.
Maybe it's all too strong, and maybe my words are far too much for you.
I know my words are far too much for me, as usual.
As the ink on the paper is slick, gliding fluidly.
The burden of what the ink resembles is anything but peace of mind.
But, I didn't know my fairy tale was ending because of a person.
I always thought it would end with age.
Not my stories' so-called hero.

Honesty:

I think my youth was never truly mine.
Instead it was filled with yelling, insecurities, and ego.
I wish it was mine.

I look back at my youth as a persistent part of what is creating me.
The yelling turned to fear of conflict.
Their insecurities turned into mine.
Their ego caused pure fear.

I want to sit down at my desk with a cup of coffee, my vinyls playing,
    and my heart beating triumphantly.
But, I can't.

Instead the coffee is antidepressants,
                    the vinyl is the silence of your words,
                              and my heart wishes to finally stop.

As much as my words want to be painted beautifully with a fantasy of my
    youth.
It can't be.
I am not a liar.

W o r d s:

Words are skeptical.
They hold too much meaning to even begin to demonstrate how I feel.

Each letter was a different part of myself.
Each word was a brand new way of expression.

It's simple and it's vague.
I wish words and I never met.

If words and I had never met then maybe I could have had a better chance.

Maybe then their phrases wouldn't affect me so much.
Maybe then I wouldn't need to defend myself.

When words and I met, I ended that day.
I was finally old enough for them to hurt. Old enough to take the pain.
God, I wish words and I never met.

Honest lies:

I don't like telling people what they want to hear.
Of course I do for small civil conversations.

But when it comes to myself, I hate it.
Don't give me the side-eye telling me to stop being truthful.
I can be in pain. I am in pain. Why is that such a problem for you?
Me being in pain is not something you can control.
Stop telling me how to feel.

I told people what they wanted to hear for years.
And, I still do. I won't lie to you.
But now, I don't do it from fear or to keep you happy.
I do it because I know what is best for me.
I guess that's the difference between my younger self and who I am now.
I don't care that my pain is affecting you so much.
I'm in pain, I'm dealing with it, so stop telling me to hide it.
I won't hide myself to make you feel better about yourself.

Stop Running Darling:

Don't be scared.
I know my words are too much.
My honesty can barely be taken seriously at times.
That's okay.
I may run away from a lot of things.
But not from my truth.
And, neither should you from your own.

MAXINE BABB

YEARS AS MENTEE: 3

GRADE: Junior

BORN: New York, NY

LIVES: Bronx, NY

PUBLICATIONS & RECOGNITIONS:
826NYC Teen Writers' Collective; Harlem Link Charter School Alumni Spotlight; Certificate for Youth Leadership Training

MENTEE'S ANECDOTE:

Agnes's encouraging words and help always keep me going. Her being by my side has made it easier to write about things that are not so easy to talk about (she makes sure I stay *Unmuted*) and she's also always there to correct my grammatical errors. I know it may not always be easy having a mentee with several other responsibilities and limited time, but we always seem to make it work. Through her kindness, assistance, and patience throughout this entire program, Agnes has become more than a mentor, she has become a friend.

AGNES BANNIGAN

YEARS AS MENTOR: 3

OCCUPATION: Writing Editor

BORN: Cheverly, MD

LIVES: New York, NY

MENTOR'S ANECDOTE:

Maxine has been my mentee for three years, and with each passing year, she inspires me with her talent and courage. The devastation of 2020–21 would have anyone wanting to remain quiet and confined in their comfort zone. But this year, Maxine has been unstoppable. She's not only *Unmuted*, she's writing in new genres—poetry and nonfiction—and sharing vulnerably. She shows me in her words and actions how writing in even the hardest times can cause breakthroughs in leadership, healing, and resilience. I'm humbled to witness her creativity and growth, and I'm proud to be her mentor.

tears of the past

MAXINE BABB

Sometimes we surprise ourselves in the ways we act in certain situations that life throws at us. This piece tells of my first encounter with this lesson.

It was a rainy, gray day. My dad, sister, godsister, and I stayed in the car while my mom went to pick up some supplies in Walgreens. All of a sudden I felt the mood change in the car. My dad looked at me with the saddest eyes (these eyes I've never seen from him before). That's when he told me that my grandma had passed away. I was absolutely distraught. I was nine, so naturally my body reacted before my mind did. I remember stopping for a few seconds to let it register—the fact that I'll never see her again. The fact that I'd have to remember all nine of the years that I've known her so that she wouldn't become just another forgotten memory (she deserved more than that). The fact that I never knew that last time that I saw her would be the last. While everything was still registering in my head, my body had a totally different reaction. I drowned out everything and started kicking and hitting everything in sight while yelling "NO" repeatedly. (It was all too much. It wasn't that I didn't believe it, but that it was all too much to believe. I can't believe I'm reliving such a painful moment now. These are the moments that I decide to put in a deep dark corner where no one can ever see them. I can't believe I just told you that either.) I felt like the whole car was closing in on me, like I couldn't breathe.

Years later, I'm actually kind of surprised that I wasn't in denial at first. Maybe I'm just not that type of person, but, now that I think about it, I was probably having a panic attack. My mother was probably so confused when she came back with a bunch of groceries and saw me ugly-crying in my dad's car. This was my first death. I didn't know how to treat these types of situations. After that day, I kept thinking about me and my grandma's relationship. Whenever she had me I would cry because I always wanted to be up under my mom, and all my grandmother ever wanted to do was spend some time with me. She would always try any- and everything just to see me smile, and I took it for granted. I knew she felt bad whenever I cried, but I never thought about that. All I was ever thinking about was getting back home to see my mom. I spent the longest time blaming myself for that, and I still partly do.

After I caused the big scene in the car, my dad held me tight. I'm pretty sure he did it so that 1) I wouldn't put dents in his car and 2) he could calm me down. It must've been hard for him to watch me in that state. My mom came back to the car pretty confused, and my dad let her know what was going on. The drive from Walgreens to our home was pretty quick. Once we got there, my little sister and godsister went into my room to play and my parents sat with me on the couch. While we sat on the couch, we were honoring her memory by talking about all the good times we'd had: like when we went to a Spider-Man Broadway play, *Turn Off the Dark*, for Father's Day; or when my mom and I went to see the movie *Hop* with her and then went to a BBQ after. I kept looking at one of the last pictures my sister and I took with her and I started tearing up again. We were in a restaurant together and she had her arm wrapped around us. I was still in shock, but I kept my composure this time. To this day, you can still see the teardrops I left on that picture.

FILOMENA BAKER

YEARS AS MENTEE: 1

GRADE: Junior

BORN: Bronx, NY

LIVES: Bronx, NY

MENTEE'S ANECDOTE:

Working with Molly has been a very easygoing experience, as we've gotten to know each other through brainstorming and writing stories together. Constantly supporting me when I was lost, she's offered guidance while simultaneously pushing me to try new ideas and methods. We're both understanding of any time constraints we have, working out alternative times to meet, taking off a lot of stress. Goal-driven, Molly wasted no time working on our dual piece to make an interesting story where both of our ideas were incorporated. Luckily, we had an uncanny amount of similar thoughts and ideas.

MOLLY VOSSLER

YEARS AS MENTOR: 1

OCCUPATION: Account
Coordinator, HBO

BORN: Hartford, CT

LIVES: Brooklyn, NY

MENTOR'S ANECDOTE:

Brainstorming story ideas with Filomena this year has been a joy. After getting to know each other early in the program, we began tossing ideas around for a short screenplay. We dedicated a few sessions to talking about what kind of films and TV shows we loved most and naturally landed on a storyline that blended black comedy and horror. Seeing Filomena quickly grasp and conquer the writing style and formatting specific to screenplays was amazing. She is so talented, and I'm very much looking forward to finishing the script with her!

A Flighty Peace

FILOMENA BAKER

The leader of an ancient tribe, tired of her war-ridden world, ignores the battle that looms behind her. But the death of her lover forces her to commit one final flight for peace.

A bird squawks above a woman, and she startles from where she gazes at a cliff's edge, head turning to find a weapon to throw at the bird. But then she pauses, and instead waves her hand, a sense of ease flowing.

It squawks once more and then it's gone.

She gets to her feet, staring out at the horizon one last time until her head snaps up, remembering the battle. Rushing to scramble up a nearby boulder, she looks at the battle that's taking place along the cliff's length miles away. She mutters a curse to a god she wishes she had believed in more as she watches.

Her mind wanders, watching the repetitive motion of stabbing weapons and blood splattering over and over and over.

Her partner throws hands and pushes for war around the table in the tent as she herself calls for peace. Her own defiant posture as she refuses to fight, her partner grasping at her hand, begging her to follow them.

"You're our leader, you have to come." She refuses—would rather stare at the sky than watch more people die. "Then you abandon us," they spit at her. Walk.

I don't need you, *her own thoughts ringing in the memory.* This fighting will mean nothing with or without me.

And then her breath catches and her mind pulls away from her memories. Far away, her partner is pinned to the ground. They resist, spitting in their killer's face. And only when the ax finally falls do they widen their eyes and scream for her.

She vomits on the stone beside her.

A shaky breath; several nods of the head; a howl of pain. She leaps off the rock and starts to run, and run, and run—until she's panting and staring at the blood, mangled faces, split heads, and torn-open bodies.

The swinging metals of death are not the easiest to deflect—her arms get skidded by a flying blade, but she stops only when she's close to the edge, hovering over a broken body. The single seed armband wrapped around their biceps—she'd given it to them—is the only indicator of her partner, their face cleaved in half. She grasps at the edge of their mangled face, but just the sight of her traitorous skin against her love nauseates her.

She remembers the last time she saw her partner: *Longing in their eyes. She stands resolute against the horizon. They plead. She laughs at them for their stupidity. They grasp her hand. She slaps their face. They walk away. She sits on the edge, dangling her legs over the jutting rocks below.*

She yanks her hands away, sobbing, unable to bear the shame. She doesn't deserve for her hands to be so soft now when they hadn't been before. To mourn. But she wishes she did.

She hiccups, looking around, and laughs with tears. No one approaches her. If *anyone* would just kill her, the head of the hawk, there would be no beak to eat the carcass. So easy.

She looks over at the cliff's edge, a squawk in the distance.

She glances down at their corpse, and fury rises at herself and everyone around them. She would end the fight. Her partner would be avenged. And she would be free.

She grabs the spear in her dead partner's hand and steals the gaze from her opponent's enemies—her allies. She nods to one man silently. He juts his chin over to the middle of the battle. Smiling, she fights through the swarm of living and dead, proud that she musters the courage to do what her partner had died for—finally ending it.

She grabs hold of the leader of the enemy tribe from behind, and holds the spear up to their throat. He gasps and she snarls. The warriors around them stop, watching with wide eyes.

She glances at the cliff's edge. So far away, but she can almost feel the breeze.

"Come close, and I kill him!" she shouts. Some look on with pride—her own tribesmen—and others cast upturned brows and snarls. The smell of piss permeates the air. She hates everyone around her.

Still holding the spear up to his throat, she shuffles the leader through the crowd, which parts like fire sizzling on leaves. No one attacks her from behind—though it'd be easy—but her own blood rushes in her ears.

The fellow leader meets her gaze; a question. She nods. He stares. He laughs at the sky.

At the edge, the horizon looms. A bird circles above her. It squawks, and swoops down to the shores below—

And she follows, tipping them both over the edge. As they scream, as the air rushes past their ears, as they hold on tight to each other, she knows he feels the same as she does.

The fighting above stops—perhaps indefinitely, perhaps not. Some drop their weapons as they stare. Some sob.

And then something swoops through the air—two birds, flying right from where the tribe's leaders had fallen. They fly through the air together, and everyone watching falls to the ground in awe.

ALEX BERMAN

YEARS AS MENTEE: 1

GRADE: Sophomore

BORN: New York, NY

LIVES: New York, NY

PUBLICATIONS & RECOGNITIONS:
jGirls; Apprentice Writer, *Blue Marble Review*

MENTEE'S ANECDOTE:

Even over Zoom, meeting and getting to know Jennifer has been an awesome experience. We clicked instantly, gushing about our favorite books and rushing to our bookshelves to show them off (one of the silver linings of this digital partnership). I was so impressed with Jennifer's many projects in writing, hearing about them is a highlight of our meetings. It was so cool to meet a real-life author! Jennifer's help has been paramount to exploring new genres and submitting to new, more imposing publications (like *McSweeney's*). I can't wait for another great semester of writing and talking together.

JENNIFER L. BROWN

YEARS AS MENTOR: 1

OCCUPATION: Writer, Actor, Tutor

BORN: Suffern, NY

LIVES: New York, NY

MENTOR'S ANECDOTE:

Working with Alex has been an incredible experience. When I first met Alex's cat named Fish over Zoom, I knew we'd get along famously. We share a wry sense of humor, a love of graphic novels, and, of course, words. Alex comes into our sessions brimming with ideas, always ready to explore new genres. I have been so impressed at the range of Alex's pieces, from heartfelt and personal to irreverent and wickedly funny. Alex is also a pretty phenomenal artist. Although this concentration of talent in one sophomore borders on unfair, I am so excited to continue working together.

The Bus Stop

ALEX BERMAN

Two girls sit at a bus stop, each wondering if the other feels the same way she does. Wondering if she could be brave enough to find out.

She is unsure, and so is she, and they are unsure together, sitting on a bench waiting for the bus that will whisk her away. She is waiting with her friend, but when the bus comes she will keep walking home. She can feel her friend's heat in the winter cold, and she dares to be hopeful.

Their hands sit side by side on cool metal slats, pinkies close but never touching. She imagines her skin would be soft to the touch if she took her hand and held it. She imagines it would feel like holding a mug of tea, if that mug were soft, fleshy, and attached to a girl that she knew. But it sits there on the bench, untouched by her, and she dares to think it might like to be held.

They are talking, always talking, but neither knows what they are saying. Something about school or parents or basketball practice. Their minds are on their shoulders, hovering within reach of each other's weary heads. Each is covered in flannel and down and wool, soft armor against an early snow. Each holds tension in the way one holds a priceless Fabergé egg, if this egg were not an egg at all but in fact a friendship. She dearly wishes to let her head fall onto the nest made of scarf and coat and backpack strap. She imagines it would be exquisite, warming her neck with her soft hair, listening to her steady pulse. As her friend looks away, she stares and dares to dream the pulse wants to be listened to.

She is afraid, and she is afraid, but neither knows it. So she sits there, unaware of her fear, oblivious to her feelings. She sits there and thinks about herself in conjunction with her, thinks about us and we and other things she cannot comprehend. She wishes to say her name in a proud way, in a soft way. She wishes to treasure her name on her tongue like a cradle holds a sleeping baby, and she dares to believe that she wants to be treasured by her.

The bus rolls up, and they say goodbye. They hug, each trying to keep her body as far away from the other as possible. Their shoulders are tense, their hands are cold, their cheeks do not touch. She climbs on the bus, and she begins to walk away, and she sits on the frigid plastic seat and wishes it were warm.

SIERRA BLANCO

YEARS AS MENTEE: 3

GRADE: Senior

BORN: New York, NY

LIVES: New York, NY

PUBLICATIONS & RECOGNITIONS:
Scholastic Art & Writing Awards:
Gold Key; Winner of National
Endowment for the Arts,
American Theatre Wing, Musical
Theater Songwriting Challenge;
original play *The Smallest Heroes*
published by YouthPLAYS

MENTEE'S ANECDOTE:

Writing with Livia is always an awesome experience. When we wrote our pair story together, it was glorious seeing how our different ideas about storytelling meshed together to create a writing style that was something unique from both our individual writing voices. Not only does Livia give amazing advice from perspectives I wouldn't necessarily think of off the bat, she also has insights into creative fields I don't know about. It's delightful to learn more about visual design from my mentor and, in turn, it's often really useful to explain what I was doing with musical or writing-style choices to Livia.

LIVIA NELSON

YEARS AS MENTOR: 5

OCCUPATION: Product Designer

BORN: Ridgefield, CT

LIVES: Queens, NY

MENTOR'S ANECDOTE:

This is Sierra's and my first year as a pair, and we've had a very "COVID" experience: we've met only over Zoom! But our Monday-afternoon meetings have become a wonderful bright spot in the monotony of quarantine life. I always look forward to hearing updates on Sierra's myriad creative pursuits, and during our sessions, we've collaborated on fiction, music, and artwork. I really hope that one day soon we'll meet in person, but until then I'm confident (and proud!) that we'll keep making new work together despite this year's unique circumstances.

Juliet and Rosalind

SIERRA BLANCO

This surrealist poem reimagines the events of the classic Shakespeare play Romeo and Juliet *from the perspective of Romeo's ex-girlfriend, Rosalind.*

Meet me at the white chalk walls, hope all drawn and leaded
There to make the dreamers fall, once "lost" is now beheaded.
Catch me at night, pale as bone, the comfort fast passed over,
There to let the dying crawl, a simple end to somber.

Sinner sleep the moon tonight, white as blinding day;
Liar turn an eye tonight, wordless what they say.

Meet me at the white chalk walls, rhyme all lost and goaded,
There to make the dreaming fall, a puppet to devotion.
Catch me at that maze's center, motion left to fester;
There to let the secrets tell the way to once and never.

Sinner sleep the moon tonight, bright as blinding day;
Liar, turn an eye tonight, wordless what they pray.

Meet me at the meat-red door, lost and never-ending,
There to turn a tail and run, promise worse for mending.
Penny for a dream they said, dance along the caverns,
There to turn the liar's head, or maybe worse his masters'.

Sinner shake the stars tonight, white as shining day;
Liar turn a cheek tonight, lips to hell and pray.

Meet me at the rust-bled door, long and always bending,
There to make the quarrelers fall, what once and never mended.
Penny for your blues they said, tomorrow will be different;
Pretty to be used, we met, and bowed before in reverence.

Sinner shake the stars tonight, white as blinding day;
Liar, turn a cheek tonight, lips to hell and pray.

Meet me where the lyric ends, though melody forgotten.
Long lost is that owl-eyed girl, the body rained and rotten.
Liar pull a string she begged, and whisked herself away
Off to darker nonsense lands where wraiths and wrongs might stay.
Left behind a message, though not far that it could spread
The story that she wove herself would barely keep her head.

A prayer for the unwitting, the lovers, last the stream;
She gave herself a talisman—a promise how it gleamed
A stolen tinsel locked away, a draught made out of dare,
A place to haunt her years away, a lock of true-love's hair.

Sinner, wake before you go, tonight will last all day;
Liar take a gasping breath before you turn away.

Meet me in the garden, like the poems she once gave
There to take the doubting breath before her lover's grave
Penny for a soldier's soul, a witch's mark, a game
Sinner steal that angel's light, and Liar steal the blame

Meet me at the white chalk walls, I will not leave it bare
Red blood door, I've done this before, I'll replicate each swear
White or dark as morning's turn, I haven't got a clue

Forgive me not, I wrote this plot, and now I'll see it through.

MADELINE SHEA BOCCONE

YEARS AS MENTEE: 1

GRADE: Junior

BORN: Brooklyn, NY

LIVES: Brooklyn, NY

PUBLICATIONS & RECOGNITIONS:
Teen Ink; The WEIGHT Journal

MENTEE'S ANECDOTE:

I met Erin this fall, and it's hard to believe that it's been only a few months of us working together. Not only does Erin do a fabulous job at showing and teaching me things I would have never considered, she's an empathetic figure who keeps me on track while taking how I'm feeling into consideration. Our weekly meeting makes me feel empowered as a writer and proud to be honing my craft.

ERIN V. MAHONEY

YEARS AS MENTOR: 1

OCCUPATION: Marketing Manager

BORN: Evanston, IL

LIVES: New York, NY

PUBLICATIONS & RECOGNITIONS:
Dwell.com

MENTOR'S ANECDOTE:

As I reflect on the year thus far writing with Madeline, it's astonishing to think we've never met in person. Our weekly sessions have allowed us to bond over our passion for food—while Madeline is a whiz in the kitchen, I excel at eating—as well as our shared love of coming-of-age stories rooted in close family ties. Though separated by Zoom boxes and the East River, our time writing together has affirmed the power of storytelling and its ability to foster connection and community.

The Miracle Fish

MADELINE SHEA BOCCONE

Miracle is a sheltered town girl with plenty of smarts. Nessa is tired of being a servant in her own home. When they run away together they have to figure it all out on their own.

Nessa grasped her hands and looked up at her with a frantic look, begging, "Come with me, please!"

"Where are you going?" Miracle asked, searching her face.

"Away," Nessa said. "Please just say yes." Miracle nodded slowly and went back into her home, bringing what she expected to need. A book of maps, her cat—whom she begged to bring—and the loaf of bread her family was supposed to eat. Soon enough they were at a dock on a boat, and seemingly so far away from home. Damn her father, Nessa thought. Damn her destiny to housekeeping, damn her destiny to marry a man as awful as he was. All she'd need was her friend to teach her reading and the boat to give her all she'd need to get by.

At sea, Miracle quickly became weary. The first days were exciting, it was the only reckless thing she'd ever done, and Nessa was so headstrong, all angry as she was from the family conflict. The two of them were filled with adrenaline and stayed up all hours, drinking from stashed bottles in the cabin and eating from the loaf of bread. A week later they were still on the water with only the stale, crusty heels left to eat, and an inability to catch any food. Nessa was still sore and it seemed like it wasn't a vacation, but a journey with no going back.

Presently, Nessa was trying to catch something—anything—and Miracle was watching, and occasionally looking out for her seasick cat.

Nessa was decent at sailing, Miracle thought, but she wasn't so good at fishing. There were only nets, no rods, and neither Miracle nor Nessa knew how to use them. They suspected it was a waiting game mostly, but neither of them was patient enough to just let the net sit. They checked it too frequently, desperate for something to come their way. Nothing ever did, only driftwood and seaweed.

At each pull of the net, Miracle could see her friend grow increasingly frustrated. When daylight began to dwindle, Nessa groaned and threw the net to the deck, Miracle came and put a hand on her shoulder.

"Why don't you take a break?" Miracle suggested gently. "Have some supper. I'll try, you sleep. Don't worry, I hear we'll have more luck at night." She picked up the net and nudged Nessa toward the cabin.

"I'll take care of it," she pressed.

"You've never cast a net before," Nessa said, sighing and trudging away.

"I'll figure it out," Miracle replied. Nessa shook her head, mumbled something about the stale bread, leaving Miracle to make some headway.

She threw the net overboard and tied it to a railing. Then she scooped up her cat and they sat on the deck, Miracle and Faith, waiting for something to happen.

The sea was a beautiful element that was as unfamiliar to Miracle as a pit of fire or a perch upon a cloud. Her parents were townspeople and her life was spent in the town square she'd always known. The only experience she had with water was her family's annual beach trip, when her father sacrificed a busy Saturday's worth of sales and her mother cleaned extra the day before to compensate. Miracle couldn't swim—she had no swimsuit—but she would often go down to the shore and watch the tide wash over her feet, and feel the ocean air rustle the long curls that fell down her back.

That was when she wore her hair down. Now she was quite grown up. Her mother had said as much one day as she left for school. She even put Miracle's hair up herself, pinning it into the simple bun she'd worn every day since. From then on, she did women's chores, spoke in a woman's tone, and went to school not simply for an education, but to show she'd make a suitable wife.

Here, she smelled the salt all around her and felt the breeze of the breathing water brush her face coolly. It was like the start of a new day. She was with Nessa, who valued her knowledge. She was far from the world of eligible young men and her looming marriage to one of them. She let down her hair, took off her shoes, and let her head fall back.

Just as she was relaxed, the rope line pulled and she snapped her head up. The heavy cord thumped against the railing and the wooden deck of the boat. Miracle let down the cat and started to yell.

"The net!" she cried. Nessa came rushing out. Nessa grabbed on to the rope and pulled hard, and soon Miracle was tugging alongside her. Whatever was caught in the net was strong, and, both of them hoped, big. They pulled, groaned, finally pulled the net aboard.

With all that effort, they had expected a whole school of fish, but when they peered into the netting, all they saw was one bright carp, flopping around in its trap. Miracle laughed, quietly at first, then a howling guffaw. It wasn't large, but it would be enough for a great feast that night.

After that night, days came and went. Faith grew used to the swaying, and the two girls sailed still. Nessa became an expert captain and Miracle never had to marry. Though they never caught another fish, they were never hungry again, their bellies still full and their spirits still high from the miracle fish they captured at the start of their new beginning.

AMY BRADU

YEARS AS MENTEE: 1

GRADE: Junior

BORN: Queens, NY

LIVES: Queens, NY

MENTEE'S ANECDOTE:

The first time I ever conceptualized a story with another person was when my mentor and I came up with the idea for our pair project. We already knew that we wanted to use a Java program to write a choose-your-own-adventure story, but what we weren't sure about was the actual contents of said story. Figuring it out together, sharing the same evolving yet abstract idea, was a really fascinating experience.

JORDAN GASS-POORE'

YEARS AS MENTOR: 2

OCCUPATION: Audio Producer at CNN

BORN: San Marcos, TX

LIVES: Queens, NY

PUBLICATIONS & RECOGNITIONS: CNN; Type Investigations; Public Radio International

MENTOR'S ANECDOTE:

Amy and I allow each other to make mistakes. We know that good writing is more than just writing. It needs a human component, one that Amy has: She's honest, determined, and trusts her instincts—and is open to alternatives to the classic Lorem ipsum. Our writing relationship is about trusting our ability to read and know when something doesn't make sense. We bring that reader's eye to our writing. We know every writer needs a reader and we take turns filling those roles when needed.

Tar

AMY BRADU

A poem on the often cruel and uncaring nature of the passage of time during the pandemic.

How it drags defines the struggle,
that it steals more moments than it is owed.
The hours, the days, the months, the years,
those would be enough,
but no, they must come,
as molasses flows.

No,
not molasses,
molasses is too sweet,
too brilliant in its color.
Too suited to the whims of men.
No, it flows not like molasses,
it feels more like

tar.

A boiling void
whose encroach is slow
and entirely merciless.

to ceaselessly toil in the rising tar,
that's what we're here for.

Haplessly typing on a broken keyboard,
completely unaware of its ascent
until at last
we are consumed.

The only difference
between now and then,
is at last we can see it
and how pathetic is that.

MAEVE ROSE BROWNE

YEARS AS MENTEE: 1

GRADE: Senior

BORN: New York, NY

LIVES: New York, NY

PUBLICATIONS & RECOGNITIONS:
Scholastic Art & Writing Awards: Gold Key and Honorable Mention; Drexel Photography Contest

MENTEE'S ANECDOTE:

Although Julia and I have never met in person, we've been able to grow as writers and teachers over the screen. Our weekly meetings are times to learn new techniques, rant about the world, and even bond over our love of Wes Anderson. Julia has also been an amazing scheduler, making sure I get everything done on time. This piece would not be complete without her.

JULIA RITTENBERG

YEARS AS MENTOR: 1

OCCUPATION: Freelance Writer

BORN: Brooklyn, NY

LIVES: Brooklyn, NY

MENTOR'S ANECDOTE:

One time, we worked on a "first lines" project where we wrote paragraphs based on the first sentences of famous novels. We had so much fun doing it, and we got the idea from a Girls Write Now Friday Salon!

Christmas in the City

MAEVE ROSE BROWNE

*I was inspired to write this piece in December when I was absorbing
the Christmas spirit in a shut-down New York.*

Christmas in New York City is like no other.

Evergreen trees shed their tiny pine needles all over the gray concrete,
festive lights line the classic brownstones, and both tourists and natives
glide along the ice ground of Wollman Rink. Films like *Elf*, *Serendipity*,
and the classic *Home Alone 2* only add to the unique holiday scene in
New York.

Of course, with the unconventional year we've had, the jolly spirit
never made its way to the city. "For rent" signs plague the city, and
boarded-up stores continue to invade streets. There are no clusters of
people straining their necks to look at the massive Rockefeller tree, nor
are there any religious ceremonies.

But even through the hardships, I've noticed the resurgence of a classic holiday activity.

One day I was on a casual stroll in my neighborhood, craving fresh
air and praying it would cure my Zoom fatigue. As I was walking, I
peered, in the least creepy way possible, into the large windows of some
of the brownstones. Every single one had a common factor: Christmas
trees. I did not pass a home or apartment without the evergreen tree
wrapped in rainbow lights.

I immediately googled if Christmas tree sales had increased this year,
and they had. In fact, sales had nearly doubled within the first few weeks
of the season.

This led me to ponder why we were all in a tree frenzy. The most logical reasons are probably due to a lack of travel—if you vacation during the holiday season, you probably won't be purchasing a tree. But thinking about this from a psychological point of view, it makes sense.

Everyone has undergone this expansive change. Life as we know it is gone, and all of the holiday joy that we felt has dissipated. But these trees in people's homes are a thing of wonder.

We're all tired of seeing the rising death toll every time we turn on the television, but at the same time we can't truly distract ourselves. But a Christmas tree is a new life; it is something that eats up our time but also connects through the action of decorating.

No matter if you are fighting with Mom or irritated by a sibling, everyone circles around the bushel of pine standing in the home.

The divisiveness in our country right now is incalculable. But all of those windows busy with bright trees remind me that, even in our most difficult times, we all come together. We latch on to each other and rely on one another to survive. Much like those lights on the trees, we are all intertwined with the goal of bringing light to our world.

GABRIELLA CALABIA

YEARS AS MENTEE: 1

GRADE: Junior

BORN: Basel, Switzerland

LIVES: New York, NY

PUBLICATIONS & RECOGNITIONS:
Scholastic Art & Writing Awards:
Gold Key and Silver Key

MENTEE'S ANECDOTE:

Writing your inner truth is scary, and even scarier is sharing that most personal self with the world. However, the moment I met Kiki, her joy, kindness, and light radiated across my screen. I knew we had something truly special. With Kiki's support, I fueled my writing with my deepest feelings and emotions, and, maybe more important, began to live unapologetically with that same fervor. I once said that Kiki helped give me my voice, but she quickly responded that it existed all along, we just had to find it. And I needed to learn to listen and trust it.

KIKI TOM

YEARS AS MENTOR: 2

OCCUPATION: Writer, Author

BORN: New York, NY

LIVES: New York, NY

PUBLICATIONS & RECOGNITIONS:
Author, *The Celestial Sexpot's Handbook* and *Angst!*; SXSW Interactive Innovation Award; NAL Quick Pick Book Award

MENTOR'S ANECDOTE:

Wednesday afternoons fast became the highlight of my week during this pandemic, as it's the time Gabriella and I connect and exchange thoughts on everything from poetry to politics. Wise, responsible, and focused, along with talented and kind, she's my Girls Write Now dream girl, the exact mentee I wanted to mentor. Riding shotgun on her self-discovery as a poet has not only given me the most wonderful flashbacks of my own trip, but also confirmed the timeless power of poetry as an eternal symbol of hope. It warms my heart seeing her carry this torch now.

shadows of the sea

GABRIELLA CALABIA

*Separated by a century, two paths intersect in a journey of identity,
legacy, womanhood, and coming of age in a painful world.*

in my dreams my great-grandmother and i are one.
our earthly bodies never took a breath together
but for a moment we froze
as she departed the atmosphere and i entered
kissing my slanted eyes she offered me her name,
our name
now our celestial forms find each other again.
she guides me through the village she never came back to
fire licks the clouds
dust in the barren fields catches the air
her house caved in from an earthquake
she says it was made of the ground and has now returned
spices that only adorned her memory waft through us
many things she doesn't recognize.
our motherland thrashes under the whip of corruption and greed.
she cannot make baby bones and mutilated child soldiers beautiful,
she was ripped away before the soft rivers turned red and
now she stumbles over bronze bodies strewn together.
a girl is raped.
relief spreads over her
when the knife cuts through her throat like butter.
this could have been her, and this would have been me.

betrothal shacked her up and no longer can she understand the cries
what she does not say is that it was one death exchanged for another.
she tells me many did not survive the passage at sea
their lifeless bodies thrown overboard
i picture all those wronged on land below the waves
their pain washed away and lulled to a peace they did not find on land
i wonder how often she wished to take her place among them,
slowly sinking
the world
drowned out.

LUZ CALIX

YEARS AS MENTEE: 1

GRADE: Senior

BORN: Bronx, NY

LIVES: Bronx, NY

MENTEE'S ANECDOTE:

Working together as a pair is very easy and the conversations flow rapidly and seamlessly. Working and sharing with Kara has always been a very easy and fun experience.

KARA GELBER

YEARS AS MENTOR: 1

OCCUPATION: Communications Director

BORN: Baltimore, MD

LIVES: Bronx, NY

MENTOR'S ANECDOTE:

It was a pleasure collaborating with Luz on this piece, and I've loved watching her grow as a writer and young woman throughout the process.

The Dream Industry

LUZ CALIX

On dream jobs, *we finally got the chance to interview a few employees from The Dream Industry, and the owner of the company himself! They had no idea this was part of a larger series!*

Inspired by NBC's The Office.

How is working at The Dream Industry—must be fun?

MIKEY: Working at The Dream Industry is a literal dream! Ha, see what I did there? As the boss or the big guy, ha, you know I try to make it as fun as I possibly can. We do roast battles all the time and are so close that some people mistake us for a family.

MAI: Uhh, well it's certainly not boring, I mean, Mikey is . . . quite the character—he surprises us with something new every day. He asked me where Zuko was the other day. You know, from *Avatar*—it was cute, I guess.

BLUE: Not that great. Our boss, Mikey, just comes up to us sometimes and insults us. My name isn't even Blue, it's Jerry, but Mikey thought I looked like Blue from *Blue's Clues* and it just stuck. Also there's no training whatsoever, so trying to figure out how to take the concept of dreams into reality for people is *bleep.*

How does one create dreams? Or, more specifically, how does the whole process work?

MIKEY: Well, let me say that it brings literal tears to my eyes when I see the process done. In more details, we see these ideas as little babies and we nurture them into something so beautiful and majestic, like a prince or princess. We raise your wishes to be your realities; it is the Dream Industry motto.

MAI: My favorite part of The Dream Industry is Cranium L.E.D. Outlet Um Device aka The Cloud. Yeah, Mikey liked the idea of having an acronym but . . . I think you can figure out what happened. From the sky they connect to your nervous system, so we can pick out the ideas from the part of your brain, and with that we send them to the Dream Mainframe where they digitize and create the scenarios before sending them back to the brain. Then ta-da! Dreams are made.

BLUE: I don't know, I just press a button and a light pops up and, boom, dreams.

What kind of dreams do you often see?

MIKEY: Beautiful dreams. We don't allow ourselves to give nightmares, but sometimes it depends on the person, you know? For example, frolicking through a meadow of blooming flowers. For the girls and the gays we even have Harry Styles in a dress waiting with open arms. It was so beautiful . . . I mean, from what I can tell.

MAI: Normal dreams of any kind. I mean, I see a lot of people who want to live in fictional worlds of all kinds, which is cool. Most want to be either a villain or the hero. Some surprise me when they just want to sit on the sidelines, but it's really fun to create.

BLUE: Oh my god, don't get me wrong, some dreams are totally epic, like last time I saw the whole anime fight scene, which let me tell you needs to be animated now, but some are just weird . . . Like who wants to swim in a glass of milkshake? I don't get it. Once Mikey got his dream cloud uploaded to the mainframe and it was him running in a field of sunflowers into Harry Styles's arms. It was hilarious, and also disturbing.

Can you tell us more about the three weeks that The Dream Industry shut down?

MIKEY: We can't disclose any information regarding the incident in respect to our clients and our employees.

MAI: Uh, well, I can't really say anything because I don't want to get fired. And you know the, umm, respect for our clients, yeah.

BLUE: *Bleep* yeah! So let me tell you, Mikey, being Mikey, wanted to send a movie scene that he created to us all at the same time while we were awake. But he spilled his papaya smoothie all over the mainframe and it electrocuted the *bleep* out of him. It was hilarious, and we saw it all since he was still connected and sharing it with us. But yeah, he messed up the mainframe, it blew up, and luckily no one died. It's one of the reasons there's a sign outside that says, "No drinks inside or else!"

Well, that's all for today. Is there anything else you might want to add?

MIKEY: The Dream Industry will always provide the best service to our clients—we love and care for you all!

MAI: Go, The Dream Industry!

BLUE: Can we maybe not share my name or keep all this off the record?

SURE! *(That was a lie.)*
After we wrapped up, we were unfortunately informed that Blue was fired, so good luck on the job search, Blue, we at News No One Wants Daily *are rooting for you!*

MICHELLE CAO

YEARS AS MENTEE: 1

GRADE: Senior

BORN: Brooklyn, NY

LIVES: Brooklyn, NY

MENTEE'S ANECDOTE:

Quite frankly and literally, one hundred words now remind me of Emily. Someone who grounds me as I navigate my weekly emotional currents. Someone who seems to know exactly what to say and do. Someone who sees me beyond my grammar mistakes. During our weekly hangouts, we share our love for food, passion for reflection, and voice for change through one-hundred-word stories that sometimes make no sense. We laugh, we smile, we chat, but sometimes sit in awkward silence too. And even then, I wouldn't choose to have it any other way.

EMILY GREGOR

YEARS AS MENTOR: 1

OCCUPATION: Content Marketer

BORN: Lawrence, KS

LIVES: Brooklyn, NY

MENTOR'S ANECDOTE:

Michelle and I have sincerely enjoyed our weekly writing sessions. We've explored one-hundred-word stories, writing about food, college essays, and more, and we're looking forward to another semester of getting to know each other!

5 Ways to Celebrate the Chinese Lunar New Year from Home

MICHELLE CAO AND EMILY GREGOR

With the impact of COVID-19, events have continued to move from large, in-person celebrations to virtual gatherings, including the sixteen-day Lunar New Year.

Lunar New Year, or Spring Festival, is celebrated in many parts of Asia, including China, Cambodia, Singapore, Indonesia, Myanmar, Thailand, Vietnam, and the Philippines. The celebration commemorates the first full moon of the Lunar New Year, and usually consists of following variations of age-old rituals and gathering with extended families to welcome the New Year.

My parents emigrated from Fuzhou, China, more than twenty years ago, but Lunar New Year remains one of our family's largest celebrations. Each year, we integrate generations-old rituals and traditions with Western influence. Every year, my family decorates the house with large posters of zodiac animals coupled with lanterns and orchids in the living room.

On the first morning, I kneel beside my mother outside as she lights the joss papers on fire and places them in the pot, one after another, chanting well-wishes to the spirits, departed relatives, and ancestors. Often, curious strangers stop by to watch and ask about it. I used to run back into the house, but now I'm beginning to appreciate my culture's unique traditions and am happy to share them with others.

We prepare seven dishes of vegetables and desserts and line up ten cups of wine and chopsticks to welcome our dead ancestors back for a New Year's meal. This is an integral way to honor their lives and pay respect to our family's elders. Roughly an hour later, we enjoy the food, reflect on the past year, and read our horoscopes.

After eating, there's usually a bit of downtime before gathering with our extended family at a local diner. We usually play mah-jongg, but last year, my mother taught me how to play a different variation of Bo Bing. When I was younger, we dressed up in fancy qipao, but now we opt to wear anything red before feasting with my father's side of the family. It's symbolic of good luck and fortune.

IF YOU'RE INTERESTED IN CELEBRATING LUNAR NEW YEAR FROM HOME, HERE ARE FIVE WAYS YOU CAN GET INVOLVED:

1. Honor departed loved ones

Paying tribute to departed ancestors and celebrating their lives is an integral part of the New Year celebration. You can pay respect by following traditional rituals, such as burning joss paper to incense, chanting, and praying at temples to ensure prosperity and good luck in the afterlife.

You can also celebrate their presence by reminiscing on memories, continuing family traditions, and inviting them back for the grand New Year's dinner. Remembrance of departed ancestors will usually be rewarded with blessings and luck over the upcoming year.

2. Gather (virtually) with family and friends

Even though it might not be safe to gather in person, tools such as Zoom, Google Meet, and WhatsApp make it easy to host video calls with your entire family or friend group. You can share a meal, reflect on the past year and plan for the new one, and play games like mah-jongg.

3. Decorate your home with red and gold

Preparing your home for the Lunar New Year is essential. Before you decorate, make sure to clean your space thoroughly to get rid of any bad luck that has accumulated over the past year.

To attract good luck, money, and health, incorporate bright red, shiny metallic, and white colors into your decor. You can also opt to decorate with traditional rice-paper lanterns, special dinnerware and vases, or even a small tangerine or kumquat tree.

4. Learn how to make traditional food

Popular foods eaten during the New Year are usually established because of their pronunciation or appearance. For instance, vegetables such as lettuce and bok choy are synonymous with luck because both are pronounced as *cai* with different tones. Dumplings, or *jiao zi*, for instance, resemble prosperity because they are made in the shape of Chinese coins.

Glutinous rice cakes, or *nian gao*, translated to "higher years," are another specialty dessert and are symbolic of eternal prosperity. While the key ingredients mainly consist of different kinds of flours and cane water, you can adjust the recipe to make it yours by adding additional toppings such as dates, raisins, peanuts, et cetera. Rice cakes also make great gifts when visiting relatives around the holidays.

5. Enjoy traditional music and dance (in parades)

While Gong Xi Ni, Cai Shen Dao, and Xin Nian Dao are typical greetings for the New Year, they are also well-known radio songs that set the scene for the celebrations. Framed around good luck, prosperity, good health, and a fresh new start, they're often played as background music, integrated into decor, and in large parades.

Parades and community celebrations are other outlets to immerse and appreciate Chinese arts. The lion and dragon dance symbolizes strength, power, and courage to scare off evil. Traditional dances such as the fan and handkerchief dance are often performed by women and represent femininity and delicacy.

Lunar New Year is symbolic of new beginnings and good luck. Although family gatherings and large-scale celebrations will not be taking place this year, let's continue to uphold century-old traditions and safely celebrate the beauty of Asian culture.

Happy Lunar New Year to those who celebrate. We wish you a year filled with love, health, and prosperity as we welcome 2021, the year of the Ox!

AMINA CASTRONOVO

YEARS AS MENTEE: 2

GRADE: Junior

BORN: New York, NY

LIVES: New York, NY

PUBLICATIONS & RECOGNITIONS:
Published in ABC News and
Medium; Scholastic Art &
Writing Awards: Honorable
Mention

MENTEE'S ANECDOTE:

As soon as Angelica stepped through the door to the New-York Historical Society the day we met, I knew she was my mentor. It was the type of face and energy that felt so familiar. I felt that I had known her forever, and ever since, our conversations have not proven otherwise. On the first day after we both shared our love for zodiac signs, Angelica took us to a French library with a ceiling of the constellations. This, combined with my favorite language, spoke to my soul and I was confident that Angelica understood.

ANGELICA PUZIO

YEARS AS MENTOR: 2

OCCUPATION: Researcher

BORN: Charlottesville, VA

LIVES: Brooklyn, NY

PUBLICATIONS & RECOGNITIONS:
womenwin.vote, *Teen Vogue*,
Journal of Adolescence

MENTOR'S ANECDOTE:

Amina and I are in our second year of deep conversations, laughs, spilling the tea, and bringing her writing to life. As the world changed drastically throughout the pandemic, our bond stayed strong. This year has not stopped Amina from pushing her writing further; her essays ask readers to hold up a mirror to themselves and think critically, often with necessary discomfort, about elements of culture that are taboo, especially for teenage girls. Amina's complexity, brilliance, and moral courage cannot be overstated, along with how lucky I am to be beside her for a second year.

Excerpt from "On the Intersection Between Teenage Sexuality and the Objectivity of Women Across Races"

AMINA CASTRONOVO

The following piece analyzes a girl's friendship with a boy at school, a friendship that shows her that taking ownership of her sexual desires should be done without shame.

Despite my best efforts to avoid him, I became quite close with a boy at my school named Vlad, a scrawny Russian twelve-year-old who *constantly* talked about sex. This friendship was mysterious to others as well as to myself. To me, he was the bogeyman of childhood innocence—an innocence that I had thrown away by losing my virginity earlier that year. How ironic. I had committed the act, but for some reason talking about it, especially with someone who would praise me for it, scared the shit out of me.

He and I were never attracted to each other, yet we enjoyed discussing the topic of sex on the regular. I had never experienced such a connection before, because I had been conditioned to believe that sex is always sexual. My conversations with Vlad opened my eyes to see that sex is just a part of life. People can experience it, write about it, long for it, prepare for it, learn about it, and, in the case of Vlad and I, debate about it. He consistently argued that sex can be used for physical pleasure, and I fervently rebutted his contention with reasons of love and tenderness. We both scoffed at each other, but I was soon to understand the validity of his statement.

One day after school, he said he needed to go to the drugstore, and when I asked why, he replied with a smirky grin and: "I need condoms." Oh, God, *that* word. Didn't he know better than to utter it out loud? What made me even more uncomfortable was the omniscience of his words. What did he need *those things* for? Was he having sex? He had never mentioned that there was someone else. Did he expect *us* to have sex and this was his way of asking me? Or, the most gruesome of the options, did he want them as a tool as he . . . did the dirty to himself? None of these questions were answered as we stepped into the Duane Reade drugstore next to our school. I darted my head back and forth to see if anyone we knew was inside. My heart was pulsing as he picked out the "perfect" type of condoms, holding two different boxes in his hands. Just there, standing openly in the aisle.

"Banana or strawberry?"

My horrified look said it all.

"You're right, banana."

As we stood in line, I had never wanted to crawl into a hole more in my life. I kept shifting my backpack between my shoulders, and I could practically hear my owl-themed pencil case screeching at me through the fabric. The man standing behind us seemed to be piercing me and my lack of virginity with his eyes as if he was the conservative messiah, there to tear down the "Open for Business" sign hanging on a string from my vagina. Of course, as we waited, Vlad picked up some Skittles from the counter, because nothing says "I'm an awkward little guy who's about to bang this depressed bisexual" quite like a plastic bag full of rainbow-colored crap. I waited anxiously for the cashier to say something as she rang us up. We were twelve-year-olds buying condoms, for God's sake! But no. She looked us straight in the eyes and asked if we were paying cash or card. A receipt had never printed for so long before.

✳ ✳ ✳ ✳ ✳ ✳

If adolescents were taught to take ownership of their sexuality, perhaps there would be less conformity into racist and sexist stereotypes. Women of all races are human, and thus they have the inherent right to express themselves sexually however they see fit. This expression can be passionate and overwhelming, or timid and slow, or anything in between. That should be the first lesson students learn in Sex Ed. Let's stop pretending that teens are not privy to one of the most wonderful aspects of life. We're teenagers, experiencing life is what we do! Teenagers are going to have sex. They're going to masturbate. They're going to go condom shopping, because they *can*. And that's good. So, to all of the teens out there: Find your something. It could be a Vladimir, an object, a book, or a website—something that replaces shame with exploration. You don't have to do anything, just observe the ways your body reacts to the liberation of sex. Looking back now, perhaps all he wanted was to put on a show for me, but I'm glad I watched. My experience with him taught me one of the most valuable lessons for a young woman to absorb: There's nothing wrong with wanting to feel another person or yourself. Vlad taught me that, and I hope that wherever he is, he's making himself very happy.

> *"Good sex is like good bridge. If you don't have a good partner, you'd better have a good hand."*
>
> —MAE WEST

DOROTHY CHAN

YEARS AS MENTEE: 1

GRADE: Junior

BORN: Brooklyn, NY

LIVES: Brooklyn, NY

PUBLICATIONS & RECOGNITIONS:
Scholastic Art & Writing Awards:
Honorable Mentions

MENTEE'S ANECDOTE:

From the time that we've spent together, we've bonded over our shared interests in television shows and writing silly ghost stories. But aside from that, we've also accompanied each other on our journeys in exploring the art of literature. I'm grateful for the experiences that I've gained from this writing relationship that has helped me become a better and more confident writer.

MARINA FANG

YEARS AS MENTOR: 1

OCCUPATION: Journalist

BORN: Albany, NY

LIVES: Brooklyn, NY

MENTOR'S ANECDOTE:

I really like that we learn from each other. We usually start each of our sessions by just sharing how we're feeling and what we've been up to, and those conversations often lead to great writing insights and ideas. I also appreciate that we are honest with each other about how we're feeling, which I think has led to a fruitful writing relationship.

reverie

DOROTHY CHAN

/'rev(ə)rē/

noun

a state of being pleasantly lost in one's thoughts; a daydream

i am a dreamer of ambition,
ambitious for a world filled with daisies and butterflies,
coupled with bright sunrises and blue skies

i listen to the sparrows chirp their morning melodies,
creating a symphony with the rustling leaves.
i wait for the sky to clear so the sun can arrive,
but that is a reality i am unprepared for.

uncovered by thick clouds and fog,
i see the wilted fields and withering grass,
illuminated by the streaks of sunshine,
hidden under ignorance and indifference,
and soon forgotten under the stroke of darkness.

i tell myself,
i am Strong and Brave, with an eye for sight.
i envision meadows of lavender instead,
bathing under bright rays of yellow,
yearning to see the butterflies once more

but they tell me,
i am fragile and weak, without a voice with might.
they took my cries calling for the birds
and threw them into the breeze,
letting them succumb to the wind.

i keep dreaming of the daisies,
waiting for their bloom,
wishing to sit and welcome the warmth,
but this reality can only be
a dream flickering in my mind

because i am only ambitious if i dream,
and i can only dream if i am ambitious.

SANDRA CHEAH

YEARS AS MENTEE: 1

GRADE: Sophomore

BORN: New York, NY

LIVES: Queens, NY

PUBLICATIONS & RECOGNITIONS:
Plan-international.org,
Dearglobalgirls.org

MENTEE'S ANECDOTE:

The past few months working with Natalie have flown by. I love how random and off-topic our conversations can get, from my hair-care routine, her lovely cat (whose name I can never remember), standing desks, abnormally huge alarm clocks, astrology, Twitter, Model UN delegate dances, and more. Not only is she a fun person to be around, but she has supported me outside our Girls Write Now space. Thank you for teaching me how to use commas and em dashes—my English teacher has thanked you in advance.

NATALIE DAHER

YEARS AS MENTOR: 3

OCCUPATION: Editor

BORN: Darby, PA

LIVES: Brooklyn, NY

PUBLICATIONS & RECOGNITIONS:
NowThis, *The Week*, *The Daily Beast*

MENTOR'S ANECDOTE:

It has been a joy to mentor and write and laugh with Sandra this year. She is a fountain of ideas and has an incredible range of interests and skills, from entrepreneurship and personal writing to her neighborhood of Flushing, Queens. Without her, I'd have been way late to discovering the perfect song "Driver's License" by Olivia Rodrigo, among other TikTok gems. I've been so proud of Sandra for taking initiative as pod chair, pushing outside her comfort zone in her writing, and making remarkable discoveries along the way. Can't wait to see where her creativity takes her next.

Commuting Up

SANDRA CHEAH

Shuttling between two neighborhoods, Flushing, Queens, and the Upper East Side, this story follows a girl's journey to school. Along her commute, she discovers her identity and the meaning of hard work and perseverance.

Oxford Languages describes middle school as "a school intermediate between an elementary school and a high school," but to me, middle school marked the realization of my identity.

Little did I know, my daily route to this small, predominantly white school would provoke years of internal conflicts. It wasn't just the difference in socioeconomic backgrounds between my hometown of Flushing, Queens, where I lived with my Malaysia-born mother and older sister, and the Upper East Side, one of New York's most desired neighborhoods. On my commute, I saw mothers frantically holding their children as they tried to sell fruit and churros to nearby commuters, and women running to catch their six a.m. buses—barely making time to eat breakfast. I saw the daily rush onto the train to grab a seat; if you didn't find one, you might sleep on your arm while gripping on to the metal poles. As I traveled to the Upper East Side, I saw my neighbors' livelihoods and hard work, the sweat and tears of working nine-to-fives.

My days began with my daily *amNewYorkmetro* newspaper, which informed me about the frequent house fires across the city or new street fairs and upcoming events. I took two trains, including a transfer, to get to the 96th Street subway station near my school. First, I took the 7 train, which ran overground, where you could look at the morning sunrise and see the skyscrapers in Manhattan, even from Queens. After a lengthy twenty-minute express ride from the first stop, Flushing Main Street station, to almost the last, Times Square, I'd get off and head toward the Q train. I'd meet my friend, Sarah G., one of the people I could relate to as a student, who also came from a district that was far from where our peers lived. Sarah was one of the few Mexicans in my middle school, and became my friend after we bonded over a game competing against tough eighth graders. The Q train was always packed at the first two stops uptown. People pushed, shoved, and yelled to get others off and their acquaintances on. At about 72nd Street, though, you could finally stand or find a seat to breathe. It felt rather calm and peaceful after minutes— which felt like hours—of being packed like Poland Spring bottles in a case.

Taking a train was the leading factor behind finding other friends who would understand me and relate to some of the uncomfortable situations I faced on a daily basis. I guess it's just a New York thing. Out of the five hundred kids in my middle school, only one took the 7 train. She lived in Elmhurst, a neighborhood in Queens not too far from Flushing, and was the only friend who could relate to the packed trains, the constant shifts in transportation, and, most important, the cultural differences. Every day on my way home from school, I saw the heads of people next to me coming closer as they fell deeper into sleep, the kids around me with their heads on their backpacks, snoring.

The little details: train stop, a game, and even my middle school played a huge role in developing my story. From a New York perspective, taking the train was more than just a way to get to school; it was a daily reminder of my life, my differences, and the extra effort I had to put in each morning. To label these differences as weaknesses is false. While they felt like barriers in the beginning, enduring and adapting to these changes helped me realize that they were my strengths. They made me a strong, independent girl from Flushing, Queens.

CHELSEA CHINEDO

YEARS AS MENTEE: 2

GRADE: Junior

BORN: Bronx, NY

LIVES: Bronx, NY

PUBLICATIONS & RECOGNITIONS:
What To Do podcast; *Taking Our Place in History: The Girls Write Now 2020 Anthology*

MENTEE'S ANECDOTE:

Pre-pandemic, Olivia and I used to meet in Manhattan at this café and share a chocolate-chip cookie while talking about our week. Even though using FaceTime is not the same as seeing each other in person, we work as effectively as we always have. She encourages me, listens to me, and brings out the best in my writing.

OLIVIA JANE SMITH

YEARS AS MENTOR: 5

OCCUPATION: Senior Editor, Internal Communications, NYU Langone Health

BORN: Rochester, NY

LIVES: Brooklyn, NY

PUBLICATIONS & RECOGNITIONS:
Ragan Communications Best Executive Letter; New York Live Arts Writer-in-Residence; Press Club of New Orleans Feature Writing Award

MENTOR'S ANECDOTE:

Pre-pandemic, Chelsea and I liked to split a chocolate-chip cookie during our meetings at Culture cafe, a tiny space where we often had to wait for a table to free up. Now we have our weekly meetings via FaceTime and have been enjoying writing daily haiku diaries and sharing them to catch up on our weeks.

Total Eclipse of the Heart

CHELSEA CHINEDO

Anna experienced a total eclipse of the heart. She had fallen for Joshua and almost lost herself in the process. This new obsession led her to compare herself to other girls on social media.

Anna, a beautiful girl from the Bronx. Smart. Driven. Kind. Talented. Lovable. Sweet. She was many things, maybe even everything anyone could ever ask for.

One day, Anna and her family went to a party in Philadelphia hosted by family friends of Anna's parents. Anna and her siblings were playing card games with all the children. One of them was named Joshua. He had changed a lot since she last saw him. As he got up to go fetch a drink he quickly smiled at Anna. His teeth glistened; it was so bright it almost blinded Anna. Joshua and Anna ended up being partners in this game.

When Anna looked at Joshua, butterflies swarmed her stomach. She was so mesmerized by his bright teeth, nice smile, and curly hair. When they were supposed to talk and generate ideas, Anna let him do all the talking and simply shook her head. "Anna, you put down a blue six on a yellow two, are you even paying attention?!" said one of the children. "Oh my God, so sorry. Haha!" Anna said as she removed the card anxiously. "There's no way we're gonna win now, I need a new partner," Joshua said under his breath. Because Anna was so nervous and this game required teamwork, they ended up losing. Joshua had a small grin on his face, like he had secondhand embarrassment for Anna. As kind as he was, Joshua had a competitive nature and wasn't too happy about playing with Anna if it meant he would lose.

The game was over and it was time for Anna and her family to return home. As Anna walked out the door, she looked back to see if Joshua was going to say goodbye. But as she turned, she saw him running up the stairs, farther and farther into the distance.

On the car ride home, Anna wondered why she was so shy and wasn't able to show Joshua who she really was. She thought he would never look her way. Not because she was ugly or boring, but because she was shy and quiet and Joshua was the opposite. Anna said to herself, "You know what, I like him a lot, but I don't think he's into me, so I'm going to drop it. Besides, he lives in Philly."

A week passed, and Anna received a follow request on Instagram from Joshua. Feelings came rushing back to her. "He had to be searching for me, we have no mutual friends, he intentionally looked for me," she thought to herself. Anna felt that perhaps she had it all wrong, and he did take an interest in her.

Anna and Joshua spoke a lot throughout the year. They became good friends, exchanged numbers, added each other on all social media platforms, and talked about all sorts of things. They even confessed that they could see themselves with each other. Anna was so worried about what Joshua thought about her that she even made a private story on Snapchat just for him. Anna would intentionally post things in the hope that Joshua would reply. When he didn't, she would get really sad.

Anna began to look through Joshua's following list and searched for girls who had his school name and graduating class in their bios, "CPA '22." "Maybe he likes white girls, maybe he likes girls who consistently post on Instagram, maybe he likes girls who play sports, maybe he prefers short girls." She began to think about everything they had that she didn't. As Anna scrolled through their Instagram pictures, she saw many people praising them in the comment sections for their good looks. *Gorgeous girly imy. You are literally the cutest person alive.* She saw pictures of them at parties and homecoming.

Anna wished she could go to parties and that her school had homecoming. She went to a small school and had strict parents, so she didn't get to hang out with friends and go to parties like other teens did. Not to mention Anna never posted on Instagram and didn't have many followers.

Joshua had told Anna that he thought she was pretty, but it was clear that he knew many other pretty girls. Later that week, Joshua and Anna were texting about Anna's love life and Joshua left Anna on unread. Joshua was probably just busy, but knowing that didn't make it hurt any less. She realized that she was being crazy. All of it, the whole thing, was just crazy. She wasn't mad at Joshua. She was the one who got obsessed and caught up and fed her mind with things.

"How can I compare myself to girls I don't even know? Their lives on social media may seem great, but social media is meant to highlight the coolest things you do, it may not be how it seems," she thought to herself. She wished she hadn't been so invasive. She kept being friends with Joshua to see where things would go, but she wished she could erase the images of his friends out of her memory.

ATIQA CHOWDHURY

YEARS AS MENTEE: 2

GRADE: Senior

BORN: Dhaka, Bangladesh

LIVES: Brooklyn, NY

MENTEE'S ANECDOTE:

My meetings with Nandita have been something I've looked forward to every week. The pandemic made my responsibilities feel even heavier, but our weekly meetings never felt like a chore to me. I love catching up with her and talking about school. Especially this year, Nandita taking the first few minutes of our meeting to ask about my college process makes me feel so grateful. She's definitely been part of my support system as a student and I love hearing about her own experiences in college.

NANDITA RAGHURAM

YEARS AS MENTOR: 5

OCCUPATION: Editor

BORN: Chicago, IL

LIVES: Brooklyn, NY

PUBLICATIONS & RECOGNITIONS:
Mashable, Vice, The Village Voice

MENTOR'S ANECDOTE:

My relationship with Atiqa has grown so much over the past two years, despite the challenges presented by the pandemic. I felt that acutely when we did one particular writing exercise. We wrote character sketches, in the form of poems, of each other. Atiqa's descriptions of me were so spot-on and accurate. She even nailed my habits and mannerisms! I'm so excited to see how she grows and flourishes as a writer and can't wait to watch our friendship and writing relationship develop further.

To the Grave

ATIQA CHOWDHURY

People tell me I can't bring my objects to the grave with me. I wanted to play around with this idea of permanence in my piece. This flash fiction explores what happens when we can.

Doctor watches Guard push a gurney into the operating room. Doctor takes in Guard's bouncing heel and tapping fingers. Guard looks at Doctor and hands him *Clipboard*.

Clipboard's robotic voice echoes data to the operating room: <u>Identifying Information</u>: *Patient is UNKNOWN years old. (RACE N/A) (ETHNICITY N/A) Woman (CHILDREN N/A) (MARITAL STATUS N/A) who was presented to ward involuntarily.*

Doctor wrinkles his eyebrows taking in Patient: Its body is covered in a film of sweat, fluorescent lights leading their skin to appear rubbery and translucent. Limbs are long and hair the color of a spider's web; their slender nails seem seconds from falling off. Doctor puzzles over the absence of veins and the floral perfume its skin emits. *Clipboard* wonders why it hasn't been submitted earlier. Guard grunts at Doctor, jutting his chin to Patient, who is still.

Guard roughly clears his throat. Doctor sees skin cracking. Guard's voice booms around the room, waking up all the instruments.

"Patient is here. It make mess on our floor. Jeremy is very tired of mopping every hour. Told to bring them here. Make stop. Getting too much."

Guard looks at the ground and his cracked skin settles into the crevices. Guard buries his hands in his pockets, Doctor notes as his toes wiggle like worms within the leather shoes. Without another word, Guard leaves the room, the door swishing softly behind him.

Doctor watches Guard's head staring at tiles the entire walk from the doors to the elevator, never once turning back to face him. *Clipboard* calls for his attention and he is directed back to Patient, whose gown is now drenched with sweat.

Guard presses the "1" button on the elevator, watching the numbers count down from 100.

Doctor checks Patient's vitals and scribbles on *Clipboard*, who enjoys the quiet of the operating room and the attention of the doctor.

The elevator is now at floor 90.

Doctor is at eye level with Patient and makes the first incision with his scalpel. *Clipboard* sits alert, surveying the movement of Doctor's wrist, the bend in his stance, preparing for Doctor to reach behind and grab the gauze lying next to him. *Clipboard* does not watch for blood, because it is his job to watch Doctor. Even if *Clipboard* was watching for blood, none would be found.

Guard taps his fingers on his thigh. The elevator is now at floor 80.

Red sap oozes from the cut on Patient's thigh and the scalpel is covered in a thick layer of crimson. The scalpel will need a good wash, *Clipboard* decides. Doctor feels the air pressure change and everything goes still. His nostrils burn from the alcoholic sweetness that Patient's skin releases. Doctor stares at the deep cut and blindly slams his hand on the table behind him for forceps. Eye level to Patient's thigh, Doctor closes the forceps around something *Clipboard* cannot see. He grabs *Clipboard* and frantically searches the room for a pen, rhythmically shifting his eyes from paper to forceps to crevice.

Guard is humming his favorite song. Jeremy showed it to him. The elevator is now at 70.

Doctor scribbles wildly on *Clipboard* and red sap begins staining his sheet. The stream of sticky petals begins dripping onto the tile. Doctor leaves *Clipboard* on the operating table and grabs a handful of towels to place underneath the flow. *Clipboard* continues surveying the bend of Doctor's knee as he crouches next to Patient. A sticky petal lies forgotten on *Clipboard*, making him squirm. Doctor leads the forceps to Patient's ragged toenail.

The elevator is now at 60. Guard begins singing the lyrics of his and Jeremy's song under his breath.

The forceps don't catch Patient's nail before it falls. *Clipboard* sees the folded piece of paper before Doctor does. He hasn't seen such a thing before Doctor did, and waits impatiently for the paper to be picked up from the ground. *Clipboard* guards the paper, worrying it would become too dirty to read. *Clipboard* names the paper *Paper*, and decides to write this on Doctor's report. Doctor is fixed in place, examining the green skin of the naked toe. His breathing is deep and quick, shaking the forceps in his hand. The movement in Patient's weblike dreads goes unnoticed.

The elevator is now at 50. Guard is belting his song in the elevator. He has never sung aloud before, and decides he quite enjoys it.

Spiders crawl all over the tile. *Clipboard* barely registers Doctor's shouts, maintaining a keen watch on *Paper*. *Paper* is *Clipboard*'s first friend and he refuses to let him out of his sight. Thankfully, Doctor has not stepped on *Paper* during his odd bursts of running, but *Paper* does move about a centimeter to the left of his original position. The gurney shades him from the fluorescent bulbs and *Clipboard* decides this was quite all right.

Guard never steps off the elevator.

Smooth out the parchment paper and find writing in sap: *We hide in you for fun. We are permanent. You are not.*

MAISHA JAHAN CHOWDHURY

YEARS AS MENTEE: 1

GRADE: Junior

BORN: Queens, NY

LIVES: Queens, NY

MENTEE'S ANECDOTE:

I can't simply call Victoria my mentor because she is so much more than that; she is my personal favorite Sims 4 player, my accomplice in exploring TV shows, and above all a lifelong friend. Victoria is sweet, authentic, and has such a pure heart. I have learned a great deal from her and I never get tired. I can definitely categorize her as the fun-loving yet the most supportive friend in a friend group. My experience with her is beyond a writing mentor/mentee relationship since we have developed this beautiful bond that has allowed personal growth for both of us.

VICTORIA CHOW

YEARS AS MENTOR: 3

OCCUPATION: Communications, Public.com

BORN: Brooklyn, NY

LIVES: New York, NY

MENTOR'S ANECDOTE:

Maisha is a truly inspiring, creative, and compassionate individual. I feel lucky to be her mentor, and to call her my friend. She's passionate about her community: She volunteers for countless organizations, and always looks for new ways to give back. Her writing on her travels to the Myanmar Refugee Camp knocked me off my feet; her empathy, self-awareness, and dedication to making the world a better place shine through. She even humors my TV recommendations! Most of all, her curiosity, playfulness, and sense of humor will take her so far. I can't wait to see her change the world.

An Eye-Opening Experience

MAISHA JAHAN CHOWDHURY

My visit to the Myanmar Refugee Camp

Fear engulfed her. Her eyes reflected the pain she'd endured. She looked around helplessly, leaving no stone unturned to find someone who looked familiar or trustworthy to ask for help. At this moment, she could not trust anyone, as her own people had turned into inhuman predators attempting homicide. She was stranded in this refugee camp.

She caught my attention when I heard a voice shout, "One more Rohingya survivor has arrived." The man behind the voice hurriedly rushed her to the registration center. She was reluctant to go. I could see she had no faith in the man. Although he wore an apron with the UNICEF logo, I figured she didn't know how to read it and thus was hesitant.

Later, when she was registered, she tested pregnant. She confessed she had been raped by one of the Myanmar military officials. They had captured her for days atop a mountain and tortured her, killed her husband in front of her. She managed to escape the horrifying torture and land into Balukhali Refugee Camp in Cox's Bazar, Bangladesh. Stories like this woman's echoed across these camps. Thousands had faced similar or even worse conditions, as victims of the ethnic cleansing by the Myanmar government.

I visited Bangladesh in January for my cousin's wedding in Chittagong. Chittagong was about a four-hour drive from the refugee camps where the Rohingya were seeking shelter. I'd read about the Rohingya crisis in the news—being so close to Cox's Bazar, my cousin and I wanted to visit the camps to provide assistance and show our support. At first, I mainly wanted to go merely for the sake of my love for photography, as the experience would give me more content for my album. Looking back, I was negligent; I had no idea of the severity of the conditions there. The news couldn't have prepared me. But the stories that roared among these camps astounded me and forever changed my perspective.

Bangladesh is a poor country in general, and I have been confronted with poverty on various occasions, but I had never seen anything like the horrifying conditions in the Balukhali Refugee Camp. More than 400,000 people lived under just bamboo shacks, with dirt as their floor, little food to rely on, and insufficient materials to survive the harsh weather. They had come to Bangladesh with next to nothing and had nowhere else to go.

I was struck by the number of children in these camps, and the number of women who were pregnant as a result of rape. They deserved so much more: a life filled with education and better health, but their fate had overturned them. I couldn't imagine myself or my sisters in such circumstances. That was the moment I realized how materialistic the world has become. In America, we often complain about not getting the latest iPhone or the trendiest shoes, while these people had lost everything and were just trying to survive.

Another thing I found shocking is the main reason the Rohingya people were attacked and tortured in the first place: religion. Based on the mere stereotype that Muslims are terrorists, the Myanmar government committed genocide. What's happening to the Rohingya is due to Islamophobia and the way society threatens Muslims today. Freedom of practicing one's religion should not be a barrier. Our society should stop judging entire religions based on the actions of specific extremist groups, and embrace equality—not just within race and gender, but religion too. Similarly, as we fight poverty, we should learn about other religions and not just base our ideas on the stereotypes that society has created in the past.

Once we entered the camp, we learned that teachers weren't allowed to teach Bangla to the Rohingya children. I decided that it was important for the kids to remember where they came from and not consider themselves as refugees in a foreign land. Although they're in Bangladesh, I thought it would be nice to still represent the flag of Myanmar. My cousin and I, with the help of UNICEF members, painted the children's hands with the colors of the Myanmar flag. Then they placed their hands on a blank white canvas, to re-create their flag. We took Polaroids of them and pasted them on the walls to create a homelike environment. The reactions I received were overwhelming; I'd never seen someone so amazed watching a picture print from the camera. The children were so excited, and their smiles made everything we were doing worth it. One teacher told me that these children don't have mirrors, much less cameras, to ever see themselves. My camera was like a magic trick. I also did a mini–photo shoot with them and felt I better understood their emotions when I photographed them. By the end, a bond had flourished between us. My goal was to bring joy to these kids through arts and crafts and technology, the way photography brought joy to me.

People refer to skydiving, doing something adventurous, or visiting their dream place as their best experience in life. But for me, this was unexpectedly the best experience of mine. I got an insight into life outside my own bubble, and how the world looks at Muslims. Although this experience lasted only a day, I gained a lifetime of understanding that not everyone is blessed with everything, and those who are should look out for the less fortunate. I learned we should all appreciate what we have at the moment and not take it for granted. Fate can change within seconds.

LAUREN CICHON

YEARS AS MENTEE: 3

GRADE: Senior

BORN: New York, NY

LIVES: Brooklyn, NY

PUBLICATIONS & RECOGNITIONS:
Teen Ink; Scholastic Art &
Writing Awards: Gold Key

MENTEE'S ANECDOTE:

I have never had a relationship with an adult as I do with Kara. I feel so at ease with her. Her passion, genuineness, and intuition are things I look up to immensely. Kara has been beside me through the most awkward transitional phases of my life; she has helped me cultivate my personal experiences into contemplative art. Because of this, I have become more comfortable with who I am today. I know that although this is our last year at Girls Write Now together, we will be lifelong friends.

KARA STILES

YEARS AS MENTOR: 3

OCCUPATION: Editor, *Forbes*

BORN: New York, NY

LIVES: Brooklyn, NY

PUBLICATIONS & RECOGNITIONS:
Forbes, msnbc.com, *Tablet*

MENTOR'S ANECDOTE:

Even after three years of storytelling and scheming with my mentee, Lauren, I wish we were just getting started. I've treasured this front-row seat to her life, where I've observed her ideas sharpen and her writing (and hair color!) evolve. For every assignment I've tossed her way, she's offered even more in return: trusting me with her highs and lows, explaining TikTok before it was a thing, and inspiring me with striking wisdom and resilience during this strange year. She may be moving on from high school (not crying at all), but she'll remain a creative partner and a dear friend.

I'm sorry. I didn't do it right.

LAUREN CICHON

This personal essay is a capsule documenting life in my bedroom and wherever else I've spent time since the pandemic upended normal life. Since March 2020, I've been daydreaming and losing time through fantasy and writing.

INSPIRATION

During the past nine months of quarantine, I've searched for comfort and an escape from daily overwhelm. As a writer, these escapes have become sentences of fantasy and bliss. Lately, I've found that I can't always write beautiful words and phrases without stopping for a moment and going dark. There are also times when I can't write at all. Although I carve out time to create every evening, I often end up doodling in my notebook instead of writing. My scribbles are agitated colors that bleed into a perplexing brown. I suppose being creative is not something you can schedule, at least for me. The entries that follow are moments of inspiration that I've selected from my Notes app, Post-its, receipts, and a variety of other mediums to document this creative rut.

SPRING

Spring evokes the feeling of being overwhelmed and resisting that feeling to the point of disassociation. When looking back at my materials, I find that I sometimes chase perfection to escape uncertainty.

3/1/2020

Eating a grapefruit. God, I love grapefruit.

I don't know what aspect of a grapefruit is so satisfying because I can't eat it cleanly. My teeth puncture the fruit and the juice splashes into my eye. I always dust white sugar on the top to counteract the sour, but the bitter stays on my tongue until the end of the day.

3/3/2020

It was that house. That house that holds our dreams of a washer and dryer. The house with the lime-green shutters and the pristinely trimmed lawn lined with peonies and begonias.

I think of you in that house because you are perfect like its flawless windows.

You're beautiful with your shaggy curls and dull brown eyes and yet I can't touch you.

4/25/2020

I sit at a laptop for seven hours a day and look at things I can't afford while teachers talk about concepts I can't grasp.

SUMMER

This summer, I felt like a shriveled version of my creative self looking for satisfaction in the color of my hair. People accept that my hair is constantly evolving: pink one week, black the next, blue a couple after, red the next month. I've been asked why I do this—change my hair so often. I really don't know.

6/11/2020

Genuinely, I can't think of any *K* words besides *kangaroo*.

8/8/2020

I'm currently reading *Gone Girl*.

8/29/2020

It feels like I don't take care of myself, but aren't I always looking in the mirror and assessing my self-worth?

9/12/2020

I'm living in a dome.

AUTUMN

It's the beginning of my last year of high school, finishing up college essays and submitting applications. The days were repetitive, so I found myself reminiscing about past routines filled with human connection. Lately, people around me talk about how much they miss simple pleasures. I, for one, yearn for dirty subways and hugs.

10/3/2020

It's that explosive flavor of lemon drops and sour candies from the deli on Fourth Place that reminds me of you. Of sugar-coated, electric-green and pastel-pink Haribo sour straws that I suck on until my tongue turns a shade of muted violet.

11/19/2020

I'm drowning in passwords I can't remember. I feel like I have five I tend to go to, but for some reason, none of them are working. I'm going to distract myself. Normally I can remember things after I distract myself.

12/17/2020

The birds didn't go south for the winter. The first thing I noticed when I woke up on that morning was the shrill song of the common blackbird out my decrepit window. The air dewy and sticky; my palms begin to sweat. I crave icy air and snow but know that I'll never have to buy a winter coat. I've been removed from the outside for too long.

WINTER

Winter is the most challenging season for me, especially now during the most bizarre time of my life. I stay inside more than I do in other months. I spend my mornings in front of a lamp that imitates sunlight so I can start my day bouncing on caffeine, emanating an artificial glow.

1/1/2021

New year. Still reading *Gone Girl*.

1/17/2021

I haven't spoken to you in months.
    But I'll see you on Tuesday and it will be so normal.
    We'll go to the pond on Elmdale and sit on the fallen leaves.
    Finally, we will feel peaceful.

1/18/2021

You are the definition of grace
You are beauty
You are an arched back in the sun
You are clear skin and gentle hands
And
Cracked palms on beach sand

You are whispers on cold nights and
Hot tea on the kettle
Why are you making fun of me for heating water in a microwave?
I'm so sorry
I didn't do it right.

1/23/2021

I want to write like a watercolor painting. I want to float across the page in bright yellows and tantalizing oranges. Unblocked and released.

BRIANNA CLARKE-ARIAS

YEARS AS MENTEE: 4

GRADE: Senior

BORN: New York, NY

LIVES: Bronx, NY

PUBLICATIONS & RECOGNITIONS:
Scholastic Art & Writing Awards:
Gold Key

MENTEE'S ANECDOTE:

Rachel has been such an appreciative mentor to me. When I share, she understands the intention in my word choice and helps me clarify my ideas even more because of that. I can be very particular about the descriptors I use, and having a mentor with a similar method to mine has helped me settle into my writing process over four years. When I break grammar rules or use odd symbols, Rachel has always encouraged me to move into the experimental. I can't thank her enough.

RACHEL SHOPE

YEARS AS MENTOR: 4

OCCUPATION: Senior Editor, CB Insights

BORN: Chapel Hill, NC

LIVES: New York, NY

MENTOR'S ANECDOTE:

This is my fourth and final year working with Brianna, and I'm going to miss her so much when she goes off to college next year! I am so proud of her. Getting to know her and reading her writing has been such a privilege. It has been incredible to see her writing voice develop—and it's such a beautiful voice. I can't wait for her to share more of her work with the rest of the world.

Translating

BRIANNA CLARKE-ARIAS

I have experienced translation as a fundamental phenomenon in my communication. I feel colonization living in my words.

> *"Translation is the art of bridging cultures. It's about interpreting the essence of a text, transporting its rhythms and becoming intimate with its meaning . . . Translation, however, doesn't only occur across languages: mentally putting any idea into words is an act of translation; so is composing a symphony, doing business in the global market, understanding the roots of terrorism. No citizen, especially today, can exist in isolation—that is, untranslated."*
>
> **–By Ilan Stavans, professor of Latin American and Latino Culture, Amherst College; Robert Croll '16; and Cedric Duquene '15. Excerpt from "Interpreting Terras Irradient,"** *Amherst* **magazine, Spring 2015**

To translate is to become new. Translation is conversion; it does not exist as it did before and its message is in the sounds broken down into new ones. I translate literally, converting my words for my grandpa on the phone just like the speaker does to my voice, but it is also an unavoidable act. I translate emotions to thoughts to sounds. I shave off parts of feelings to make them words, but I make them larger through that act of sharing. I do not know if it is intentional how similar a community is to communication, I know that sharing is whittling the shape of my lips, my accent collected from the English of my parents and the Spanish of my grandparents, and making new meaning of my words the more they are received, unpacked, recognized.

I noticed recently, in my last year of Spanish class, that there was something so rough in my thoughts and tense in my arms when I could not force out my words. My English words do not exist in another language, I have run them through so many filters, I have strained them, stained them, packed them with meaning. The sting of *S* in my *sorry*s, the grounding edge of *R* growling in my throat instead of rolling on my tongue like my mother's. My big words, my small ones: melancholic, coffee cup, alienation, car door. I have grown up.

I have forgotten the sway of Spanish. I hear my grandmother crying, the bend of the stairs beneath my bare feet, *Elena!* The EXCLAIMING AT PARTIES! THE SLAM OF DOMINOES! MY GRAND-FATHER'S BIG BELLY LAUGH! The curve between my grand-mother's neck and shoulder where I slept, *cosita, mi linda* . . . My dry cheeks when she moved away. The soft skin of her hand, the thumbs that peel apples and wash them in lemon juice, where she stood by the stove. Her pots and spoons in the cupboard, dented with use, the faint scent of spices cooked into the metal, as if she has just cooked sancocho, mangú, baked the sweetness into the air to greet me as I enter the house. The empty kitchen.

The image of my house, of its walls, its stairs, the railing, the curve of my mattress around my body as it holds me while I sleep. I trace the dirt of my bedroom wall where I put up my feet in impatience as a child in tears because one day poetry would run out. The wood and metal and drywall hold me up; they are visible to me through this quiet consciousness in the absence of language.

SHERIDAN COLE

YEARS AS MENTEE: 1

GRADE: Junior

BORN: Queens, NY

LIVES: Bronx, NY

PUBLICATIONS & RECOGNITIONS:
Scholastic Art & Writing Awards:
Honorable Mention

MENTEE'S ANECDOTE:

My relationship with my mentor, Meghan, is fun and a learning experience. We both come up with outlandish ideas, and we have the most interesting conversations. Whenever I don't know something, Meghan will explain it, or if she doesn't know, she'll find the answer. Meghan has also helped me grow tremendously as a writer, and with our recent submission to the anthology, we've both had to learn together. Honestly, Meghan feels like an older sibling and I couldn't ask for a better mentor.

MEGHAN McDONOUGH

YEARS AS MENTOR: 2

OCCUPATION: Journalist

BORN: Stamford, CT

LIVES: Brooklyn, NY

PUBLICATIONS & RECOGNITIONS:
Films: "Invisible Monsters and Tomato Soup" published in *The New Yorker Documentary*; "What Is Home?" published in *Atlas Obscura*; "What Makes a Voice Human?" video published in *Scientific American*

MENTOR'S ANECDOTE:

I had a hunch that I'd enjoy collaborating with Sheridan when we learned in our first-ever video call that we had both been sorted into Slytherin by a Harry Potter quiz on the Internet. That hunch would soon be confirmed by her sharp sense of humor, upbeat nature, and creativity. I got to witness all of this in the form of a thoughtful rant she wrote recently on behalf of a 132-year-old maple tree for our pair project, which was a screenplay. Laughter is what we all need right now, and Sheridan makes it easy to come by.

Sword-Lily

SHERIDAN COLE AND MEGHAN McDONOUGH

A college freshman arrives on campus with her loyal guide dog. Whispers from the trees lead her to question her purpose: Will she be an advocate or a bystander?

EXT. COLLEGE CAMPUS—DAY

> BIRD'S-EYE
>
> STEPHANIE (nineteen, quietly observant, dry sense of humor) and HERBERT (sixty-five, grandfatherly, earnest) trail a dog up an expanse of grass toward a dark forest. A crowd of students ambles toward them and the dorm on the other side of the lawn.
>
> Stephanie is blind and accompanied by her guide dog, GLADIOLUS (three, German shepherd mix, loyal), her eyes to the world.

> HERBERT

You look nice in your student ID photo, honey.

STEPHANIE

Oh! I can't see it, obviously, but thanks?

HERBERT

Steph, please just humor me.
                    (tears fill his eyes)

This is the last time I'll be with you before you're
on your own.

STEPHANIE

Pops, there are people around.

HERBERT

You're growing up so fast. I still remember when you
were up to my knee . . .

LOW ANGLE

        Herbert continues speaking in the
        background. It's a sunny afternoon in
        late August, but the world looks dusky
        from the dog's perspective.

        Footsteps approach, fast and loud. Gladi
        starts getting antsy and begins to bark.
        The person doesn't slow down or change
        direction.

        Gladi tugs on the leash to pull
        Stephanie to a stop. In that moment, a

person's legs brush roughly past,
shoving Stephanie back.

                    HERBERT

Well, that wasn't very nice. I hope they get nothing
but coal for Christmas!

                    STEPHANIE

Pops! It's fine. They're probably just late to
orientation or something.

                    HERBERT

I hope everyone on campus isn't like this.
                    (pause)

The audacity of some people.

          A strong wind sweeps through the forest,
          which the trio is just entering—getting
          smaller and smaller as the woods get
          larger. The rustling of trees overwhelms
          the scene and carries us into the
          next day.
                    MATCH CUT TO:

INT. STEPHANIE'S DORM ROOM—MORNING

          Stephanie wakes to the sound of trees
          rustling through the open window.

                    STEPHANIE

Morning, Gladi.

Gladi's paws balance on the windowsill as she stares out the window at the trees. Stephanie slowly rolls over to the worn wooden desk drawer and unravels a bag of dog food.

STEPHANIE

Gladi, are you ready for breakfast?

Gladi pays Stephanie no mind, her ears perked and body stiff.

Stephanie starts to pour the dog food, waiting for the quick pitter-patter of paws that always follows the ring of food hitting the metal bowl.

She pauses. Nothing.

Stephanie picks up a bottle and tops off the water bowl.

STEPHANIE

Gladi.

Gladi remains unresponsive. Stephanie furrows her brow and instinctively touches her left-hand fingers to her ear, waiting.

The wind blows one final exhale, and Gladi turns quickly to greet Stephanie with a nudge of her hand before dropping her head to the bowl. Stephanie relaxes, dropping her hand from her ear.

Behind her, a dark green vine pokes through the open window into the room.

CUT TO:

EXT. COLLEGE CAMPUS—AFTERNOON

Through the branches of a maple tree, we spy a circle of eight students lounging on the grass. Gladi pants loudly.

STUDENT ONE
(shrugging)

The.

STUDENT TWO
(giggling excitedly)

The ancient.

STUDENT THREE
(looking up, bored)

The ancient tree.

TIM (eighteen, lanky, pale) wears an oversized sweatshirt and absentmindedly ruffles the grass.

TIM
(whispering)

Hey, what's your dog's name?

                    STEPHANIE

Gladiolus. I call her Gladi.

                       TIM

Is she working right now? I don't want to be rude.

        GLADI looks over and sighs in his
        direction.

                    STEPHANIE

No. She says go for it.

        Tim offers his hand for Gladi to sniff.

                  STUDENT FOUR

The ancient tree is.

        Stephanie shivers with a sudden chill.
        The branches of the MAPLE TREE (132,
        strong, majestic) wave wildly in the
        wind above.

                   MAPLE TREE
                 (in subtitles)

The ancient tree is . . . watching in judgment as
you humans ruin my land. Maybe ancient, but still
gorgeous. And supreme.

        Stephanie's eyebrows furrow together and
        her mouth opens in shock. The wind
        quiets down, and there is deafening

silence as the whole group stares at her in confusion.

ORIENTATION LEADER

Hey, Stephanie? You're up.

STEPHANIE

Uhhh, sorry. The ancient tree is quietly . . . watching? And gorgeous?

A pregnant pause. Then a few students erupt in laughter, followed by the rest.

Tim looks at Stephanie closely as the icebreaker game continues.

TIM

You were gone for a while there. You're still here, right?

STEPHANIE
(still shaken)

I'd like to believe so.

Gladi nuzzles closer to Stephanie, who touches a hand to her ear below the shifting leaves.

ALTHEA COLLIER

YEARS AS MENTEE: 1

GRADE: Junior

BORN: New York, NY

LIVES: New York, NY

MENTEE'S ANECDOTE:

Kelsey always greets me with a warm and beautiful smile. No matter what I am doing, or how I am feeling, she makes me feel so comfortable and loved. I was worried that I would not get along with my mentor, but she just makes me want to spend hours writing and chatting together.

KELSEY WEEKMAN

YEARS AS MENTOR: 3

OCCUPATION: Writer and Editor at Verizon Media

BORN: Raleigh, NC

LIVES: Brooklyn, NY

PUBLICATIONS & RECOGNITIONS: *Billboard*, CBS News, Yahoo

MENTOR'S ANECDOTE:

After a long day of doing nothing but writing, I'm burnt out, but Althea always provides that creative spark that reminds me how much I love writing as an art. She's like one of the super-cool it-girls from years past, but comparing her to someone else feels cheap. She's bright and entirely her own. She may be ten years younger, but she pushes me to think outside the box in a way that makes me wonder who the mentor is here. What a treasure.

Spring Sunday

ALTHEA COLLIER

As a child, my church congregation had a small garden that we grew vegetables and fruits in every year. After many years, the garden was sold and converted into a new apartment building.

It is spring Sunday. I have pulled on my white dress and tied it with my favorite blue ribbon. Tights and pinching shoes. But I cannot wait for later. Later, I go to the Garden. At two o'clock I run to find my dad. He grabs my hand and I skip along beside him.

Corner. Man. Nod. Gate. Lock. Key. Grass.

This is our Garden. Tucked between two old buildings, it's been tended by my family and community since I was born, and I will tend it today. Thrilled eyes wide open, I toss my tights and shoes into the grass and run across the little lawn, under the arch of spindly vines. In the back, empty plots are waiting for the energy that spring brings.

My brother, who has run in behind us, has brought bags of mulch and manure. I roll up the sleeves of my Sunday white and dig my hands in the dirt. Turning, pulling, pushing, my little hands bring the old, hard earth to grow between my fingers. New sun beating on my back, I can feel the warmth of life come back to the dirt. In my white dress, I am rooted in the earth. Soon, corn, tomato, squash, basil, cucumber, and strawberry will find their place next to mine.

It is summer Sunday. Embay parts the thick, warm vines and hands me a prized, juicy, plump tomato. I hold it in my hands, loving, eager. Under the shade of the six-foot-tall corn, its juice runs down my chin. Beautiful, tart, and sweet. We are all gathered here today. I cup my treat between my hands and peer out from the vines at my family and friends gathered on the grass. Barbecue and ice cream in their mouths, the Garden in their hearts. The girls and boys whose smiles have brought me here, the hands of those who have lifted me up, day after day. Returning to my tomato, I smile.

It is fall Sunday. I pull roots and pick squash for Mom. The vine archway is turning rusty orange, the strawberries are gone. Dead tomato vines piled in my small arms; the Garden goes back to sleep. My father stows away shovels and bags of dirt as I lie in the grass.

"Until next summer," I whisper.

It is winter Sunday. It has snowed so much that my short legs are engulfed by a wave of pure, sparkling white. Joy hidden under my scarf; I throw the first. My brother; the second. Klyde; the third. We fall and run and throw until our fingers are red and sore and our faces wet and frozen. As my father locks the gate behind us, I remember: Spring is almost here.

It is spring Sunday.

Corner. Man. Nod. Gate. Lock. Key. Grass.

This is not our Garden. Tucked between two old buildings, our Garden is gone. Sold years ago; nothing grows here anymore. Instead, there is a concrete tower. Hard, cold. No more am I rooted in warm earth, juicy tomatoes, vines, and grass. My Garden is gone forever, living only in the whispers of old memories in my heart.

DALYA CORDEIRO

YEARS AS MENTEE: 2

GRADE: Senior

BORN: Curitiba, Brazil

LIVES: Queens, NY

PUBLICATIONS & RECOGNITIONS: *Taking Our Place in History: The Girls Write Now 2020 Anthology*; *We the Writers* literary magazine (Academy of American Studies High School)

MENTEE'S ANECDOTE:

Working with Paige is always a riot. I come in with a harebrained idea and half of a plan, and with much laughter and enthusiasm, Paige helps shape it into something concrete, something I'm proud to show off to everyone I know. She jokes with me, critiques my work, and transforms my ideas, but I never feel like I'm being condescended to or insulted. This is extremely cheesy, but what we do together is definitely a kind of magic, and I'm infinitely glad to have her with me.

PAIGE CARLOTTI

YEARS AS MENTOR: 3

OCCUPATION: Marketing Manager

BORN: Erie, PA

LIVES: New York, NY

PUBLICATIONS & RECOGNITIONS: *USA Today, Forbes, Men's Health, Prevention,* Furthermore.com, Redbook.com; interviewed Michael Phelps

MENTOR'S ANECDOTE:

The continual exchange of knowledge is what I love most about working with Dalya. Although I'm technically the mentor, I'm not the only one doing the teaching in this relationship. I am so grateful to have the opportunity to learn from someone with such a fresh perspective on what's happening around us. I am a firm believer that a person should never stop learning, and working with Dalya through Girls Write Now has given me the space to do just that. I am extremely eager to see what Dalya will accomplish as she continues to find her voice through writing.

the infinity thing

DALYA CORDEIRO

In other words, a quick analysis on the true scope of what is "infinite," and how humankind as a species utterly fails to grasp it.

infinity is a concept i have repeatedly dissected. i think of it while looking at the sky and the sea and the stars and i think about it after i read love stories with their happily-ever-afters. i cannot grasp the concept of infinity because the human mind is not meant for it, and that is why it's so infinitely compelling. how do we understand forever? we can't, and that's that. we must come to terms with our own insignificance in the universe, and that is our only taste of infinity. is it fair? not really, but it's true.

perhaps you believe in eternal life, but you cannot truly comprehend it. you simply can't, and it's arrogant to believe you could. shortsighted, even, because you'll wonder what comes after eternity, not capable of internalizing that there is no after. it is a similar phenomenon when we read that the earth is billions of years old, brush it off laughingly, make a joke, shamefully repressing how pathetically useless the human brain continues to be as it vainly attempts to perceive incredible numbers, to fit them into a linear, coherent little picture of reality—so pitifully overshadowed by the vast immensity of the truth of the universe none of us can grasp tight enough to keep.

we are limited in this way, tragically so, constantly stretching out hands and fingers toward the enormity of space in the fragile, broken hope of feeling it reach back, entwine hearts and minds in a oneness so fully incomprehensible yet desperately sought after. our true essence is nothing but endless, plunging void, gaps waiting to be filled, so daunted when seeing our own infinity reflected back at us, so unable to capture the core of what makes us human.

instead, we watch as our sprawling forevers unfurl into countless directions, spanning the width and breadth of the cosmos and yet packed into tight little agglomerations of atoms and dust, confined into delicate, impermanent bodies destined to ultimately shatter and deliver their minuscule infinities back into the stars they descended from. finite infinity is what we are, what we repeatedly dissect, what we are utterly incapable of internalizing.

ALEX CRUZ

YEARS AS MENTEE: 1

GRADE: Junior

BORN: Brooklyn, NY

LIVES: Bronx, NY

MENTEE'S ANECDOTE:

I'm really glad I ended up doing Girls Write Now. I didn't know what I was expecting, but this was better. Alicia always knew the right things to say and the best advice to give. I've never had someone be so knowledgeable about writing in my life and I'm very glad I could have this opportunity. I'll definitely remember everything about this experience for years to come.

ALICIA KORT

YEARS AS MENTOR: 1

OCCUPATION: eCommerce Writer

BORN: Batavia, IL

LIVES: Brooklyn, NY

MENTOR'S ANECDOTE:

Over this past semester, Alex has impressed me with her dedication to writing and her creativity. I can't wait for others to read her work. She's even inspired me to write for fun again, which I haven't done in years.

Morning Shade

ALEX CRUZ

It's the perfect morning in Brooklyn.

The quiet of the night quickly vanishes as the tenth alarm sounds, filling the room with the sound of tolling bells. It felt like only a day ago when a phone from below would wake up the room with ABBA's "Lay All Your Love on Me." But that was a month ago, when the room occupied two instead of one.

The old wood planks of the mattress creak as the soft blanket with its red-and-white Christmas pattern is thrown to the side in a lazy manner. There is a bad taste left behind by the night before, and the world fades away in bursts of consciousness with the lull of sleep still weighing heavy. The lingering world of a colorful dream slowly retreats. The phone's clock is bright with a blurry image behind the numbers eight and ten.

It is still early in the morning for the rest of the house. Those still slumbering prefer to sleep in on weekends and be woken naturally rather than by the aggressive jolt of an alarm clock. Of course the loud alarm was annoying, and it always felt better to wake up by daylight, but sometimes, well, most of the time, an alarm was the only way to go for an early start. It always felt wrong to start the day off with only a handful of hours remaining, almost a disservice. A couple minutes passed and the bed remained still.

Creaks sound from the top of the bed and travel methodically to the end, nearing the ladder next to the bed. The movements had become muscle memory, and the fear of falling from uncoordinated steps was only a passing worry. There was the sound of four creaking thumps on wood until a final thump was heard on the floor, which felt like ice.

The room was small, and it took only four small steps to reach the beaten-up and yellowing air conditioner that loudly blasted an artificial gust of air into the room. It was a wonder it still worked after all these years. The groaning sounds were a comfort while sleeping, but it was time to wake up. It was shut off before the clack of pink Adidas slippers signified its way to the kitchen.

Just the sight of the kitchen was rejuvenating. Starting a new day right felt like the immense weight being lifted—when starting a new story after finishing the last. Ingredients from all over the kitchen flew onto the counter: a carton, a mason jar, a container of speckled sweetness, and last, a cup of ice cubes. A small button was pressed with a blue light and the machine whirred to life, filling the once sleeping kitchen with noise. The mason jar was perfectly placed under the machine until a dark brown liquid poured into the jar, filling the kitchen with its bitter yet tempting aroma.

Not a second could be wasted, and the day's dance began with a calming rhythm. Almond milk, brown sugar, and the ice cubes, one after the other. Too much or too little of any of them and it would be ruined. Once it was done, it was topped off with a metal straw. The perfect iced coffee was complete.

The mason jar floated through the air and landed on the white desk in the room. It never got old. It was something that could be controlled. It was always the same. With all the unsure things in life, at least there was still this. The one time in the day where nothing mattered and the background would disappear with the cold sip of coffee.

The early-morning sounds of New York faded away, and you could be anywhere in the world. Thoughts of the day's activities jumped around, so many possibilities. Yoga, knitting, writing, cooking. So many things were in store and the day was its own to shape.

Everything in life is finite and soon events and people would just be distant memories, remembrances of a different time. But right now.

Right now, this one moment was forever. This routine had become the one, the only thing that stitched each day together, proof that each day had passed and a new one was beginning. The seconds passed by easily as a wandering mind continued to think and wonder. There was a book that still had to be read, a story to be written, and a day to conquer. Slowly the mason jar was depleted, pure contentment. A sigh of happiness. Was there nothing this perfect coffee couldn't fix?

Once the morning was over and the mason jar was empty, then nothing could be predicted, and that was a scary thought. But for now, there was no need to worry about such things, because now there was only this moment and this morning. And when this is gone, something else will take its place.

GRACE CUDDIHY

YEARS AS MENTEE: 1

GRADE: Junior

BORN: New York, NY

LIVES: New York, NY

MENTEE'S ANECDOTE:

Every time I meet with Caroline, I am filled with joy and inspiration. Whether we are laughing together about Furby cults, or Caroline is patiently letting me rant about my life, Caroline is one of the most intelligent, caring, and empathetic people I know. She has been an incredible mentor to me, and has taught me not just about writing techniques, but about adult life with disabilities. It has been a really meaningful experience. Caroline has taught me so much about myself, and she has given me so much confidence by always being my best cheerleader and supporter. Love you, Caroline!

CAROLINE SHIFKE

YEARS AS MENTOR: 1

OCCUPATION: Freelance Writer

BORN: New York, NY

LIVES: New York, NY

PUBLICATIONS & RECOGNITIONS: *HuffPost, Teen Vogue*

MENTOR'S ANECDOTE:

My mentoring session with Grace is always the highlight of my week. Whether we're laughing hysterically as we plot out a parody true-crime podcast about a Furby-led cult or we're dissecting the ins and outs of living with invisible disabilities, Grace brings a level of maturity, thoughtfulness, and care to every task at hand. I'm in awe of their activism and engagement in their school community—Grace is constantly working to create a better world. They bring a fresh perspective and beautiful voice to their writing, and I'm so excited for them to continue sharing their work.

"What does it mean to be in my body?" and "Part One of Thirteen Ways of Looking at Being Female-Bodied"

GRACE CUDDIHY

My two pieces "What does it mean to be in my body?" and "Part One of Thirteen Ways of Looking at Being Female-Bodied" both explore my physical experience in the world.

What does it mean to be in my body?

Being in my body means playing with my hands, twitching my fingers back and forth to keep myself distracted. A slight crack in my knuckles, my fingers clicking every time I move them. It means a dull, throbbing headache in my temple that I can't escape no matter how much water I drink or meds I down. A headache that starts from the base of my head and blooms forward across my brain. Headaches that cause white spots and flurries to dance around my eyes, meaning that I need to blink hard four times before I can read the writing in front of me.

Being in my body means tits, not particularly large ones but ones large for my frame and that developed quickly, leaving them always feeling like an external strange part of me that doesn't belong. Tits that leave me with back pain. With faded, stretched-out old bras that never fit right, and shirts I can't wear because they leave me with weird looks from strangers. It means adult men that stare at me, gazing at me with a predatory glare from across the train car because I made the mistake of locking eyes with them. It means boys that harass me, sneering, telling me that I am leading them on by having boobs and being nice. Teasing me in front of friends, teachers. Snapping my bra strap because I started wearing bras before everyone else, leaving me with a stinging sensation on my back and a sense of shame.

Being in my body means walking around at night terrified, gripping keys between my fingers and looking behind me whenever someone gets too close or makes too much noise. It means wearing different clothes on the way to the party, then, on the way there, covering up on the train and on the sidewalk because if I get assaulted wearing something provocative it'll be my fault. It means putting down my drink and not picking it back up again. It means not being able to trust anyone.

Being in my body means EEGs, EKGs, emergency IVs. Leads glued to my body, my head, my chest. Spending the night in the hospital. My mom doing an IV before my math test on a Tuesday morning. It means avoiding scheduling plans based on the weather, for fear that if it rains my head might explore. It means bringing a "makeup bag" everywhere I go that's actually filled with medicine. A makeup bag that rattles when it's shaken, one that people accidentally open and look in horror as piles of orange pill bottles spill out.

Being in my body means being beautiful. It means feeling the low grumble of my dog's snores as he lays on my lap. It means smelling the scent of a brand-new book when I open it for the first time. It means sucking in thin cold air while going for a run in the wintertime. It means licking cookie dough off of a spatula while baking. It means feeling sand under my toes while swimming in the ocean. It means being a lover, a caretaker, and a friend. It means being an older sister, a daughter. It means turning pain into art. It means being alive.

Part One of Thirteen Ways of Looking at Being Female-Bodied

I sat in Port with my legs curled up on the floor, leaning up against my bunk bed. Peeling teal paint stuck to patches of the floor. Some of the girls in my cabin were leaning over the sides of their bunk beds, and some were spread over the floor. On the other side of the cabin a pretty, smart redhead curled up against the wall. She was older than us and had more experience. We clung on to her every word. She told us about a time that she had experienced sexual harassment.

"It's terrifying," I said. "Especially if they get increasingly agitated with you because you aren't acknowledging them or whatever." Even in an all-girls environment, the memory of that fear was enough to make me hold my legs for protection.

"Yeah, it's very scary," she said. "But it's very important that all of you girls listen to me. Whenever a guy comes at you in the street, or you feel as though they are following you, you cannot show them that you are afraid. It is important that you don't give any signs of being scared, or even increase your pace, because that is enticing for them. Don't ever run. Prey runs."

DOMINIQUE DE CASTRO

YEARS AS MENTEE: 2

GRADE: Senior

BORN: Queens, NY

LIVES: Queens, NY

PUBLICATIONS & RECOGNITIONS:
Scholastic Art & Writing Awards:
Gold Key; First place winner of
Center for Fiction's National Teen
Storyteller Writing Contest; High
Commendations at John Locke
Institute Law Essay Competition

MENTEE'S ANECDOTE:

It's no secret that this past year has been challenging amid protests against police brutality and a debilitating pandemic. Despite these life-changing events, I have found comfort in being able to talk to Courtney about what has been happening and how it affects me. She's been an amazing mentor who has helped me grow not only in terms of my writing, but emotionally and intellectually as well. She has been an amazing friend, and I can't wait to see what the future has in store for us.

COURTNEY STEVENSON

YEARS AS MENTOR: 2

OCCUPATION: Editor

BORN: Greenwich, CT

LIVES: Brooklyn, NY

MENTOR'S ANECDOTE:

Dominique and I have been friends for two years now, and while most of our friendship has been virtual at this point, getting to talk and write and laugh together has been a bright spot in the weirdest year ever. She is so dang smart, and I've loved watching her create in all different kinds of formats (including baking PIE!). I'm excited to read all the plays, poems, horror stories, and more that she will write, and I can't wait to give her a hug IRL when the world is normal again.

The Crows

DOMINIQUE DE CASTRO

Broken family ties and ominous crows haunt Jo as she faces the dangers of the forest.

"Jo! Come back!"

My father's voice ripped through the trees, echoing off their dampened bark. The rain had eased its ceaseless pelting, but water still dripped from the near-impenetrable canopy above.

I glimpsed the grassy expanse I'd left. Chairs sat organized in neat rows, empty and white as skeletons. My father stood at the front, a lone black crow screaming bloody murder.

"Come back here, Jo! You piece of shit!"

Despite his taunts, he didn't follow me. He stood rooted to the ground as if he were chained to the casket behind him.

The casket was the most beautiful part of the scene. Surrounded by gardenias and lilies, it shined like precious amber. It was the perfect vessel with which to glorify the life of Josephine Corvus.

But I didn't want to glorify the woman who'd cast me aside.

I clenched my fists in frustration and kept running. I sprinted through brambles and stumbled over tree roots. Before I knew it, the forest had swallowed me. Fog hung in the cold air, and I shivered as it sunk into my skin.

"Caw! Caw!" Crows mocked me from the tree boughs. I shrank under their piercing stares.

"Who's there!" I shouted. Out of the corner of my eye, I thought I saw a girl hiding in the mist. I felt as if the trees and the earth were watching my every move, waiting for me to stumble and fall into their waiting jaws.

My breathing became rushed and heavy. I wiped my palms, slick with sweat, on my clothes and pulled my wet hair out of my eyes. There was thick brush and trees wherever I turned, but I decided to head back the way I'd come. Funeral formalities were preferable to an eerie forest.

As I marched back to the funeral, I could feel the forest choking me and pushing me back into it. The brambles thickened and scratched me. The branches lowered and swatted my face. Even the mist became thicker, suffocating me.

"Ow! Fuck!" I screamed in pain as I fell.

Shit! My ankle's busted. I coughed and spat mud out of my mouth.

I'd tripped over a large tree root that had been covered in moss and vines. I heard the rush of birds' wings flapping overhead and looked up. A murder of what looked like hundreds of crows stared down at me in complete silence.

"Get away from me!" I wailed. I grabbed a nearby stone and threw it at them. They didn't move and merely watched as the stone feebly fell back to the ground. Hundreds of eyes then returned to my frail form, covered in mud, sweat, and tears. I could feel their stares burrowing into my soul.

I had to escape. I tried to stand, but I immediately felt shooting pains radiating up from my left ankle.

I began crawling through the mud. The pain in my ankle was so intense that I began shaking uncontrollably. I could hear the trees laughing as I scrambled past. As I crawled, I noticed a clearing ahead of me.

There was a well in the middle of the clearing surrounded by lush grass and daisies. Perched like a dove on the edge of the well was a little girl dressed in a pearl-white dress.

"Oh! Are you hurt?" she asked as she fluttered over to me. She lifted me up and slung my arm over her shoulders. She held me as we hobbled over to the edge of the well. Upon closer inspection, it was extremely old, with decaying bricks and a bucket with a rope slick with moss.

"My name's Josephine, but you can call me Jo!" she twittered. She looked up at me and smiled. The wind toyed with her raven-black hair, so it flapped like crows' wings. I touched my own raven locks.

"What a coincidence. My name's Josephine too. I was named after my mom," I said.

"Oh, really?" Josephine said as she slid onto the ledge of the well and sat right next to me. She gave me a cheeky smile. "Would you like to see her again?"

Before I could answer, she placed her hands on my chest and pushed me into the well. The darkness of the well filled my mouth and lungs, stifling my screams. As the light of the surface began to disappear, I saw the shape of my mother grinning down at me while I plummeted to my death.

I awoke surrounded by lilies and gardenias. My father stood over me, his eyes filled with tears, no trace of the anger from before. I tried moving, but my limbs felt like stone. I tried to speak, but my throat felt like it was filled with cotton.

"Come on, dear, it's time to close the casket," chirped my mother's voice from somewhere out of my eyeline. My father nodded and began to close the door above me shut. All I could do was watch my vision blur with tears as I took my last look at the light of day and listened to the trees sing goodbye.

AMIHAN DEL ROSARIO-TAPAN

YEARS AS MENTEE: 1

GRADE: Freshman

BORN: New York, NY

LIVES: New York, NY

PUBLICATIONS & RECOGNITIONS:
Scholastic Art & Writing Awards:
Gold Key

MENTEE'S ANECDOTE:

To me, conversation is one of the most important things in life. Through it, you gain perspective, understanding, and new ideas. And every meeting with Tess is full of rich conversation. Whether it be conspiracy theories, philosophy, books, politics, or anything else, my mind is always buzzing after our meetings end. She's introduced me to new styles of writing and pushed me creatively. Because of Tess, I end every week on a high, drunk with knowledge. And that is the power of great conversation with a brilliant mentor.

TESS McCLURE

YEARS AS MENTOR: 1

OCCUPATION: Journalist

BORN: Wellington, New Zealand

LIVES: New York, NY

MENTOR'S ANECDOTE:

After my first meeting with Amihan, I stood up, wandered to the kitchen, and said to my roommate, "Well, she seems like a genius. I don't think she needs a mentor." This year has been a hard one to write through—locked in by a pandemic, isolated, cross-eyed from hours on Zoom. Still, it's been a pleasure to watch, even over bad-quality video calls, as Amihan excavates her ideas, sharpens her work, and trusts her own instincts. That impression from our first meeting has held true—she doesn't need a mentor, but it's nice to be along for the ride.

As a Woman

AMIHAN DEL ROSARIO-TAPAN

This piece is about the double standards that plague society and force women to be small.

As a kid, I was called bossy. All the time. People would tell my mom, "Oh, she's a bossy one, isn't she?" or "Oh, she's sassy!"

As a kid, I wasn't taken to any Eagles games, and I didn't get to go to the Super Bowl parade. Instead, I was brought to musicals on Broadway. My brother is four years younger than me. He's been to two Eagles games and went to the Super Bowl parade.

As a kid, I was told to sit like a lady. That meant that even though I had jeans on like my best friend Aidan, because I was a girl, I couldn't sit comfortably. I forced myself to learn how to sit uncomfortably, squeezing my knees together.

My dad grew up in Philly and is a hardcore sports fan. So I grew up admiring the Philadelphia Eagles, blindly loving the team. I jumped when Papa screamed touchdown and was upset when they lost. And I called the Dallas Cowboys "the Cowgirls" like him, my cousin, my uncle, and my aunt. I teased my elementary school crush by telling him he hit like a girl. Now I can box.

November 8, 2016, was my tenth birthday. It was also a historic presidential election. The night of my birthday, before I went to bed, I told my mom that the only birthday gift that mattered was gonna arrive tomorrow morning when I wake up to the first female president of the United States.

America wasn't ready. Hillary Clinton was perceived to be emotional and, therefore, weak. One Trump supporter said a woman couldn't be a president because they had too many hormones and would start a war too quickly. Yet in America, every war has been started by a man. The phrase "be a leader, not a follower" has been preached since I was little. But when I would advise people what to do in projects and organize who did what, I was bossy.

I was conditioned as a little girl to think that I was inferior to men. "You hit like a girl," "Stop being such a little girl," "You sound like a spoiled little girl," or even "You're such a pussy," versus "You got some balls." And so men are told to man up, that crying makes them weak, so when Harry Styles wears a dress on the cover of *Vogue*, society says to "bring back manly men." Double standards. Gender norms. They are breaking everyone.

As a tween, I was told to dress modestly.

As a kid, my grandma told me to be careful. She would tell me to always watch my surroundings, and specifically, the men surrounding me. I've never heard her tell my brother to watch his surroundings.

It is hard to function in society when you are seen as less because you are a woman. Having to live in a society where you are constantly looking over your shoulder makes it that much harder.

I found an online study from 2007 that showed 99 percent of women have experienced some kind of street harassment. Out of these women, 81 percent have been subjected to sexual comments. This violation of catcalling has been normalized in society. It is just something that happens.

As a tween, I was warned one day that a complete stranger would ask me to smile. That it was normal, and I should just ignore them.

And as a teen, I swipe through my Instagram Explore page to see videos of women giving tips on what to do if they feel uncomfortable in an Uber. I save videos of fake phone calls of a random woman telling me she'll meet me on the corner instead of outside her house. I train my eyes to never make contact with a man staring at me. And I know better than to ever let my guard down

alone, because anything can happen in a society built to bene-fit men.

White men are free to walk the streets as they please, go on late-night jogs without fear, and whistle at women with the peace of mind that they will get away with it. To them, there isn't even anything to get away with. They don't have to worry that they will be assaulted if they choose to travel the world alone. They have the privilege of street survival.

I stay up late because of how quiet it is. My mind moves at 60 mph, and being alone slows it down. Clears my mind. After four months of quarantine, in July, I went for a walk in the city, alone. At that moment, I decided that I was going to solo travel the world.

But as I kept on walking, I remembered how men's eyes would travel down as I walked past them. The study of 2007 came back to me, and the fear crept in. And this is what it means to work harder because I am a woman. To have danger be my shadow, but to continue being despite it. Because one day I will see the world.

JAIDA DENT

YEARS AS MENTEE: 2

GRADE: Junior

BORN: Brooklyn, NY

LIVES: Brooklyn, NY

MENTEE'S ANECDOTE:

I have been working with Jalisa for two years now, and I cannot see myself working with another mentor. She helps me better my writing in any way she can, and I feel like because of who we are as people, we can easily relate to each other. I have been able to give her my true self, which I cannot do with many people. She makes me feel comfortable all the time, and she truly is someone that I love working with, and she has made me a better writer.

JALISA WRIGHT

YEARS AS MENTOR: 2

OCCUPATION: Freelancing Creative

BORN: Brooklyn, NY

LIVES: Brooklyn, NY

PUBLICATIONS & RECOGNITIONS: Every Girl Deserves to Blossom Student Writing Competition: First Place; Placed top ten in Brooklyn Lit Match Teen Writing Contest

MENTOR'S ANECDOTE:

This year Jaida was committed to stepping out of her poetry comfort zone, and she did just that. It has been my pleasure to support her in developing a portfolio and online presence as a teenage writer. Jaida is inspired by everyday life. She takes snippets from her corner of the world and sounds from the city to create written and multimedia pieces that are relatable for her generation and beyond. Virtual was our reality this year, but it did not hinder Jaida from exploring the world outdoors in her writing.

Snow Days

JAIDA DENT

"Snow Days" is a slow-burn love story about two people who need each other more than they realized. This is the beginning of what a full book would look like.

She followed a routine: go into the apartment, take care of the child, wait for Ryder to come home, and then leave. Skylar didn't expect to have her routine come crashing down the same way the storm did that day. She was gathering herself and waiting for Ryder to come home; snowstorm warnings rang on the television. The weatherman warned of heavy snow and high winds for tonight. Even in the middle of January, the snow was intense. It was clear Mother Nature was angry tonight.

He made it home just in time. Ryder, the CEO of Asset House Corp., spends hours at his office in D.C., but tonight he couldn't risk it. The forecast called for snow, and it was going to be a big one in this winter season.

Held captive in the home of her boss with his young daughter, Bria, she was privileged to get to know the mysterious man who kept her life afloat. She learned of his past and how he is the way he is now. Before this moment, she would've thought the only thing they had in common was their love for the little girl. But now, it is something else.

"I didn't think you were the type to lose your sanity over a woman."

"I didn't either."

Babysitting was just her side hustle. Skylar didn't intend to have this job for too long. As a student at Georgetown University studying digital marketing and creative design, she just needed something that would provide her with enough cash to pay to finish school. Somehow she managed to land a goldmine part-time job babysitting for a young and handsome CEO.

Ryder's last nanny ended up quitting on short notice. She was moving away to California to be closer to family. He was worried his little girl, Bria, wouldn't be able to connect with another nanny as she did with the last one. Alas, he needed the help, and he took a chance on Skylar. Not only did she have a good résumé and no criminal background (which is always a plus), she was a very pretty girl. Yet Ryder couldn't allow himself to be distracted by that. He hired her and only hoped that things would go well and he wouldn't have to look for a new replacement again.

On Skylar's first day, she decided she would arrive early. Being punctual is something she was always good at. She always had this constant fear of making people wait on her, so she did her best to always abide by a schedule. As she was traveling, she finally had a chance to think about what she was stepping into. She actually had known nothing much about the company he worked for other than it mainly surrounded finance. She also wasn't focused on appearance herself. She could care less if he was an older, less attractive man; money was money, and it was just babysitting. However, when her brown eyes were met with his hazel ones, she was slightly taken aback not only by his looks but his talent. A man his age looks to be in his early thirties, meaning he had his daughter in his mid- to late twenties, and he was still able to build a company. Impressive in her book.

On Skylar's first day, she was early, which made things easy for Ryder because he was able to get out the door quicker. "Money waits for no one" was a common mantra he always had. The plus side to being early on her first day was being shown an extra layer of kindness from her new boss. Ryder wasn't unfamiliar with people being late. Because of how punctual he was, he often wondered if everyone was just on time when he was early. He liked to make sure he was always running on schedule, yet it was always difficult when you had a seven-year-old daughter. He always thought that she took after her mother, with the same brown curly hair, doe eyes, and rounded nose. Ryder couldn't help but see his former lover when he looked at Bria's face. Unfortunately, the girl's mother was never able to see it herself, as she passed away giving birth to their daughter. A part of Ryder has never recovered from that, and he always wondered if he would ever find a woman suitable in his life, not only for him but for his daughter as well.

"Thank you for being able to start on such short notice."

"No problem, Mr. Daniels."

"Ryder is just fine."

"Okay, Mr. Ryder." He laughed. Even with the privilege of calling him by his first name, she still kept it professional.

"It's a respect thing for me and it's just what I am comfortable with. For now." She grinned. *What a pretty smile,* he thought.

As the man left for the day, he wondered how things would go back inside the apartment, how his daughter would react to a new sitter, and how the girl with the pretty smile could possibly change his life.

CAROLINE DER

YEARS AS MENTEE: 1

GRADE: Junior

BORN: New York, NY

LIVES: New York, NY

MENTEE'S ANECDOTE:

Through pair sessions, workshops, and the events that Girls Write Now has hosted, I've found that no question is too silly and no matter too small to discuss and laugh over. Orla has helped me discover more of who I am. It was during the romantic fiction workshop when we bonded joyfully over our shared appreciation for and fondness of romance novels and movies that I realized Orla was not just a writing mentor but a lifelong one. In Orla, I find an unwavering cheerleader full of amazing advice and anecdotes, love and lessons, and I am endlessly grateful for that.

ORLA MURPHY

YEARS AS MENTOR: 1

OCCUPATION: Speechwriter to the President of the United Nations General Assembly

BORN: Cork, Ireland

LIVES: New York, NY

MENTOR'S ANECDOTE:

Throughout 2020 and 2021, there have been unprecedented political events, and my first text is always sent to, or received from, Caroline—sometimes even before the *New York Times* alert! We were both participating in a Girls Write Now Saturday 360 Series romantic fiction workshop when I learned of President Biden's election, and I furiously texted Caroline before switching on CNN. A few months later, Caroline messaged me on a Wednesday afternoon relaying the news that crowds were storming the US Capitol. We often joke about being soul sisters living through history together!

Our Tree Topper

CAROLINE DER

*A teenager is expected to carry out another year of her family's bru-
tal tradition. Tormented by reservations and her conscience, she
makes a decision that changes the course of her family celebration.*

For as long as I could remember, our family had a Christmas tradition
that was either mildly unpleasant or horribly disturbing, depending on
your perspective. Sure, it was a bit cruel, but so is Thanksgiving for the
turkeys that unwillingly make the ultimate sacrifice so that human families can gather and pretend to enjoy one another's company.

Why the double standard for hamsters? Besides, we don't eat them—
we're vegans. Every year, a family member chooses a hamster. This year,
the task fell to me, and so I went to Petco with Delphine, a friend from
school. The drive there was silent, bar some stilted conversation where
she reminisced about her first hamster.

"Have you thought of names?" she attempted after a particularly
painful lapse of silence.

"No," I replied.

I'd read an obscure book once, in middle school maybe, by a cattle-
man who said he never named his cows because leading one with a name
to the slaughterhouse was unnatural. I agreed with his rationale. But I
remembered Delphine didn't know about our tradition, so I kept quiet.

Soon we pulled into the Petco parking lot, desolate save for an aston-
ishingly red convertible. I strode purposefully to the hamster aisle. This
year they were nearly all a boring beige, mindlessly climbing on top of
one another, just like dumb goldfish. Pathetic.

"Ooh, I like this one." Delphine pointed to a black-and-white hamster that stared beadily up at me, forlorn. A salesperson came shuffling uncomfortably close and cheerfully announced, "Oreo and you seem to have a connection!"

"Interesting," I said, although it was quite the opposite. "I'll take it if it's not pregnant."

The saleswoman looked startled. I explained the catastrophe of 2009, when the hamster unexpectedly gave birth, then promptly ate her offspring just hours before Christmas. She laughed uncomfortably and assured me that Oreo was not pregnant. Twenty minutes later, the hamster was all mine.

Later, as I made my way into my childhood bedroom, I kept a firm grip on the carton so as not to make it dizzy. I was considerate like that. We had the cage from last year's hamster ready; Dad had cleaned it the night before. I lifted the hamster out. Instead of squirming like the particularly feral hamster of 2018, she lay still in my hands, nibbling the tip of my index finger. I was struck with the crazy urge to give her a quick pat like one does to a child.

"Oreo's a name for dogs," I told her, my voice hard.

Her eyes pierced me indignantly, and I relented, giving her not one but two pats.

A couple of weeks from now, she'd be our Christmas tree topper, and those beady eyes would haunt me from their new fixed position perched atop the tree all through the holidays. I shook off a wave of repulsion for her impending fate.

Oreo was subsequently rechristened Beady, yet the day of her execution crept upon us like a malevolent shadow. As I fed her, I tried to avoid her inquisitive nose, which was always sniffing for a hint of my guilt.

At dinner, my family discussed taxidermy poses with increasing excitement. I felt sick and was building up the courage to admonish them until my sister recalled how I'd enthusiastically suggested the winning pose in 2013.

I slept fitfully, my dreams plagued by images of a permanently still Beady. As the days went by, I couldn't bear the thought of my playful little pet forever unmoving. I unlocked her cage and felt compelled to share some parting words with her. I steadied myself and took a deep breath, "This is it, Beady . . ."

She snorted, and warmth suddenly flooded my veins.

"You know what, Beady? You're not dying. Not this Christmas."

I informed my family that Beady would not be adorning our tree, ever.

"Are you kidding me?" my sister scoffed.

"She's my pet," I explained, watching their bewildered faces.

Frantic attempts to buy another hamster were spurned. My brother came back from Petco empty-handed that evening. "Sold out," he said and shrugged. My distressed mother became even more hysterical.

As Christmas loomed, my family threw me increasingly resentful looks for "ruining Christmas."

Their hostility was palpable, and I feared for Beady. I had to do something, so I bought a gaudy angel topper, similar to the ones around town. Personally, I felt it lacked the sophistication of a hamster. But to my surprise, my family found it serene. My dad even pondered aloud why we hadn't done this every year, and my mother emphatically agreed, as if they weren't the ones who had created the tradition. Hypocrites, the whole lot of them.

Nevertheless, in the end, I had saved Christmas, my beloved Beady, and all future hamsters. I considered myself somewhat of a minor hero.

LENA DIBIASIO

YEARS AS MENTEE: 1

GRADE: Sophomore

BORN: New York, NY

LIVES: Queens, NY

MENTEE'S ANECDOTE:

Hayley and I worked really well together, and our writing styles and personalities complement each other nicely. We were so excited about our idea for our pair piece that we originally wrote much more than we needed to. We've bonded over the wonders of Taylor Swift and mug cakes.

HAYLEY ALTMAN

YEARS AS MENTOR: 1

OCCUPATION: Data Analyst

BORN: New York, NY

LIVES: Hoboken, NJ

MENTOR'S ANECDOTE:

Lena and I have become fast *virtual* friends during the Girls Write Now program. I have really enjoyed reading and discussing her work and talking about all things pandemic, politics, and Christmas movies. It was a lot of fun to lean in to our inner old ladies and cowrite our pair piece.

A Tale of Two Grandmothers

LENA DIBIASIO AND HAYLEY ALTMAN

Two grandmothers meet and form a close bond, only to discover that the nursing home they live in is up to no good.

RUTHIE

The worn-down Nissan Sentra puttered along the road, Ruthie's hands practically reaching above her head to clutch the wheel. She was in a moment of reflection, as one does while driving *themselves* to an old folks' home. It was Benjamin's idea, her oldest and most obnoxious child. He had flung into her living room proposing the idea of Crystal Springs, as if visiting his lonely mother once a year earned him the say-so. It was an assisted-living home, but that was code for "place that smells like pee where I can dump my naggy mom."

"Make a RIGHT turn," Ruthie's phone shouted at its typical ear-splitting volume.

Ruthie loved Siri. Ruthie loved a lot of things—she loved baking, knitting, and frogs. Her house was decorated with all kinds of amphibian-related knickknacks, which were all self-gifted, because she barely received Christmas or birthday presents anymore.

She had to admit, despite dreading the idea of being shipped off to live with people who would forget her name instantly after she told them, she was in dire need of a friend. Did she want to leave her home? No. Did she have any desire to socialize with people who watched *Judge Judy* for fun? Also, no. As she pulled her car into the dismal gray parking lot, she tried to smile.

Maybe this will work out. Maybe.

BEATRICE

Swoosh. Swoosh. Swoosh.

The gliding force of the wheels beneath her was irritatingly familiar. A powerful sound from her youth now a condescending reminder of her incapacity. Thin rubber tubes and sharp metal spokes separated her calcium-deficient bones from the waxy, colorless floor. Oh, how she had come to hate her insides. Aging was a contact sport, and the medical chart in her aide's hand was the referee—the results were in, and she wasn't celebrating.

She had been a known force on the basketball court at sixteen. The kids in her neighborhood—a congested square mile of tenements in the upper Bronx—would hang on the chain-link fence surrounding the concrete court and yell, "Betty for the Block! Betty for the Block!" Her ears would buzz at the sound of their confidence, and adrenaline sent her five-foot-eight stature soaring.

Swoosh. Swoosh. Swoosh.

RUTHIE

Crystal Springs was *exactly* what Ruthie had expected it to be. She had settled in quite nicely, in her opinion, making a few friends here and there. Each day during arts-and-crafts hour, they would sit in a very silent circle to knit identical scarves. Ruthie didn't hate it, but she certainly didn't love it.

Ruthie couldn't help but notice the woman in the corner during these hours spent in the cramped community room with floral-covered walls. Every day, without fail, she would roll briskly into the room and set up a little card table. She sat and played solitaire by herself, muttering and cursing under her breath all the while. She never wore the cute cardigans that Ruthie and the other knitters did; instead, she always donned a giant T-shirt with a slogan like "THINK OUTSIDE THE BOX" printed inside a small box. She also wore Air Jordans, and Ruthie had a sneaking suspicion that she would never be caught dead in a knitting circle.

Ruthie felt a spark of spontaneity, in addition to her usual boredom, as she finished the thirty-sixth row in her scarf. She hoisted herself out of her rocking chair and headed straight toward the source of her captivation.

"Good morning!" Ruthie said with a grin as she reached the card table.

"Mornin'." The woman's eyes stayed glued to the deck in her hand.

"I'm Ruth! Ruthie, if you want."

"Beatrice," she answered, and looked up begrudgingly.

"Mind if I join you? That is, only if you don't mind making it a game for two."

Beatrice looked surprised, as if no one had ever offered to play with her.

"Come on, then, have a seat."

Ruthie noticed a hint of a smile dance across Beatrice's lips as she rolled her wheelchair over to make room for the Shirley to her Laverne.

BEATRICE

Ruthie proved to be the antidote to Beatrice's abrasiveness. The constricting environment of Crystal Springs often catalyzed her banal rants, as she complained to every staff member paid to listen that the soup at dinner was too hot or the Friday movie was chauvinistic. She knew she could improve her delivery, but a syrupy-sweet follow-up by Ruthie seemed to do the trick instead. Their influence quickly received attention from other residents, and a makeshift town hall evolved to organize the persistent requests.

"Those orange horse pills always get stuck in my throat."

"I'm wiped out by noon every day."

"I forgot to take mine, and I feel like a million bucks."

Each morning at ten a.m., the aides passed around Dixie cups filled with a Technicolor assortment of pills. Small red ones treated high blood pressure; the blue, cholesterol; and the green, reflux. This practice seemed standard in a house of the living dead, but fifteen worrisome comments signaled a grave pattern.

"They're drugging us," Ruthie said in a firm whisper while collecting soiled paper goods left behind by the recent attendees.

"Well, of course they are. Where would we be without those damn Dixie cups? Probably in the morgue, and then *poof*—how would Mr. Springs afford all this crystal?" Beatrice answered with contempt.

"No, you don't get it," she repeated, this time with a sharp edge to her voice. "They. Are. Drugging. Us."

DENISE DOMENA

YEARS AS MENTEE: 1

GRADE: Senior

BORN: Brooklyn, NY

LIVES: Brooklyn, NY

MENTEE'S ANECDOTE:

Emely and I share a lot in common when it comes to our interest in writing genres like poetry, and our enjoyment in writing about our Latina identity. When we write together, we are able to brainstorm ideas and critique each other's work with utter ease and comfort knowing that we have the best intentions for each other. Writing with Emely is always fun, adventurous, even therapeutic. I couldn't have asked for a better mentor.

EMELY PAULINO

YEARS AS MENTOR: 2

OCCUPATION: Research Associate

BORN: Queens, NY

LIVES: Queens, NY

MENTOR'S ANECDOTE:

Denise is a passionate writer who always brings her authentic self to her work. From the beginning, I was impressed by her willingness to experiment with different writing styles and desire to grow as a writer and scholar. Our mutual love for Latinx literature inspired many conversations about the complexities around language, culture, and identity. I look forward to reading the powerful work she creates as a mentee at Girls Write Now and beyond!

Siempre Boricua

DENISE DOMENA

This poem focuses on my experience growing up in Brooklyn, New York. It addresses the challenges and stereotypes that Puerto Ricans face in the neighborhood.

I wish your voice was just white noise.
Something I can block out like
The rumbling of the subway braking harshly in the city
Or the blaring sirens of police on call.

Instead, I stop and freeze
When you jokingly question me
For it no longer feels like a tease,
But a dissociation from others like me.

I'm from Bushwick, New York.
Balancing the border of Brooklyn and Queens.
The overachiever with straight A's.
The one who cries over silly mistakes.

I'm also the youngest of two.
My *abuela*'s *cuquita*,
My parents' little one,
And my sister's loving pain.
The unspoken glue that holds this family in place.

Without knowing any part of me
You say I must be oblivious to my culture and roots
Because I don't speak Spanish
Or have the same accent as you do.
As if I haven't been trained by my *abuela*'s routes.

And yet, despite our language barrier,
I still manage to understand her.
Some might call it broken English
But actually, it's music to my ears.
Something I've learned from and listened to over the past few years.

Her voice guides my course,
Against this frictional force.
It teaches me how to move my hips
To the blasting speakers of our Brooklyn district.

It leads me to the back of the shady projects
To watch the *viejos* play endless rounds of dominos.
Tracing my fingers along the dotted indents.
Hoping to pull off a *capicu* in just a matter of minutes.

It shows me why *piragua* hits different than
Any sprinkled ice cream from Mister Softee
And how Vicks is the solution to any sickness
For a coat of it can cure just about any illness.

Not to mention smelling her authentic *pernil* richness
After watching her sprinkle the adobo on like it's nobody's business.
Learning the familiar sound of *chancletas* down the hall
And feeling dirty if my bare feet touch my house floors at all.

These small things bear heavy significance
To who I am as a Puerto Rican.

I will no longer allow you to question
All of these fond memories.
Pretty soon, your noise will fade
Into just another muffled voice during my commute,
Indicating my train is delayed.

Just like with the train conductor, I won't hear you
Because my pop indie rock is consuming you.
Tuning out your opinions
That have been blinding you
From seeing that I am
And always will be
Boricua.

ILANA DRAKE

YEARS AS MENTEE: 3

GRADE: Senior

BORN: New York, NY

LIVES: New York, NY

PUBLICATIONS & RECOGNITIONS: Scholastic Art & Writing Awards: Gold Keys, Silver Key, Honorable Mentions; *Pandemic Notebook*; YR Media

MENTEE'S ANECDOTE:

When most girls are asked who their role model is, they might say Ruth Bader Ginsburg or Michelle Obama. My answer is a bit different, although my role model exemplifies the same characteristics of these prominent women. Throughout the past three years, I have been extremely lucky to know Erica as a writer and a person. Erica's tenacity, empathy, and charisma are all traits that I hope to acquire in larger doses. Erica has taught me not only how to become a better writer and strive for success, but also how to be the best person I can be.

ERICA DRENNAN

YEARS AS MENTOR: 3

OCCUPATION: PhD Candidate

BORN: New York, NY

LIVES: Amherst, MA

MENTOR'S ANECDOTE:

Three years ago when I first met Ilana, I could already tell that she was the most enthusiastic person I had ever encountered. I soon discovered that she is also a brilliant writer who is generous and wise beyond her years. Hanging out and writing with Ilana every week has gotten me through the pandemic. Her boundless energy and beautiful writing make everything brighter, even over Zoom. I am so proud to know her and call her a friend. I can't wait to keep reading Ilana's words and asking for her writing and life advice for years to come!

journey while traveling

ILANA DRAKE

My piece "journey while traveling" was inspired by my high school experiences and transformation into a young adult. This poem starts with me as a young teen and progresses into my exploration of adulthood.

i. courage

i used to swim in a sea of fear
dreams floating on the blue surface
but i picked my fins up
and held my breath

my eyes swelled
like the times my body burst
with shattered fins and fragile bones
yet, i kept swimming

i swam in circles
fins flailing as waves crash over
i couldn't reach the coral reefs
so i switched directions

the bluefish watched me
the clownfish gossiped
the angelfish looked away
while i flipped like a fish shouldn't flip.

ii. flip

see the world upside down
and you realize that
the sea might not be the world
because the birds swoop down

their yellow beaks skim the water
my home broken into
fish trying to swim down near me
hiding in the reefs

i learned to dash
i tried to sprint
but then i realized our eyes never met.

iii. together

those dark brown eyes
glimmered in the water
right above me

my small mouth gaped
eyes wide as the ocean is deep
except, i found hope

tranquil waters shaken by hurricanes off the coast
thunder that lasts for days
rain that keeps pouring

drip drop drip

halcyon sands to the east
troubled times to the west
we start the new day together.

AMOYA EVANS

YEARS AS MENTEE: 2

GRADE: Sophomore

BORN: New York, NY

LIVES: New York, NY

MENTEE'S ANECDOTE:

At the start of the program year, I was interested in learning more about fiction. Then as the year went on, I found myself thinking more about history and its effect on our current moment.

JULIA CARPENTER

YEARS AS MENTOR: 4

OCCUPATION: Journalist

BORN: Atlanta, GA

LIVES: Brooklyn, NY

PUBLICATIONS & RECOGNITIONS: New York Newswomen's Club Award of Excellence; National Association of LGBTQ Journalists Award of Excellence

MENTOR'S ANECDOTE:

At the start of the program year, Amoya and I discussed exploring new genres, like horror writing and speculative fiction. I've loved seeing her at work in so many different areas.

Between the World and Me
& James Baldwin

AMOYA EVANS

At the time, this piece was inspired by one of my favorite books, Between the World and Me. *Everyone should read this book and these writers.*

The book *Between the World and Me* is a letter to Ta-Nehisi Coates's son. It expresses the struggles of racial inequality and the consequences of living in a Black body in America. Coates confronts the history of slavery and racism during the periods of his letter to a younger generation. Coates points out how the abuse of power within the police force needs urgent change and to understand that "broken-windows policing" is another branch of a long history of racism in America. According to most sources, the broken-windows theory is a criminological theory that shows how visible signs of crime create an urban environment that encourages further crime and deaths based on racial bias or microaggressions.

In *Between the World and Me*, Coates states that his son was being harassed by a woman trying to prove she is on a "higher level" than him. I think this is because the younger generation needs to know that the world they grew up in is not equal. Middle schoolers and high schoolers should read this book because it is educational. It educates you on microaggressions, bias, and racism. The actions in this book are current and are very relevant. James Baldwin was an American novelist and was especially known for his essays on the Black experience in America. He says, "This innocent country set you down in a ghetto in which, in fact, it intended that you should perish." According to a study done by the New York Civil Liberties Union in 2014, New Yorkers were stopped by the police 45,787 times and 37,744 were innocent (82 percent). 24,319 were Black (53 percent). This relates to the message of Baldwin, who says this country set Black people down in the ghetto and let them perish. James Baldwin also says, "It comes as a shock" that your country didn't evolve a place for you. This quote shows racism in America leads to inequality. James Baldwin and Ta-Nehisi Coates both make relevant points.

James Baldwin's and Ta-Nehisi Coates's letters have some concepts of implicit bias, the matrix of oppression, and racism. Racism is the belief that one race has an "advantage" over another race, which often results in discrimination and prejudice toward people based on their race or ethnicity. Implicit bias is a specific judgment of particular qualities to a member of a particular social group. The matrix of oppression is a pattern that explains issues of oppression that deal with race, class, and gender. I know this because in Baldwin's quote he explains how "this innocent country" set his nephew down in a ghetto in which it intended him to perish. That section is a concept of implicit bias. I think James Baldwin's nephew is being placed before being known. Coates explains this in multiple parts of his book, and he also explains racism. There is a big difference in these quotes. Baldwin's was written in 1962 and Coates's in 2015.

In my opinion, a lot of things have changed since the 1960s. James Baldwin and Ta-Nehisi Coates might have written at different times, but they both discuss the issues involving concepts of implicit bias, the matrix of oppression, and racism. *Between the World and Me* expresses many racial issues in America. It educates you on microaggressions, bias, and racism. Everyone should know that the messages in this book are important and very relevant.

EMELY C. FABIAN VASQUEZ

YEARS AS MENTEE: 1

GRADE: Senior

BORN: Santiago, Dominican Republic

LIVES: Bronx, NY

MENTEE'S ANECDOTE:

It has been a pleasure and much more to have a mentor/friend help me improve my writing skills through Girls Write Now. With Shanice's help, I tapped into my poetic side. I recall our first call, when she asked the different genres I was familiar with and I told her I was willing to try something new and I also mentioned my dislike for poetry due to its complexity. And here I thought poetry would be out of the question and then Shanice pulls me out of my comfort zone and helps me publish my own poem.

SHANICE ANDERSON TCHAMAMBÉ

YEARS AS MENTOR: 1

OCCUPATION: High School Educator

BORN: Washington, D.C.

LIVES: New York, NY

PUBLICATIONS & RECOGNITIONS: *Embers: A Collection of Poems*

MENTOR'S ANECDOTE:

It has been a pleasure watching Emely find her voice as an individual and as a writer. I'm happy that others will get to read her words.

La Niña y La Del Barrio

EMELY C. FABIAN VASQUEZ

The privilege to read someone's story is great, but what counts the most is the experience you leave with after you reach the last page.

Raised by a strong Dominican woman
Her strong character many times overshadows mine

I enjoy listening to hip-hop
while my mother
enjoys her salsa and bachata
I like to wear my hair curly
and she likes hers blown out

My mother believes in God
and follows the ten commandments
I identify as a spiritual believer

My mother identifies as Latina
Dominican
Her safety net
All she's ever known.
I identify as Afro-Latina
I am Black,
But, I am also Latina

I grew up surrounded by Black culture through my community
Streetwear

slang
The city
The projects
MTA
While my mother grew up around the trees
El colmado
La música
El campo

All my life
I went by everything my mother told me and hid parts of myself

All my life
I swallowed so many words to keep the peace

It grew overwhelming
To have someone teach me who I had to be
To meet
expectations
needs
desires

I couldn't stay quiet anymore
I was trying to save the world from my mother's judgment
but who was to save me
I had to save myself this time and so I did.

My mother doesn't always agree with how I choose to express myself
Our differences are what makes us
unique
What makes me
Me
And her,
her

So I stopped comparing
Stopped fixing what wasn't broken

Now I see myself
Emely
The one coming from behind the shadows

ABBY FAVORITO

YEARS AS MENTEE: 1

GRADE: Junior

BORN: Phoenix, AZ

LIVES: Brooklyn, NY

MENTEE'S ANECDOTE:

Stephanie is not only a profound writer but also a new friend. When I first came to Girls Write Now, I was intimidated because I had barely dipped my toe into the writing world. However, I had Stephanie there to help get me started and guide me through. She helps me discover new styles and edits my pieces so they come out magnificently. Stephanie has helped me gain confidence in my writing and made sure that each project or exercise we do is enjoyable. Overall, my time with Stephanie has been a time of growth and lots of fun!

STEPHANIE GOLDEN

YEARS AS MENTOR: 7

OCCUPATION: Author, Journalist, Book Doctor

BORN: Brooklyn, NY

LIVES: Brooklyn, NY

PUBLICATIONS & RECOGNITIONS: *The Startup*, Aeon.co, *Tricycle*

MENTOR'S ANECDOTE:

After six years of person-to-person meetings with mentees, I was a bit apprehensive about trying to develop an online relationship with a new mentee. I'm still eagerly awaiting the moment I can meet Abby in person, but I was happy to find that it wasn't hard to develop a real connection through Zoom. We're a good match since, like me, Abby is thoughtful and introspective. She comes up with wonderful, subtle word images to express her feelings. And her ability to edit video awes me.

I am from change

ABBY FAVORITO

The idea to write "I am from change" appeared in one of the first Girls Write Now workshops I participated in. I wrote a few lines then and decided with my mentor to continue to work on it.

I am from the burning pavement of Arizona
rocking under my feet.
From the boiling heat of the sun
blanketing across the bridge of my nose.

I am from dry lips and cracked skin
From the rattlesnake that hid under a rock in the park,
only coming out once in a while to say hello.

I am from tightening the straps on my goggles
to the point where they leave a crimson rim around my eyes.

I am from jumping into my backyard pool,
sometimes naked if the weather called for it.
From blowing air bubbles out my nose
and descending to the bottom,
Just sitting there,
In the silence,
In the peace.

I am from salty tears running down my cheeks,
Making vertical streaks on my eight-year-old porcelain skin,

My youthful eyes,
That once gleamed with joy,
gone dull.
From goodbyes and
"We'll visit in the spring!"
I am from taking a plane and soaring thousands of miles to Brooklyn,
A new place,
Maybe scary,
I am from change.

I am from putting my Barbie-pink flip-flops into storage and taking
    out my Bearpaw boots instead.
I am from a tight-knit community of hugs and
"Have a nice day"
To practically watching the smoke rise from that middle-aged man's
    head when I accidentally bump him on the sidewalk.
To the rush of cars and motorcycles
Racing outside my window.
To cramming into a pack of people on the subway.

I am now from the high of New York adrenaline I feel coursing
    through my veins,
The rush of independence,
At only sixteen,
Swiping a plastic yellow card in between two pieces of metal
Descending steep stairs
Rocking my heels on the platform edge
The breeze of the incoming train weaving through my hair and kissing
    my cheeks,
From hopping on that train,
And just going,
Going,
Going,
From the city that is always going.

I am,
Now,
From the city that never sleeps.

I went from peace and quiet,
The light buzzing of crickets and hummingbirds,
The swish of tumbleweeds.
I'm now from
The light cooing of pigeons and the rapid flutter of their wings,
Squirrels that scale the trees in the park,
The smell of coffee and "Nuts4Nuts" peanut trucks.

From the awkward bump,
I shared with that man,
But appreciating a new face,
Even with the smoke rising out of it.
From a rainbow of culture, fashion, and faces,
Where no two people are the same,
Where no experience is the same,
Where no day is the same.
I am from fear of change,
But adapting,
Growing,
Learning,
To love the change I once dreaded.

ANAÍS FERNÁNDEZ

YEARS AS MENTEE: 1

GRADE: Junior

BORN: San Francisco, CA

LIVES: Queens, NY

PUBLICATIONS & RECOGNITIONS:
Scholastic Arts & Writing
Awards: Honorable Mention

MENTEE'S ANECDOTE:

Kayla and I both expressed an interest in playwriting early on in our relationship. During our first attempt, we were both on the same Google Doc, each taking on a different character and writing out their lines in response to each other. Both of us come from a background in theater, and translating improvisation from the stage to the page was a really unique and fun experience. It was a way for us to learn each other's writing styles while also exploring the world of playwriting.

KAYLA THURBER

YEARS AS MENTOR: 1

OCCUPATION: Copywriter and
Copy Editor

BORN: Boca Raton, FL

LIVES: Brooklyn, NY

MENTOR'S ANECDOTE:

When I first met Anaís, I wanted to get to know her really well. I knew we needed some icebreakers to get the ball rolling, so I came up with a bunch of random questions that we could ask each other, from "What's your favorite color?" to "If you could have any superpower, what would it be?" We laughed together and learned a lot about each other, but then I posed a challenge: Write a poem about the other person based on the answers to the questions. The end result was two lovely poems that I cherish to this day.

A Passenger's Library

ANAÍS FERNÁNDEZ

An exploration of ghostly subway rides during the COVID-19 pandemic.

the faces on this train used to tell stories

good stories
stories like the ones passed down from our mothers
stories that feel like
speeding through space or
maybe through a darkened subway tunnel

the faces on this train used to tell stories

with all the figurative language my English teacher
could ask for

I could find similes in their smiles
metaphors in their mouths
imagery right behind their eyes and
always irony
tucked into the corners of their lips

the faces on this train used to tell stories

sad stories

stories of cold nights and not enough to wear
stories that sound like clinking coins in cups
stories printed in black-and-white, flipped through
and left behind for the next person

loud stories
stories of boombox bass and beat and beat-up baseball caps
stories that start with *it's showtime, folks*
and read like limber limbs around steel poles

the seats on this train used to tell stories

stories of lost things
of umbrellas and MetroCards
mittens and hats
they say that one man's trash is another man's treasure and
I imagine if all the lost things on the subway were turned into
    illustrations
they would create the most beautiful picture book

sticker stories
graffiti graphics
call me written in red and a phone number
ads and ads and ads and

the bodies on this train used to tell stories

in the summer they would shine
and in the winter they would disappear
only to come out again too early
forgetting the snow always has the best April Fools' Day trick up its
    sleeve

the subway was my favorite library
no overdue policy
and the shelves were always stocked but never the same

I treated the threshold between the platform and train car floor like
a steel-bound front cover
and when the man tells me to *stand clear of the closing doors*
it sounds like a dedication

the faces on this train

are few now
covered and concealed
by a cloth veil

I know that behind the mask
there is still a story
but for now
all the titles are the same:

keep breathing.

JAZMINE FLORENCIO

YEARS AS MENTEE: 1

GRADE: Junior

BORN: Queens, NY

LIVES: Queens, NY

MENTEE'S ANECDOTE:

My relationship with writing has never been the best, but when I met my mentor, Mary Darby, that changed. For the first time, I felt like I was finding my voice as a writer. I feel more comfortable when I open a document or flip to a fresh page in my notebook. I am able to discover who I am as a writer without being intimidated. I feel very happy to have such an experienced and amazing writer as my mentor.

MARY DARBY

YEARS AS MENTOR: 3

OCCUPATION: Writer and Editor

BORN: Peekskill, NY

LIVES: Brooklyn, NY

MENTOR'S ANECDOTE:

I look forward every week to meeting with Jazmine. She is a beautiful spirit and a joy to work with, because of both the person she is and the fact that she is so committed to her writing. This is the first poem she's ever written, and she worked hard on it. I'm proud of her and what she's accomplished. I can't wait to see what she does next.

Las Manos de mi Mamá

JAZMINE FLORENCIO

My whole life I have been fascinated with my mother's hands and how they are changing over time. I decided to dedicate a poem to them.

Dry, cracked, hard.
These hands, once soft,
Now long for attention.

Years ago they changed my diapers,
Soft and moisturized, they greeted me in the mornings
And tucked me in at night.

My mom's hands prepared hot coffees for years at our family's bakery.
They packed orders and stocked fridges,
Her bare fingertips flipped tortillas over the scorching stovetop,
And our tiny kitchen filled with that smokey aroma I grew up with.
Her hands heated up my own little hands on cold New York City
   winter days,
Squeezing them to remind me that I was safe.

But now her hands no longer function like they used to.
These hands, once filled with life, are drying up.
Now, these hands change my little sister's diapers.
And now I am the one who warms her dry, cracked hands in mine.

GABRIELLE GALCHEN

YEARS AS MENTEE: 3

GRADE: Senior

BORN: New York, NY

LIVES: New York, NY

PUBLICATIONS & RECOGNITIONS:
Nancy Thorp Poetry Contest:
Finalist; *Apparition Lit* magazine;
Soul Talk Magazine

MENTEE'S ANECDOTE:

Whether it was in our weekly coffee shop dates or on our current FaceTime calls, Emily always seems to understand my mind in a way no one else can. Especially during the pandemic, she has taught me that writing is simultaneously a catharsis, salve, and way to console others. For once, words fail to truly express the empowering impact she has made on me as both a writer and person. I will truly miss having her as a mentor in college, but I am forever grateful for the three past wonderful years.

EMILY BARASCH

YEARS AS MENTOR: 3

OCCUPATION: Writer

BORN: New York, NY

LIVES: New York, NY

PUBLICATIONS & RECOGNITIONS:
The Jerusalem Post, Vogue, i-D

MENTOR'S ANECDOTE:

If working together with Gabi in Girls Write Now last year was about finding her voice, this year has been about exploring her new, complex, and unique ways of expressing it. From playwriting to poetry to podcasting, Gabi has challenged herself and come out on the other side with brilliant work, tenacity, and wisdom that surpasses her years. I particularly revel in the way her work can emotionally move me, from a genuinely terrifying (and riveting) play to more candid and heartfelt work.

A Certainty

GABRIELLE GALCHEN

This poem focuses on the philosophy of interpreting life objectively; there is a certain calm in accepting reality as is, and taking pleasure in the mere fact of our existence.

The only fact is that existing rings
Kinder chimes than thinking,
A sickness which questions too much
To waltz through time passing.
Trees do not breathe,
Waves do not beat,
Winds do not whistle,
Birds do not sing,
The world does not exist
For us to think about it.

If it did, trees would inscribe
Letters along the veins of leaves;
Waves would whisper their messages
Within the mouths of seashells;
Winds would echo words
Born of every hemisphere's wisdom;
Birds would sing in front of audiences
Larger than squirrels and sky.

But trees grow leaves to grow leaves,
And waves beat to beat,

Winds whistle to whistle,
Birds sing to sing,
And this is so because it is so.

I am, I am, I am,
And that's it.

ANGIE GALINDO PEREZ

YEARS AS MENTEE: 1

GRADE: Senior

BORN: New York, NY

LIVES: Queens, NY

PUBLICATIONS & RECOGNITIONS:
The Baysider

MENTEE'S ANECDOTE:

My relationship with Kym Richardson brings a surprise weekly. We have similar interests, whether it's about astrology, stars, cultures, thrillers, Star Wars, or science fiction movies/series. My mentor has become my guide in my writing exploration and someone I can confide in when life gets hard.

KYM RICHARDSON

YEARS AS MENTOR: 1

OCCUPATION: Early Childhood Learning and Development Digital Editor

BORN: New York, NY

LIVES: Silver Spring, MD

MENTOR'S ANECDOTE:

My relationship with Angie is an inspiring journey into creating work and sharing interests and aspirations. When we recorded our podcast, *How a Poem Comes to Be*, Angie read her poem-in-progress. I interviewed her about why writing is important to her and what her process is for making a poem. After we played back the audio, Angie let me know that this was the first time she'd heard her own voice. I was grateful to be able to share this moment of wonder with her and to see how it impacts the work she is creating.

Pozole

ANGIE GALINDO PEREZ

A heartwarming moment between a mother and daughter. Cooking pozole, a Mexican meal, and learning about their roots.

As my mami took the groceries out of the bag, I could see the excitement in her eyes as we would soon begin our Mexican Christmas tradition. Soon, Mami would show me how to make Mexican pozole, the recipe her own abuelita taught her.

"Put your hair up in a bun, wash your hands, and help me cook, Mija," Mami said to me, as she started playing cumbia music on the stereo.

"Okay, Mami. Relax," I said.

"Sorry, Mija, I'm just excited that my little girl is finally going to take part in our family traditions," she said, as she put on the pork to cook.

"Before I start telling you the story, can you please chop up some onions and garlic?" Mami said as I reached into the grocery bag.

"Our ancestors, the Aztecs, were smart. I always wonder, how did they know which plants were edible," she said.

As I struggled to chop the onions and garlic, I almost cut my fingertip with the small, sharp knife. Mami glanced over and motioned for me to step aside. In a flash, Mami chopped up the onions and garlic, dropped them into the pot of boiling water with the meat, and placed the lid on top.

"The Aztecs were one of the greatest empires in Mexican history," Mami said. "The Aztec empire had strong warriors whose victories honored their gods. Especially the god of war and of the sun, Huītzilōpōchtli. The Aztecs' prisoners of war would be used in a human sacrificial religious soup that they called *pozole*. But the colonizers of

Spain arrived and changed the Aztecs' customs. The Spaniards converted the Aztecs to Christianity. Through these new and enforced beliefs, the Aztecs were taught human sacrifices were wrong and that they should use animals such as cows and pigs for their practices, instead."

As she talked about the Aztecs, my mouth dropped open wide. Mami saw my face of horror and she laughed. Then she stroked my hair back to my ear.

I sat quietly for several minutes, thinking about everything Mami just said. As Mami lifted the lid from the pot, the steam warmed the house from the cold winter breeze. Mami took out the meat from the boiling pot and placed it on a separate plate. She opened the can of white hominy and poured it into the same boiling water that had cooked the meat.

"Wait, Mami. So, how did your abuelita teach you how to cook pozole?" I asked.

Mami looked outside the window and sighed. I could see the expression in her eyes. She missed her abuelita.

"My abuelita was the gem of the town and was loved by everyone. My abuelita's name was Flor, which means flower in Spanish, and her name fitted her personality. She always wore traditional flowered blouses or skirts and always smelled like flowers. Every day she would wake up at sunrise and set out to collect all types of flowers. Did you know I was Abuelita's favorite grandchild? Shhhh, don't tell your uncles and aunts," she said as she put her finger to her lips.

Mami opened the lid to check if the hominy was cooking. She pinched the hominy to check its softness.

"It is a bit hard, but it's cooking nice," she said. "Now it's time to put in the seasoning. For this pozole to taste good, you need to add oregano and salt."

When Mami put the seasoning in, it fell down gently like the snow.

"Anyways, she took care of my siblings and me when my parents immigrated to the United States," Mami said. "One day, my abuelita called me to come into the kitchen and told me to help her cook pozole. She showed me what ingredients to put into my pozole and which method works to get that delicious and unique taste."

"Those were the best days," Mami said. "The days that remind me of my childhood. I wish you could have met my abuelita. She died six years ago. I wish I could have been there for her during her last days. She went away peacefully in her sleep. Abuelita's legacy continues and I can see her reflection in you." She pointed her finger at me and tapped me gently on my chest.

"Why do you say that?" I asked.

"You have her determination, kindness, and curiosity," Mami answered, as she patted my head. Then she walked to the stove to taste the pozole.

"Mija, come here and taste how good our pozole is," she said, and motioned with her hand for me to come over.

My mom handed me a spoonful of pozole. As soon as I tasted it, I imagined Mami and her abuelita tasting the pozole with all of its flavors: the oregano, the soft pork, the saltiness, and the white hominy.

"It's ready to be served!" Mami announced.

Soon we will share our pozole with the whole family!

VICTORIA GAO

YEARS AS MENTEE: 3

GRADE: Senior

BORN: New York, NY

LIVES: Queens, NY

PUBLICATIONS & RECOGNITIONS:
Scholastic Art & Writing Awards:
Honorable Mention

MENTEE'S ANECDOTE:

For the past two years, I have always looked forward to meeting with Soyolmaa to brainstorm new story ideas and explore different writing and multimedia genres. Her feedback and excitement to read my latest works always motivate me to continue writing. A memorable part of this year was working with Soyolmaa on our pair piece "Forging Melody" and experimenting with podcasting.

SOYOLMAA LKHAGVADORJ

YEARS AS MENTOR: 2

OCCUPATION: Assistant Editor at
Harper Design

BORN: Ulaanbaatar, Mongolia

LIVES: Brooklyn, NY

MENTOR'S ANECDOTE:

Now that Victoria's senior year is coming to a close, it feels bittersweet to announce her last Girls Write Now reading. First, I would like to thank Girls Write Now for bringing Victoria and I together, as we've spent the past two years writing, chatting, and getting to know each other. She's shared with me some of the most creative short stories I've ever read, and I know you too will be on the waiting list of people who are looking forward to reading more of her work. I can't wait to see what the future has in store for her wherever she goes!

Spinning Genes

VICTORIA GAO

This story highlights the positive and negative impacts of gene-editing tools on a person's health and personality with the use of time travel and the fantasy character the Immortal Wish Maker.

At Van Cortlandt Park, I cheer as Samantha approaches the finish line of a 5K race. With swift repetitive movements, she propels her body through the other runners and crosses the finish line first. As I approach Samantha to congratulate her, she suddenly stumbles and clasps the sides of her head in pain. Her legs crumple underneath her and her body lands on the concrete with a loud crack.

When doctors open the operating room doors, I rush forward to help them wheel Samantha's stretcher. Her head is wrapped in white bandages with specks of blood.

Once Samantha falls asleep, I schedule an appointment with the neurologist who performed the MRI. An hour later, the doctor shows me black-and-white snapshots of Samantha's brain taken from different angles. He points to a large white lump in the bottom right part of the brain and says, "A brain tumor has permanently impaired Samantha's facial-recognition and hearing abilities. Ms. Campbell, I'm sorry to tell you, your daughter has been diagnosed with Stage Three brain cancer."

"W-W-What are the next steps for treatment?"

"I recommend getting surgery to remove her brain tumor. Afterward, Samantha will need radiation or chemotherapy treatments to stop the cancer from spreading. Here is a list of potential costs on the hospital bill."

I accept the slip of paper with shaking hands, realizing that all the money saved for Samantha's college tuition is not even enough for more than one treatment.

Outside the hospital, I watch the sky darken and feel water droplets snake an icy finger down my spine. I'm in disbelief of my daughter's dire medical state. If only I could go back in time and remove Samantha's mutated genes before she was born to significantly lower her chances of getting cancer.

Sixteen years ago, my partner Jake and I visited a laboratory every three weeks to combine our reproductive cells to form frozen embryos. Via CRISPR technology, we removed genes associated with bad traits and inserted genes for perfect health, athleticism, and intelligence. However, the genetically modified embryos wouldn't grow inside my womb for more than a week. As I approached menopause, the chances of conceiving a child diminished. The last time I visited the lab, I told the lab technician to implant only unaltered embryos, despite Jake's vehement protests.

One of the unaltered embryos successfully developed inside me. On the day Samantha was born, my heart was singing and I couldn't wait to show the baby to Jake. Instead, I was greeted with my belongings and bills from fifteen failed embryo implantations scattered across the front porch. There was a new brass lock on the front door, and I was left to raise Samantha as a single mom. Who could have guessed what the decision to have an unmodified baby would bring.

Suddenly, the rain stops falling. As I round the corner of a street, the streetlamp illuminates a lady wearing a sparkly white wool cloak. She holds up a disk that spins and flashes groups of numbers and letters every few seconds.

01-10-2112 15:30. 40°N 74°W.

"I can let you travel back to the hour before Samantha's embryo was implanted in your womb if you agree to be my apprentice for the rest of my life. When I pass away, you will replace me as the Immortal Wish Maker," the lady says.

"What does an Immortal Wish Maker do?" I ask.

"Travel to different universes and time periods to grant other people's wishes if they are willing to pay a price."

I shudder at the thought of leaving the world I am familiar with. But the possibility of changing Samantha's fate gives me the courage to accept the Wish Maker's terms. She presses the center of the spinning disk and vanishes in a flash of white light. A gust of wind blows around me, and when I open my eyes, I am sitting in the lab technician's office. He hands me a contract stating the cost and risks for implanting unaltered embryos.

Feeling confident in the fate of this embryo's success, I ask the lab technician if we can remove the oncogenes associated with brain cancer before it's implanted. The lab technician nods and has his assistant edit the genes of the embryo. Nine months later, a baby girl is born. Doctors delivering the baby exclaim that she is healthy and will become an outstanding athlete. At the age of four, she already has the endurance to run a mile every morning. As she grows up, she wins medals at every race she participates in. At the age of sixteen, she doesn't develop brain cancer and is qualified to try out for the Olympics. She wins gold medals for the USA but brings them home with vacant eyes. With a genetically modified body, she wins races without setbacks or hardcore training. I smile as I see my daughter grow into a young adult with a bright future. Before long, I see a flash of light and a spinning disk. The time is ripe for my apprenticeship.

CLAIRE GIANNOSA

YEARS AS MENTEE: 2

GRADE: Junior

BORN: New York, NY

LIVES: New York, NY

MENTEE'S ANECDOTE:

Anna gives advice in such an effortless way. If I could, I would want to soak up every word from our conversations together. I have always admired Anna's quiet strength; she is a natural leader and carries herself with tranquility and kindness. Anna has pushed me further than I ever thought I could go, and it is because of her that I can continue pushing myself. And although we have not been able to see each other in person for almost a year now, I feel our relationship has only strengthened.

ANNA HUMPHREY

YEARS AS MENTOR: 3

OCCUPATION: Speechwriter

BORN: Lexington, KY

LIVES: New York, NY

MENTOR'S ANECDOTE:

If I had to choose one word to describe Claire, it would be *brave*. This year alone, she has been brave enough to begin writing her first novel, to submit her poetry for award consideration, and to share her experience living at the epicenter of a global pandemic. Although we haven't been able to see each other in person for nearly a year because of that pandemic, I probably get more out of our virtual pair sessions than she does—because I learn just as much from her bravery, and her writing, as she does from me.

Field of Memories

CLAIRE GIANNOSA

This poem captures the essence of childhood nostalgia, contrasted with older adolescence. It is a realization that our innocence has turned into something darker.

Remember when the grass tickled our toes and we screamed at the
    critter crawlers that dared invade our space;
Remember when we saw the world through a smaller lens, only
    capable of two emotions, how gasps were really a big gulp of fresh-
    tasting air;
Remember when we were elastic—our muscles expandable, able to
    bend and curve and pull and run
        and run
            and run
      so far away we didn't even—
Remember when we didn't know what pain was, when we confessed
    our love with the conviction of infants, latching on to what was safe,
    easy, and warm;
Remember when promises were dandelions, something we could give
    freely and never take back, before we realized they were made of
    glass;
Remember when webs were for spiders, and not the sticky mess of lies
    we cradle in our laps, forgetting we fed our monsters.

KATHRYN GIOIOSA

YEARS AS MENTEE: 1

GRADE: Senior

BORN: Queens, NY

LIVES: Queens, NY

MENTEE'S ANECDOTE:

Carol has helped me grow as a journalist and essayist by helping me learn to appreciate my dual identities. Through working on college essays and personal narratives, she has taught me to value my family and culture much more. I've enjoyed talking to Carol about her past in activism for women's rights and connecting about our shared interest in advocating for social justice.

CAROL HYMOWITZ

YEARS AS MENTOR: 4

OCCUPATION: Journalist, Writer, and Editor

BORN: New York, NY

LIVES: New York, NY

MENTOR'S ANECDOTE:

Throughout this year of COVID-19, spending time with Kathryn on Zoom is always a high point of my week. This fall, she spent a lot of time writing and rewriting many college essays, and through these I've gotten to know about her Taiwanese/Italian family and her bold and passionate involvement in social activism, fighting against climate change and for racial justice. Her essays display her talents as a descriptive and compelling writer who's willing to reveal herself to reach others.

Noodles and Pasta: Different Yet the Same

KATHRYN GIOIOSA

I wrote this piece to reflect on my favorite tradition every year— my family's Christmas Eve dinners, demonstrating my multicultural background through the food that we eat.

On Christmas Eve, for as long as I can remember, I open the door to my aunt's house and get attacked. She owns five huskies and runs a dog-sitting business, so as soon as I arrive at her home with my parents for our holiday celebration, about twenty dogs of various sizes jump on me and tackle me to the ground.

As a child, I would recoil and try to run away. My parents, who stood behind me, were seemingly the more desirable targets, since they held plates of food—but they were left untouched.

Now that I'm a teenager, and much taller, I enjoy the dogs' rowdy greeting. After they jump on me and lick my face, I enter my aunt's dining room, away from the dogs' smell, and inhale the sweet odor of scented candles and freshly baked chocolate cake, along with the spices in dishes still being prepared. I'm with the Italian side of my family, so our holiday meal includes a lot of pasta and the traditional seven dishes of seafood. We usually have lobster, crab, calamari, salmon, and my and the dogs' favorite—shrimp.

But there is always one outlier.

My Taiwanese mother brings homemade noodles to dinner, which everyone enjoys. Her light brown noodles, smelling of sesame oil and vinegar, stand out on the dining room table next to the bright red baked ziti.

To me, these dishes are the same. Although noodles and pasta represent cultures from opposite sides of the world, they're both composed of flour, eggs, and water.

Since my mother emigrated from Taiwan to New York on her own in her twenties and her mother, her siblings, and their children all live in Taiwan, my Italian relatives who live near my family in New York are my closest extended family. Whenever I'm with them, I feel accepted. My aunts and uncles try to teach me Italian and share stories about relatives who died before I was born. In turn, I share updates from my relatives in Taiwan, if I've recently visited them.

When Taiwanese relatives do visit, they're always fascinated and delighted by the intricate Italian dishes they're served and the loud backgammon and poker games happening in the background. Shouts of "Come on, give me doubles" are a staple as my paternal uncles bet on games of backgammon while others present crowd around them to see who will win.

Still, I've struggled to come to terms with my dual identity. I'm often seen as just Taiwanese or not Taiwanese enough. My Chinese is mixed with an American accent, and I know only a few words of Italian. I have a gold fortune cat necklace, rosaries that have been passed down for generations, and other items and symbols from each of my cultures, but I've had difficulty finding ways to connect them.

Food, however, is one of the few things in the world that has the unique ability to bring people together—especially food that overlaps different cultures. On Christmas Eve, when I watch my aunt eat my mother's noodles and my mother devour my aunt's ravioli, while I consume portions of both dishes, I feel complete—and at home. And I'm reminded to embrace not only my dual identity but many different cultures around the world, and to appreciate their similarities.

LILIANA GREYF

YEARS AS MENTEE: 1

GRADE: Junior

BORN: New York, NY

LIVES: New York, NY

PUBLICATIONS & RECOGNITIONS:
Scholastic Art & Writing Awards:
Gold Keys

MENTEE'S ANECDOTE:

Annie and I are many things—we are writers, thinkers, women, friends—but mostly we are people who care for each other. I am lucky to trust her with my writing, and luckier to have her one step away whenever I need her.

ANNIE BRYAN

YEARS AS MENTOR: 3

OCCUPATION: Digital Editor, *The Philadelphia Inquirer*

BORN: Philadelphia, PA

LIVES: Queens, NY

PUBLICATIONS & RECOGNITIONS:
Society of Professional Journalists
Mark of Excellence Award: First
Place; *Off White*; Fringe Festival

MENTOR'S ANECDOTE:

When we get on a Zoom call, the worries of the world disappear (at least for a little while). Our sessions are both therapeutic and challenging, comfortable and experimental, energizing and calming. There is a kind of magic that happens when two people who truly understand each other write together, and we have found that in each other. I think the world of Liliana and I am incredibly excited to see what she does with her infinite talent to distill the complex, unflinching watch on the inequities of the world, and true compassion for everyone who crosses her path.

Night Swimming at Summer Camp in New Hampshire

LILIANA GREYF

The girls swim in the lake at summer camp. It is the only place around them that is cool.

It is mid-August and the hair on our legs has grown long, even below the knee. The days are hot and slow. We wake with our backs damp and our ankles blistered. We braid our hair in the mirror and paint our toenails light pink. We hang the straps of our bathing suits on the porch, let them drip lake water into the grass.

In the afternoons, the air becomes impossibly still. We lay on the floor of the cabin with our belly buttons showing, exhale hot air toward the ceiling, and open all the windows. Even the silence is sticky with warmth. We count one another's birthmarks and kick our feet over the rails on the bunk beds. We shuffle decks of cards and hope for a breeze to blow through the room. The world grows heavy with our waiting.

We watch the sun move through the sky until the windows become stained with purple light. This is how we know that it is time. We slip off our dresses and walk the wooded trail hand in hand. We stumble through tree roots and glide beneath branches. We close our eyes and do not open them until we feel the dirt turn to sand on our heels.

It is dark by the time we have reached the water. Now it is the lake that is still. The air has begun to move. We run and crawl and tiptoe and breathe. We do not stop until we feel the lake seep through the lines on our palms.

The water is dark with chill and depth. We sink our hips into it, bury our faces into its quiet. We push ourselves into the throbbing blue. Under the surface, we listen to its murky breaths. We think we can hear it speaking to us, calling us to move deeper, further, quickly. Every night seems to be the first cold we have ever felt, and we swim through it as if we will never experience it again.

We remember the first night of the summer, weeks ago now, when the water still felt new, piercing, bold. We think of our clumsy apprehension, our unknowing gaze. We recall how we stumbled through the heat without anticipation of night. Now we have internalized this thrill. We do not suck in our bellies or raise our arms. We do not shy away from the cold.

We float on our backs and watch the constellations rearrange themselves, the leaves flutter and pulse. We let the ends of our curls drift loosely beneath us. We open our eyes and let them be flooded with wind, let them sting and blink and see.

We are submerged by the solace of liquid deep. This is what brings us back to the present. During every moment that is not this one, we are in mourning for the days we have already experienced, those we cannot get back. We retrace the faded calendar that our counselors drew with chalk on the porch. Cross out another day. Step back to measure our progress. We wonder how long it will be before there are no days left. Here, under the surface, there is no tomorrow. There is no end to this summer. No final campfire, no last breakfast. Here, we are just existing. Girls, together, swimming in the lake at night.

Tomorrow morning, we will wake up slow and heavy again. Only the roots of our scalps and the spaces between our toes will hold memories of what we saw. Only our eyelids will flicker with cool breeze, dark chill, crisp water. Only our hearts will beat with the rhythm of the lake's ripple. We will only wait to swim again.

ERYNN GUTIERREZ

YEARS AS MENTEE: 1

GRADE: Senior

BORN: Ridgewood, CA

LIVES: Queens, NY

MENTEE'S ANECDOTE:

It never occurred to me how much you could connect with someone, even through a computer screen. From the start, Sarah and I knew that we wanted to step out of the bounds and explore mediums we hadn't tried before. And we've done just that. As we recounted our lives through memoirs, letters, and poetry, working with Sarah has shown me the value that life has to offer. We write to share experiences, to cry and to laugh over. We write to remember. Through our shared memories of childhood music rehearsals, affinities for Trader Joe's, and golf (somewhat haha), I'm glad that I have Sarah by my side to bounce off all these feelings and experiences with. Thank you, Sarah, for not only being my mentor, but a wonderful friend and confidant. I am so grateful to have you by my side!

SARAH FIRSHEIN

YEARS AS MENTOR: 1

OCCUPATION: Journalist

BORN: Hartford, CT

LIVES: Brooklyn, NY

PUBLICATIONS & RECOGNITIONS:
The New York Times, Condé Nast Traveler

MENTOR'S ANECDOTE:

After more than six long months marked by disconnection and distance, I nearly jumped for joy when I first met Erynn. I could tell immediately that we'd hit it off—our first conversations came naturally, as if we had known each other for years. I'm continually impressed by her work ethic, passion for extracurriculars and social justice issues, and humble, kindhearted nature. I was honored to help her shape her wonderful college application essay, and I beamed with pride (and bragged about her loudly to anyone who would listen) when she got in—rather unsurprisingly—to her first-choice school. In short: Erynn is a superstar, and our sessions have become a real bright spot in my week.

The Pieces of Us

ERYNN GUTIERREZ AND SARAH FIRSHEIN

Do physical things mark the passage of time? What we hope to reveal is that these seemingly mundane objects have lives beyond the obvious—and that they're filled with love, pain, stress and hope.

Sarah's Crab Socks

Much of the postpartum period is about loss. Sure, you've gained a baby; maybe you've gained a new title—mother, parent—as well. But you've lost things too: your body, encumbrances, money, freedom.

Some of us also lose our ability to reason, which explains why, a few weeks after my son was born, I found myself on hands and knees, furiously overturning the apartment in search of a pair of tiny, light blue baby socks stitched with illustrations of crabs.

After scores of hormone shots and hours shuttling to appointments on the Manhattan-bound R train, I got pregnant. Diapers and changing tables be damned: What my future child really needed was a pair of overpriced novelty socks. They were the very first baby-related thing I purchased, an emblem of all that was to come.

One afternoon, when the minuscule crab socks fell prey to the crevice between the washing machine and the wall, the exhausted new mother in me spiraled. What would happen if the socks were lost?

They weren't; I found them. And babies, I soon learned, grow anyway, whether you want them to or not. My son, as it happened, wore those socks exactly once.

Sarah's Delta Wings

Most travel writers boast about highly impractical things: scouring an entire nation on foot for a single bowl of soup, for example, or taking a twenty-three-hour flight across the world and not feeling an iota of jet lag.

My braggadocio had always been about underpacking, about how far the very little I stuffed into a suitcase could take me: Vietnam for three weeks, a road trip across France, a lazy, sun-dappled honeymoon split between Portugal and Morocco.

Then I had a baby. My packing became a study in maximalism; my suitcases a sea of specialized "just in case" items for all manner of ailment: rashes, bug bites, fevers, teething pain. There was formula and purified water; supplements and purees. The wheeled, hard-shell suitcases that had, in my twenties, filled my passport book—and, in doing so, launched my career—were suddenly overstuffed shrines about worry.

But we were determined nonetheless to travel with our infant son. On his very first flight, from New York to Cancún, the Delta flight attendant handed us a tiny gold pin. Now they hang, framed, in his room as a reminder of his wings: wings that I hope allow him to fly.

Erynn's Origami Cookie Tin

The red tin box sits in my closet. On it, an old ripped label remains intact: "Trader Joe's European Cookie Collection." Covered in dents and scratches, the box held cookies eight years ago, until they were shortly replaced by paper.

Zebra print, bold red, golden tint, and flowers flash before me when I lift the lid. The faint scent of dark chocolate and caramel kissed on each piece, the past folds of my youth extending their reach as I sift through the box. Origami cranes, frogs, flowers, Santa Clauses, and pumpkins, folded into themselves among the lifeless pieces below them.

Taped on the bottom of the tin is a sticky note with a wish I wrote when I was ten years old (sorry, it's a secret!). They say if you fold 1,000 paper cranes, you will become an origami master, and your wish will come true. I wouldn't call myself an "origami master," but my ten-year-old sister does. As I teach her the valley, crimp, and pleat folds, I can almost see myself back in my old living room, my hair dangling in front of my face as I squint at the instructions in front of me. Cher Lloyd plays in the background as I whisper the words under my breath, trying to fold 1,000 paper cranes to make my wish come true.

Erynn's White Denim Jacket

Fur coats, an orange blazer, flared pants, and a Gildan T-shirt printed with the word "SPAM," all lined up on hundreds of racks.

My fingertips flitted through the hangers, fearlessly tugging the multitudes of fabrics—lives that reside in this place. The space was empty; no one came to the thrift store on an early Sunday morning. It was just me, the smell of dank cotton, and the decades: 1960s, '70s, and '80s.

As I looked at those fur coats, I imagined their previous owners waltzing out of Tiffany on Fifth Avenue and hailing cabs to soirees on the Upper East Side of Manhattan. Those flared pants: a roller skater on Astor Place who'd fallen on her butt many times, but got up and kept going anyway. They peeked out the racks, ready for new experiences.

What had caught my eye, though, was a white jean jacket: '80s-esque, with black, rounded, jewel-like buttons and black-and-white polka dots lining the inside. I owned nothing like it.

Its denim radiated a clean slate, fervent to hit the ground running. So I picked it up from the rack, slung it over my shoulder, and set off to tackle whatever the world had to throw at me.

INSTAGRAM HANDLE: @thepiecesofus_GWN

FRANCIS GUTIERREZ

YEARS AS MENTEE: 2

GRADE: Senior

BORN: New York, NY

LIVES: New York, NY

MENTEE'S ANECDOTE:

Working with Ashna these past two years has been amazing! She has helped my writing grow so much and honestly makes the process so much more enjoyable. She always gives helpful and constructive feedback and makes sure we work our way together through my pieces. I am honestly so grateful to have her as a mentor; she makes the process so much more enjoyable and worth it.

ASHNA SHAH

YEARS AS MENTOR: 2

OCCUPATION: Brand Strategy Consultant

BORN: Chicago, IL

LIVES: Brooklyn, NY

MENTOR'S ANECDOTE:

Working on this piece was another glimpse into the mysterious mind and talent of Francis. I find myself in awe of the insight and fresh thought brewing under the surface! We started with one piece and realized that while it used all the right words, her truth was missing. Starting over with a free-write, Francis reached deeper within herself—coming out with a thread of honesty and clarity and even some pain that we both felt hit a different note altogether. I enjoyed not just the end result you're about to see, but the entire process of discovering it.

A Generational Blessing

FRANCIS GUTIERREZ

Oftentimes I tend to focus on generational curses, the bad traits I've received from my family. My piece reflects on this and the generational blessings passed down.

Passed down from my grandmother to my mother to me
a box you do not want to open but you need
And it's stuck in the core of your being
It's full of tears and heartaches
Full of complacency and ignoring your mistakes
A raw kind of sadness that hurts your soul
and makes you question life and growing old
but if you look hard enough and stick your hand deep enough
you'll find a string of pearls
each showing perseverance and hard work,
unconditional love and friendship
that string of pearls is brighter than the rest
It makes opening this box
More of a treasure than test

LENA HABTU

YEARS AS MENTEE: 3

GRADE: Junior

BORN: Addis Ababa, Ethiopia

LIVES: New York, NY

PUBLICATIONS & RECOGNITIONS:
Scholastic Art and Writing
Awards: Honorable Mention

MENTEE'S ANECDOTE:

Time and time again, I'm left acutely aware of this twist of fate that brought Sammi and me together. I leave each of our sessions with an overwhelming sense of gratitude—for the creativity and adaptability she carries with her into every meeting, for her endless supply of prompts that never fail to strike chords of inspiration within me, and always for our invaluable time together.

SAMMI LaBUE

YEARS AS MENTOR: 3

OCCUPATION: Founder of
Fledgling Writing Workshops

BORN: Moorpark, CA

LIVES: Brooklyn, NY

PUBLICATIONS & RECOGNITIONS:
Words in Progress

MENTOR'S ANECDOTE:

After our sessions I'm often left to wonder if Girls Write Now has some crystal ball for placing mentors with mentees. It would be too reductive to say we have a lot in common, but it seems clear our paths were meant to cross as women and artists. In our third year together and one unprecedented to the world, we seem to have focused our efforts on the not always simple task of writing "honest" poetry. In that way, we are helping each other continue to become in a moment of global pause.

palatable

LENA HABTU

"palatable" is a product of my experiences as a young black girl at a predominantly white school. Particularly, it's my examination of the concept of palatability, and what it means to prepare yourself for consumption.

palatable

i've always known i was black.
i knew the basics: my body was encased in a chocolate skin, and my
    hair defied gravity in the most wondrous ways.
i knew the abstracts: that Way Back When, people like me couldn't do
    the things that white people could for some reason.
the cloudy obscurity of racism was a foreign concept, and i slept
    soundly knowing that i lived in the Now, when things were
    Good.
it came with the elation i felt seeing the headlines broadcasting
    the election of the "first black president of the united states of
    america."
i never questioned why there hadn't been one before.

i understood my blackness in the way one claims to understand
    gravity,
i knew it was there, but i'm not sure i could explain to you what it
    meant.
i knew my blackness in its purest tangibilities and the hushed stories
    we'd tell of the Dark days

but then i stepped into the white white world of cookie-cutter girls,
      powdered sugar pale, with their lululemon leggings
      and dull, lifeless hair.

      i wasn't one of them, and it **showed**.

my mom did everything she could;
she took me to lululemon and bought me the leggings, silver iridescent
    logo glistened on my calf, a receipt of my belonging

i told myself that i was different, but in a good way. i didn't straighten
    my hair or lighten my skin. i loved my curls!!!1!1!
i didn't try to fit in.

didn't i?

didn't i nod and smile and muse and hum and play along when my
    peers mentioned White
        People Things, dropped tidbits into conversations i'd never be
        able to relate to.
didn't i make it a point to prove my worth when i could? centuries of
    social mobility neatly
        wrapped up in whether i
            (this silly little black girl)
        knew the name of the obscure broadway show
            (spoiler alert: i did)
didn't i make it a point to be more sweet than spicy, to sugarcoat my
    complexities,

i'd pat myself on the back for refusing to conform then turn around
    and pretend to navigate this white white world with ease.

and even now if i laugh too loudly with the cocoa-skinned girls,
    the girls like me,

and one of the pale cookie-cutter girls glances over, toothpick thin and
    sickly sweet, i smile
        (demurely,
           we are not threatening creatures)
and pipe down and i wave, making my body, my voice, and my being
    soft and small enough for them to sink their teeth into with ease.

because really who am i if not palatable?

IRENE HAO

YEARS AS MENTEE: 3

GRADE: Senior

BORN: New York, NY

LIVES: Brooklyn, NY

PUBLICATIONS & RECOGNITIONS: *The Stuyvesant Spectator, Teen Ink, Canal Street News*

MENTEE'S ANECDOTE:

Lauren has immensely contributed to and been the highlight of my high school years, whether as a guide throughout the college process or as a mentor and advisor in not only my writing, but also my life. I look forward to our Whole Foods/Sunset Park/Center for Fiction/Zoom meetings every week to talk and vent about our week, collaborate and brainstorm fun projects, and write and work in comforting silence. Wishing us both the best of luck in future endeavors. I hope to look back on these years with a fond smile.

LAUREN VESPOLI

YEARS AS MENTOR: 3

OCCUPATION: Freelance Journalist

BORN: New Haven, CT

LIVES: Brooklyn, NY

PUBLICATIONS & RECOGNITIONS: *The New York Times, Vox, Atlas Obscura*

MENTOR'S ANECDOTE:

I've loved getting to see Irene grow as a writer and person over the past three years, from our weekly snacks in the Whole Foods café, to seeing her songwriting in action at her school's *SING!* performance, to now catching up on Zoom. Her creativity and talent for world-building is always inspiring, but most of all I've loved just hearing her observations about her school and daily life. I can't wait to see what awaits her after graduation this year!

Seepage

IRENE HAO

Spilling thoughts on paper; the unrefined, unfiltered, unmuted musings of Lavera Yul.

Lavera Yul needed to sort out her desk.

Her hands were sore from switching back and forth between the different-colored Muji pens on her desk. Why was her chair wooden? She should buy a pillow cushion. She glanced at Maria; her sister was in class, stumbling, awkwardly laughing. At least she was participating.

Sleepy, she wanted to sleep. Why does sleep exist? If she didn't have to sleep, if she could stop time, she could finish her homework. Everybody says they'd love to have the ability to travel back in time or to stop time to right their wrongs or whatever, but she'd do anything to stop time for an hour just to catch up on what this teacher was saying, and maybe rest. Too fast. That slide went by too fast. She should message Kelly for notes. If she could find the time.

She pushed her chair back, attempted to step out, but tripped on the charger wires to her phone, laptop, tablet. Lavera peeked under her desk: "What an absolute mess."

"Then clean it."

"Don't have time," she retorted to her sister. "And pay attention to class."

"I am," she huffed. "You're too loud."

Had Lavera been like this back then? Sure, she was quiet, angsty; she had some dark thoughts. Did she ever project them outward? Perhaps on paper, never aloud. She's older; she should help her sister. But a shower; that's what Lavera needs now.

She grabbed some towels on the bedside railings. Lavera loved afternoon showers. Hers have always been long, sometimes fifteen, thirty minutes; once, when she was twelve, she showered for an hour.

The apartment was quiet. Mom must've gone out for groceries. The bathroom was hers.

She stretched, heard a bone crack, cranked up the shower.

Hot. A bit too cold. Warm, but not lukewarm. The water was like a warm blanket. She inhaled, raised her face to the showerhead. If she angled her face right, the water would drown out the sound. A dull, muted soundscape. She was underwater, a mermaid, about to be reborn, but no, she can't hold her breath any longer. She opened her eyes. The light, the bathroom was too bright. She raised her arms in flowing movements, her ballet lessons from nine years ago. Weightless, no clothes keeping her down, flying in a spotlight of sprinkles; the water dripped from her fingertips. She swirled them around; she was waterbending, controlling oceans like Moses. That *Prince of Egypt* movie was good. She should watch it.

The bathroom mirror, fogging up, was the perfect target. Water splattered on the mirror and dripped down, the hot water cutting through the foggy cover. It's like blood; no, Picasso, or Pollock. Abstract, shapeless; she made that. She was a waterbender.

There was a new bump on her shoulder blade. And another. Mosquito bites? Acne? Goose bumps? She couldn't see. There was that idiom, or superstition, that people had a butterfly on their back, beautiful wings that everybody could see but themselves. What would her wings look like? Would they droop in the water or freeze and break in the cold like Tinker Bell? No, she wouldn't want wings. Everyone wanted to fly like Peter Pan or hop buildings like Peter Parker, but no, what if she fell? Or the web broke? Heights are scary. The higher you go, the more people pull you down, the more people can see you.

Back in her room, towel in her hair, waiting for it to dry. The desk was messy on the left, but on the right, the Instagrammable shelf was perfect.

Aligned bookshelves, colorful pins, bobbles, and gifts; her gaze wandered. There were her yearbooks, the leather notebooks where her classmates wrote comments and farewells. The smell was undeniably dusty; "You're so smart," and "You have such neat handwriting," and "Wish I knew you better," in gold ink, upside-down text, scribbles on each page.

She wished she'd known them too. If she could go back in time, when would she go back to? Middle school? No, there's a chance she would've never met her best friends. High school? She'd have to retake physics. Would she retain her knowledge? If she could, she'd go back to her infancy. Reborn a prodigy, genius. Like Matilda Wormwood, or Akeelah at the Spelling Bee. Every parent hopes for their child to be one, to carry on their hopes and dreams. She was an idea to carry on their legacy, but what is a legacy? "It's planting seeds in a garden you never get to see," says Lin-Manuel Miranda. Her ideal, unattainable dream: be the next Miranda, the next multitalented creative mind that could create a masterpiece. Songs, poems, books, podcasts: not something that just rocks on the first listen or read, or something that "grows" on you. Something that rocks your world; something that won't evaporate.

Her phone buzzed. Her Google Calendar reminder; brainstorming session in five minutes. Then dance practice; then algebra tutoring; dinner; homework, however long that will take. Rest, then morning will come. A sigh. With so much to do, surely she'd feel accomplished by the end.

MAY HATHAWAY

YEARS AS MENTEE: 2

GRADE: Senior

BORN: New York, NY

LIVES: New York, NY

PUBLICATIONS & RECOGNITIONS:
Hobart After Dark; YoungArts: Honorable Mention; *PANK* magazine

MENTEE'S ANECDOTE:

Having Alena as a mentor has been such a gift! From brainstorming college essay ideas to analyzing the short story "Cat Person," we've had so many edifying conversations and fruitful writing sessions. Our meetings are always a highlight of my week—I've really enjoyed our discussions and jokes. Though it's sad to think that we won't have these meetings next year, I know Alena's revolutionized not only the way I write but also the way I think about writing, and I'm so grateful for the time we've been able to spend together.

ALENA GRAEDON

YEARS AS MENTOR: 2

OCCUPATION: Writer and Assistant Professor

BORN: Durham, NC

LIVES: New York, NY

PUBLICATIONS & RECOGNITIONS:
Fellowship, The Lighthouse Works; Creativity and Research Grant, Monmouth University; *Los Angeles Times*

MENTOR'S ANECDOTE:

May is a wunderkind. So brilliant and creative. And somehow also a kind, grounded, and humble person. Working with May each week for the past two years has been a great joy of my life, and it's been such a pleasure to watch her thrive. I've loved witnessing her evolution as a writer, and getting to see so many of her pieces published and recognized. A special highlight, though, was hearing her words performed in front of a live audience for her high school's *SING!* celebration last spring, just before the coronavirus shut down the world. May is unstoppable!

codetry

MAY HATHAWAY and ALENA GRAEDON

We have used computer code as a form for poetry that also reinforces its content. By deploying functions and conditionals to drive narrative, we interrogate the value of art versus other modes of expression.

narrative.c

May Hathaway

```
# include <stdio.h>
# include <string.h>
# include <stdbool.h>

bool am_i_selling_out;
bool good_person;

void produce_art() {
int pride = 10;
printf("aren't you glad that you didn't sell out?");
printf("aren't you?");

}

void exist() {
printf("you are a person.");
}
```

```
void exist_upgraded() {
int pride = 0;
printf("you are a person with money.");
}

int main() {
if (am_i_selling_out == true) {
exist_upgraded();
}
if (am_i_selling_out == false) {
good_person = true;
}
if (good_person == true) {
exist();
}
return 0;
}
```

#/usr/bin/python/biological_weapon*
Alena Graedon

```
def permutations(elements):
#the
if len(elements) == 0:
#the virus
yield elements
#the virus they
else:
#the virus they killed
for result in permutations(elements[1:]):
#the virus they killed the elders
```

---

* This poem was heavily inspired by Lillian-Yvonne Bertram's "//three_last_ words" from *Travesty Generator*.

```
for i in range(len(elements)):
#the virus they killed the elders with
yield result[:i] + elements[0:1] + result
```

#the virus they killed the elders with
#was a biological weapon

NATALIE HENRY

YEARS AS MENTEE: 1

GRADE: Sophomore

BORN: Brooklyn, NY

LIVES: Brooklyn, NY

PUBLICATIONS & RECOGNITIONS:
Scholastic Art & Writing Awards:
Gold Key

MENTEE'S ANECDOTE:

From the first day we met, there was an instant connection between our personalities that created a bond that still grows to this day. After only a few meetings, I felt comfortable seeing Danielle as more than my Girls Write Now mentor. Danielle is an adult who I trust to talk to about school, forms of art, our interests, or anything we wanted. Having this relationship has produced a partnership that allows us to be honest with each other and our writing voices. The parallel of having a mentor and a friend is certainly what I didn't expect but needed.

DANIELLE M. CHERY

YEARS AS MENTOR: 2

OCCUPATION: Author, Artist,
Teacher

BORN: Brooklyn, NY

LIVES: Brooklyn, NY

PUBLICATIONS & RECOGNITIONS:
Peers, Cheers, and Volunteers

MENTOR'S ANECDOTE:

We virtually meet on Sundays. We chose Sundays because it's the perfect day to reflect on the week. I usually have my coffee and Natalie has her tea. Our choice of hot beverages inspired the name of our podcast, *Bean to Leaf*. We catch up, exchange laughs, talk about the pandemic, and then we dive into writing. We value wellness, and seek out ways to dig deeper into the definition of self-love. I'm mostly inspired by her writing as she reads it, because she genuinely breathes into each word—a true writer.

If Only You Knew

NATALIE HENRY

Subconscious writes a letter to assure Natalie of the doubts she has about her self-worth.

Life isn't what you thought it would be. No late-night high school parties. No teenage love affairs. No sleepovers to gossip about school drama. No making stupid mistakes that you would regret in your twenties, and later laugh at in your forties. Just home: waking up, logging on, and falling asleep, just to do it all over again. It's different, it's hard trying to live life with only four walls, a laptop, and a window. One with sunlight flickering through but not quite the light of life. Just you with yourself. Just you with your thoughts.

If only you knew that texting "lmao" while having a mental breakdown doesn't show mental stability. Saying that you're fine when you're not doesn't help anyone. If only you knew that people can't read your mind like they do in rom-coms. It's a fantasy; one that would've been magical to have but shouldn't be relied on. I know it's hard to let people in when you still get the same sorry result for a friend. The ones who barely reach out. The ones who are overly obsessed with what you do. Even the ones who completely switch personalities on you. Trust me, I know, but if only you knew that your true circle is on their way. The circle that inspires one another. The circle that will be there no matter how far you go. The circle that will make you happy without causing you to suffer first. That's the circle that you've been waiting for. I mean, no one can quite top myself, but if only you knew.

If only you knew that during the wee hours of the night, when you lie awake wondering why you have no one to talk to, I was right there; that I was always there. If only you knew that the value of conversation with others is just as important as communicating with yourself. You don't have to wait to tell someone your regrets to reflect, nor wait to share your achievements to celebrate. I know the satisfaction of sharing those moments is adoring, but sometimes the only person you need to talk to is me. I know what you're thinking before you even say it. I know what you're feeling before you even acknowledge it. I know you, so why can't you trust me?

Instagram says you're pretty, but if she had your lips, your hips, your hair, your flare, she would be just beautiful. She is light-skinned; a fair-looking lady who would be "just beautiful." But if only you knew that loose curls aren't good hair. Light skin may be desired by society, but you are my desire, my entity, my greatness, my beauty. If only you could look past your tall awkwardness, covered with various shades of melanin, topped with your kinky hair, just to see that beauty. Seeking your allure through all the world's madness makes you incredible. The strength it takes may be immeasurable, but if only you knew that you were born with that greatness.

If only you knew that love and happiness doesn't come from another, rather, yourself for others to build upon but never for them to plant. Loving yourself starts with assurance. You know that I always tell you that you're bright and beautiful. But you've always taken little regard simply because you're not assured of it. You don't believe me? Why? Is it because you're blind to your beauty and intelligence, or is it because you don't know how to hold your head high with such assertiveness. Well . . . let me tell you what I see. I see an amazing young lady whose drive carries her to great lengths. Who goes after anything she wants. Who always looks for ways to improve, not only for herself but for others too. She has inspired many, close and afar, which she may not even know, but I do. I know that she's sweet. She's kind. She's smart. She's beautiful.

Everyone has demons that they'll spend a lifetime fighting. Grades will slip, friends will come and go, self-worth will even leave you in the darkness. Your demons will forever be, but it's time you stopped fighting.

It's not your fight, nor is it mine either. It's about our spirit shining light on the parts of us that've been dark for years. An equal and opposite source, exceeding the power of such negativity. I'm not telling you to forge happiness, I'm telling you to be with me. When we're together, there's no division between good and bad; just us. Is that enough for you? Just being with me? We could sparkle and shine like diamonds. If only I could be your rock like you are mine. The force that's so valuable that you can't live without. *But if you only knew, if only you knew.*

CELINA HUYNH

YEARS AS MENTEE: 1

GRADE: Junior

BORN: Queens, NY

LIVES: Queens, NY

MENTEE'S ANECDOTE:

I loved my time spent with Liz. She is very open, understanding, kind, and cool. I think we are a great match; it's wild that we have so much in common, despite being thirteen years apart. I appreciate having a mentor whom I can talk to and look up to. We like to discuss all sorts of topics together, and we both feel comfortable addressing sensitive, personal topics in our writing. I feel close to her, like she is not only my writing partner, but my friend, which I hope extends beyond our time at Girls Write Now.

LIZ VON KLEMPERER

YEARS AS MENTOR: 1

OCCUPATION: Teacher

BORN: Darien, CT

LIVES: New York, NY

PUBLICATIONS & RECOGNITIONS: *The Rumpus, Tin House*, Lambda Literary

MENTOR'S ANECDOTE:

We put a timer on and let ourselves free-write for ten minutes. I see Celina's face in the corner of my screen, concentrating. At the end of ten minutes, we compare. I am always amazed at how our experiences overlap, whether it's related to mental health, sexuality, or family dynamics. I love how writing and conversation blend together, allowing us to create and bond despite our age gap. It's weird to know I've formed such a connection with Celina despite never actually having met her in person, but I'm looking forward to it!

Free in My Mind, My Body

CELINA HUYNH AND LIZ VON KLEMPERER

*During our pair sessions, we have been discussing our shared expe-
riences related to the shame, pleasure, and destigmatization of female masturbation. Below are our reflections.*

Celina Huynh

Desire lures me
I try not to give in,
but, what's the harm?
I let go and enter a world of bliss
Pleasure at the command of my fingertips
My imagination runs wild
sensations feed my mind and body
Until the rapture peaks
and I sink into my bed,
melting in contentment
until accusatory thoughts penetrate my mind
I feel so dirty, impure
But why?
My mom says masturbating is what men do
Am I to hold off my pleasure for that of a man
Am I selfish, greedy, for craving satisfaction
Am I too young
Am I too "girl"
Am I tainting my purity?
Are these feelings so dirty?

it's so natural
divine
My body is mine.
My instrument to strum.
a sweet song to myself.

A Way Back

LIZ VON KLEMPERER

When I was a teenager, I went to the doctors a lot. My body wasn't mine: They took blood, slid gloved fingers up my neck. MRI machines swallowed me up. After they cut me open, I tried to separate myself from my body. I joked that I'd rather be a brain in a jar, and it was true. My body was an inconvenient thing I couldn't control. For many years I couldn't locate pleasure in my body because I didn't believe my body was capable of it.

I didn't learn how to touch myself until I was in college. Celina and I have been talking about ways to describe it: masturbating, pleasuring oneself, getting off. None of these phrases really fit. They all seem too serious, too silly. Maybe it's something that exists outside my brain, outside words. Something that forces me out of the jar my brain has yearned to exist in. Here's what I do know: It's a portal back into my body, a way for me to feel good on my own terms.

Bouncy Castle

LIZ VON KLEMPERER

Kick off your shoes
climb inside.
In the past it's been
a frenzy of bodies
arms, legs jostling but today

it's just you.
At first you go slow,
stabilize
socks stumbling against a wobbly floor.
You bend your knees, spread your arms out
testing ways not to fall.
Eventually you start bouncing.
That's why you came here, right?
You go higher, your heart snagging, catching air
as your body ascends
sharp inhale and
arms float up
your mouth does too and then
stillness.

After,
the castle lets out air
flattening on a sun soaked patch of grass.

SHEYLA JAVIER

YEARS AS MENTEE: 2

GRADE: Senior

BORN: Queens, NY

LIVES: Queens, NY

PUBLICATIONS & RECOGNITIONS:
Taking Our Place in History: The Girls Write Now 2020 Anthology

MENTEE'S ANECDOTE:

Despite the pandemic, Shannon and I managed to do all the things we did last year, just through a screen. Reflecting on how chaotic the past year was, we wrote about all the crazy obstacles we've encountered, as well as all the fun distractions, and how much we've grown. She is always willing to listen to my stories and rants about anything and everything going on in my life, which makes it all easier.

SHANNON CARLIN

YEARS AS MENTOR: 6

OCCUPATION: Freelance Journalist

BORN: Ronkonkoma, NY

LIVES: Brooklyn, NY

PUBLICATIONS & RECOGNITIONS:
Refinery29, The Lily, Bustle

MENTOR'S ANECDOTE:

When the world turned upside down, my meet-ups with Sheyla were a welcome bit of structure that allowed time away from all my worrying. We started a diary, writing back and forth about our pandemic day-to-day. We chatted about finding inspiration in the hardest of times and Mercury in retrograde. She applied and got into college(s). Times are hard, but having a front-row Google Hangout seat to her growth as a writer and human makes it bearable. I get sad thinking about our weekly chats coming to an end, but I'm more excited to see what she does next.

The Journey

SHEYLA JAVIER

During these times, I learned how important it is to find happiness in the small moments. Reflecting on life pre-pandemic, I was inspired to write about the little things in life that bring me joy.

I knew happiness was a journey rather than a destination when I found
　　bits and pieces of it along the way.
The smallest things sparked instant joy in me.
I realized I hadn't longed for and wouldn't miss them after they
　　were gone.
It was laughing uncontrollably over the funniest joke when I hadn't in
　　the longest.
Someone's eyes lighting up as they go on and on about what sets their
　　soul on fire.
Losing track of time; getting caught in the moment doing something
　　you love.
When you realize you might miss a moment while you're living it,
So you make sure to cherish every second.
When things are weirdly working out in your favor,
So you try not to question it
And just let the good times roll.
When you finally face your fears and do that thing you were so
　　afraid to do,
And it doesn't end up being so scary.
The big drop on a roller coaster; adrenaline rushing throughout your
　　body.

When the weather starts to get warmer
Waves crashing along the shore
Receiving good advice
When your gut is right
Best friends
Random luck
The phrases
"I love you"
"I'm proud of you"
Things I never thought twice about until now.
Happiness is the journey without a destination.

JESSICA JIANG

YEARS AS MENTEE: 2

GRADE: Senior

BORN: Brooklyn, NY

LIVES: Brooklyn, NY

PUBLICATIONS & RECOGNITIONS:
QuestBridge Scholar; Scholastic
Art & Writing Awards: Silver
Key; Jack Kent Cooke Finalist

MENTEE'S ANECDOTE:

When we began the new semester in October, I exclaimed to Kelly, "I can't believe we've known each other for a year now!" because it felt like we've known each other forever. I cannot imagine being where I am now without her guidance, and though I groan and mutter and protest, her edits, on both my writing pieces and my life, have been one of the most transformative parts of my life. Do not tell her this, for she will protest this statement, but I aspire to be like her when I start "adulting."

KELLY MOFFITT

YEARS AS MENTOR: 2

OCCUPATION: Engagement
Editor

BORN: St. Louis, MO

LIVES: Brooklyn, NY

PUBLICATIONS & RECOGNITIONS:
MJ Bear Fellowship; Fellowship at
Auschwitz for the Study of
Professional Ethics

MENTOR'S ANECDOTE:

In all the madness this crazy year has offered, my weekly meeting with Jessica has been a constant comforting, creative, and centering space. Even though we disagree on the purpose of rereading books, we agree on all things Ocean Vuong, *Hamilton*, and *Throne of Glass*. After a summer filled with college essays and COVID stress, we made a pact that our sessions this year would be lighter and more focused on fun. In leaning in to this, we've discussed all things under the sun. I'm so proud to see this growing writer coming into her own as she heads to college.

A Suitcase of Lost Things

JESSICA JIANG AND KELLY MOFFITT

Two women, quarantining apart for a year, exchange disposable cameras and the stories of lost-and-found parts of their worlds, eight miles apart. These are the stories they uncovered. Visit girlswrite now.org to see the photographs.

Ode to the City

I think I will always love you like this; from afar, you are only an idea. I fill the space of you in my mind—I pave your streets with asphalt; I build skyscrapers and hang lights upon your windows so that you gleam; I fill you with people, of all skins, of all walks of life, and of all types of love. I am still too far to feel your heartbeat, but I imagine it beneath my fingertips, pounding and trembling, as ferocious as a horse galloping, as tender as a baby's chest pressed against a mother's palm. Over the water, you duplicate, your edges blurred and hazed, as if you are Atlantis, lost but found again in my imagination. I will always remember you like this; from afar, I am not yet a stranger from a foreign land for whom you are responsible, only a daughter arriving home, laden with expectations, which is to say I still love you completely.

A Suitcase of Lost Things

She collects lost items left on the streets of the city—a slap's sting at the footstep of the World Trade Center, the sound bite of a mother's harsh scolding strapped to the Thunderbolt, a first kiss laid gently on a bench in Central Park, and more. She pauses when she finds them, lips pursed, a little furrow between her eyebrows, because for a second they are so familiar that she had mistaken them for hers. But no, her first kiss had been under the dark of a movie theater, her mother scolded her constantly but always in the confines of home, and she had been slapped only once, drunk, in Natalia's basement. It takes her breath away—this familiarity—as if she had not known she had been lost until the city offered someone else's memories as beacons, their memory becoming her own. In a suitcase of lost things, the asphalt is skin, the skyscrapers limbs, the rivers blood, the parks a pulsing heart—she is found in the reflection of the city.

Fire Escape

You touched my face and said, "I know you're happy, baby, I'm happy too." My face, between your cold hands, shivered and shook in your trembling. The future is a hippie town; I'll be bleached white when I return to your erkuai and cong you bing. I had imagined that when I left, it would be down the fire escape, burning from your words, your hate lashed on my back. I did not imagine it like this, leaving with your blessing and this ease between us.

On the Staircase

She: "I didn't know God was a woman."

They: "I am not; you just wished I was."

A suitcase of lost things between them.

She: "How do I get rid of this?"

They: "Leave the city on the staircase."

Mama said: Leave your shoes at the door, don't bring the dust from the outer world in here. Prop your shoes against the wall to make sure no mice or insects make their homes inside. I don't care if your feet get cold standing on the concrete, as you fiddle with your keys at the door. These are my rules; you must follow them.

Papa said nothing, but when the mice left droppings in his shoes, Mama still washed them with care. In pursed-lips silence.

There is a saying in my mother tongue: "Only the good leave, the evil ones stay." I've spent years trying to parse these words so often spoken in the days after my sister was killed in front of me, scooting along carelessly, like the child that she was. In the precarious moments after my mother wailed beneath the wheel well of the truck, her words carried on the wind. "Only the good leave, the evil ones stay." Am I evil? For Sama means sky and I was cursed with the name Omar, long-lived. I did not choose to be the evil, it was foretold, and I still don't know where to go from here.

Meat Shop

Tiered flesh,
tidy, but greased
like some bodybuilding
contest for fowl, I stare spellbound,
Starving.

Ritual

Every day, I find my way to the folding chair
It is not comfort, but it will suffice
for I am but a man, and though you may stare,
a man must sit if he is to avoid the vice.

It is not comfort, but it will suffice
to see the children run past, free.
A man must sit if he is to avoid the vice
and remember what it meant to just be.

To see the children run past, free,
I bow my head as trains rush by

and remember what it meant to just be
when I was small but felt like God and sky.

I bow my head as trains rush by
gasping softly, remembering the air
when I was small but felt like God and sky.
Every day, I find my way to the folding chair.

AKIKO JINDO

YEARS AS MENTEE: 1

GRADE: Senior

BORN: New York, NY

LIVES: Bronx, NY

PUBLICATIONS & RECOGNITIONS:
Instagram: @littlespontaneities

MENTEE'S ANECDOTE:

While our writing styles couldn't differ more, we have found extremely interesting themes to write and talk about. I always love having a non-poetic view on my poetry, as well as writing that isn't poetry. Once, we decided to write based on a piece of furniture in our house. I wrote about my cabinet and the violin that rests upon it, hinting at various aspects of my childhood, while she wrote about her old chair. It is always interesting to choose random themes as such and freely write. We get along surprisingly well, despite our sessions being virtual.

LINDA CORMAN

YEARS AS MENTOR: 11

OCCUPATION: Freelance Editor

BORN: Newton, MA

LIVES: New York, NY

MENTOR'S ANECDOTE:

I feel it is still early in our relationship. I suspect meeting remotely slows down the process of getting to know each other. But one of the moments that stands out for me was when Akiko told me she was tutoring students in Spanish, and that she knows four languages. Another moment that stands out is when Akiko told me she played the violin. I thought how wonderful— this was the solution to the challenge of producing multimedia pieces. She and I could play chamber music together. Unfortunately, though, Akiko's violin is out of commission.

Whale, Well

AKIKO JINDO

A list of problems that increase in scale as we progress throughout the week. In a sense, they all reflect the world growing heavier to bear, an incessant drowning of some sort.

MONDAY:

Whispered *I'm Okays*
Minute-long yawns
Under-eye luggage
    From trips to unwanted flashback resorts with flat pillows

TUESDAY:

Withheld secrets
Avoidance of eye contact,
    Her contacts twinkle in permanent violets of *Leave Me
    Alones*

WEDNESDAY:

Picking at pickled delicacies
Mom's cooking tasting so foreign
The loud little people chasing each other around
Like press offices and Times Square streets
    An incessant and unbearable chaos

THURSDAY:

Deeper dents in the lockers across mine

Screams resonate and stolen lunch money lies scattered on the floor

We'll deal with it

Fretting parents with cut-off wallets and their toes not reaching the ground on the M4 bus like their dusty five-year-old selves

Utter helplessness for themselves and others

FRIDAY:

Piled Coke cans and clutters of old Christmas gifts

The cars zooming carefree while they leave their deadly residue

Browned waters to match the soil, an unwanted sort of harmony

The ozone layer falls to bits like the plaster on that ceiling

SATURDAY:

Pencil stops in place as the bottom of an undying Kindle has been found

24/7 has been maxed out, and yet there's no brown bag of lunch

Her arms' existence means society will crush her down

While the only one percent she'll ever attain is the one on her chemistry test

SUNDAY:

Third class, third world

A problem stemmed in greediness and the loss of the sixth sense: morality

The embers in the orphaned child's emerald eyes no longer glistening,

Even the tears have dried, leaving a single salt grain

The world has grown too heavy like earth whales

SYDNEY JOHNSON

YEARS AS MENTEE: 1

GRADE: Sophomore

BORN: Los Angeles, CA

LIVES: Los Angeles, CA

MENTEE'S ANECDOTE:

I've always been shy of sharing work, and I don't really know where it comes from, but I've been that way about myself for a long time. So when I read a piece for the first time to Natasha, my voice was wavering and I had the shivers, but her response to it was so kind and encouraging that I forgot about my nerves. I was much more comfortable sharing after, and all of Natasha's comments are so helpful, thoughtful, and make me think too, which I appreciate enormously.

NATASHA PIÑON

YEARS AS MENTOR: 1

OCCUPATION: Video Script Writer, *Mashable*

BORN: Los Angeles, CA

LIVES: Los Angeles, CA

MENTOR'S ANECDOTE:

Meeting Sydney (in a Zoom breakout room!) was an immediate and obvious highlight to an otherwise grim pandemic era. From our very first conversations, we quickly settled into an easy back-and-forth chatter, covering everything from the politics of the NFL to Yoshi from Mario. Sydney is generous with her laughter and careful with her words, a quality I came to appreciate even more as the year went on. I made a private promise to never jump in and finish her sentences, no matter the length of the pause, and the result was a magic glimpse into Sydney's beautiful, roving mind.

things hidden on the surface of skin

SYDNEY JOHNSON

These stanzas are the documentation of the pieces of people I'm allowed to see.

there is a woman who carries one-hundreds in her purse like they are
    twenties
she wears robes around her house even when she has guests
and laughs like the world is ending

there was a man who brought the nastiest protein bars to me
he lived in an empty house with empty decor
i know very little of him but i know his generosity

there is a girl whose first instinct is to judge
she does it as naturally as humans become envious
it seeps out of her like facial oil
it is part of her all the same

that same girl talks to me about literature
her face and limbs contort on top of the car seat with marvel
when she is tired you can see it in the way she walks
it practically seeps out of her

there is a person who thinks long before they speak
it is not a testament to their ego, i think, but instead of their genuity
to answer after thinking can rest between arrogance and sincerity

i can sense no ill intent in their silence
i could be wrong

the same person writes songs as if they were letters
and has a strange, strange atmosphere to them
i could not tell you why

they remind me of an awkward conversation when the sun is lowering
   in the sky
and the steam from a childhood tea recipe curls into the air,
only seen in the escaping beam of light
from the drowning sun

FARIYA KABIR

YEARS AS MENTEE: 1

GRADE: Sophomore

BORN: Dhaka, Bangladesh

LIVES: Queens, NY

MENTEE'S ANECDOTE:

One of my very favorite quotes by an unknown author says, "A teacher takes a hand, opens a mind, and touches a heart." Every time I meet my mentor Ms. Cailey, I am reminded of that quote. She is one of the most supportive, caring, and cutest teachers I have ever had. She always helps me with my writing, gives great advice, and corrects me. As I love to talk, she is always there to listen to me as well. I am super-annoying, but she never gets irritated by me and loves me a lot.

CAILEY RIZZO

YEARS AS MENTOR: 1

OCCUPATION: Writer

BORN: Buffalo, NY

LIVES: Brooklyn, NY

PUBLICATIONS & RECOGNITIONS:
Travel + Leisure, Today, Vice

MENTOR'S ANECDOTE:

It has been a joy to meet with Fariya and forge a new connection during a time of isolation and social distance. Even though our meetings are virtual, we have navigated the highs and lows of a tumultuous time in history together. I always feel brighter after seeing her sunny smile on my screen. Through my talks with Fariya, I am able to see the world through the eyes of a teenager again—and remember the reasons I first fell in love with writing. It has been incredible to witness her growth as a storyteller through Girls Write Now.

I did raise my boy to die . . .

FARIYA KABIR

My poem explores a mother's emotions about sending her boy to war.

I still remember your first sign of existence, the most precious word
  "positive" . . .
Your first kick at my stomach . . .
Your first flap of eyelids . . .
Your first sight of me . . .
Your first drop of tears . . .
Your first smile . . .
Your first hug . . .
Your first call, "Mom" . . .
Your first fall . . .
Your first footstep . . .
Your first birthday . . .
Your first ABC . . .
Your first day of school . . .
Your first report card . . .
Your first day of high school . . .
Your first night away from home . . .
Your first crush . . .
Your first speech at school in public . . .
Your first day of college . . .
Your first love . . .
Your first heartbreak . . .
Your first misunderstanding with me . . .

Your first sorry . . .
Your first career . . .
Your first uniform . . .
Your first day you left to join the soldiers . . .
Your first drop of blood on the ground . . .
Your last face before your death.

I still remember everything, my love
Through all those firsts,
I never thought I was raising my boy to die.
I was raising him to live in the heart of every mother, of his
    motherland.

RACHEL KELLY

YEARS AS MENTEE: 2

GRADE: Sophomore

BORN: New York, NY

LIVES: Brooklyn, NY

MENTEE'S ANECDOTE:

I loved working with Lauren so much this year! Lauren is so kind, and we work well as a team. She has made me feel motivated when it's tough to stay focused being at home. She helps me grow my stories by making them more suspenseful and enticing and helps me develop wonderful plots, even for the side characters. We always text to show each other how the project is going, and I love all the laughs we have on Zoom calls. I'm lucky to be able to call Lauren my mentor and so proud of what we made.

LAUREN KIEL

YEARS AS MENTOR: 3

OCCUPATION: General Manager, Bloomberg Green

BORN: Wilmington, NC

LIVES: New York, NY

MENTOR'S ANECDOTE:

Rachel is amazing! It has been an incredible silver lining of the challenging COVID-19 era to see how she has captured this moment in time through the experiences of her character Adelaide. I have really enjoyed brainstorming story ideas and editing scripts with Rachel, and she has done an amazing job filming and editing this project. I'm constantly impressed by Rachel's creativity, and I can't wait to see how this character will continue to evolve in future films.

Nothing Is Normal

RACHEL KELLY AND LAUREN KIEL

*This is the written version of "Nothing Is Normal." This film con-
tinues Adelaide's story from "Far Away Is Closer Than You Think,"
an original short film featuring the same main character. She realizes life isn't going back to normal yet . . . but what is normal?*

Thursday

Hey.

It's Adelaide, and welcome to my very, very, boring life.

I was writing in my journal when suddenly the alarm to go to school
went off. *BEEP! BEEP! BEEP!*

Ugh! So I have to attend virtual classes, during which time goes by so
slowly and lunch goes by so fast. You have to pay attention even though
there are lots of distractions, and I definitely don't doodle in class. I wish
the virus would just go away! I think we all do. To be able to go to school,
meet people on the subway, go to my locker, I even miss the not-so-great
things, like getting to class late. If only we could . . .

"Adelaide, what did you get for question fourteen?" asks Ms. Scott on
the screen.

"Oh, right, Ms. Scott, question number fourteen, ummm . . ."

I looked down at my phone to see a classmate texted me the answer.
"Thirty-seven," I say.

I've made a couple friends since my friend June moved away. It's
crazy that my family didn't move away first. My family has a habit of
not staying in one place for very long. Even though I've lived in New
York for two years now, I don't have any close friends here, which makes

independent lessons unbearable sometimes. Listening to music can help, but sometimes I can't resist checking my phone where everyone's life looks so perfect. I really like this account by @letteringw.lottie. I'm thinking that I might start my own, but it would never get popular. It's just a fact, Adelaide isn't popular . . . but it IS anonymous!

Well, that's my very, very boring life, see ya later.

XOXO Adelaide <3

Friday

I decided to start a similar account. It's so hard to wait during my morning online classes. Charlotte was my partner in our math breakout room. I felt like she was silently judging me the entire time. I know she wants to do a project with Kaila. I'm sorry Ms. Scott paired us together.

She asked me if I needed help with the conclusion. Of course, I shyly said "no" even though I was confused and could have used a second set of eyes.

Finally, it's lunchtime! I start to film the quote I made, but everything is getting messed up. That's not right, there's a shadow in it, it's too dark, you can see my legs. Okay, it's done . . . and so is lunchtime.

I log on to the Zoom meeting for class and ask, "Hey, Ms. Scott, can I turn off my camera for a second and get something to eat?"

And of course she replies, "No, you just had your lunch period."

Right. But the feeling of hunger was worth it, because when I checked my phone later that day, I saw a comment on my posted video from @letteringw.lottie: "I love it!!!" Yes, you heard right, I got a comment from @letteringw.lottie. Maybe I'm not so hopeless after all!

Saturday

I'm so excited that Halloween is finally here. To celebrate Halloween, my neighbors and I all put out candy on our doorsteps for everyone in the building to take. But that's not why I'm excited. Neither is my costume, which makes my cat and I look like identical twins.

I'm so excited because @letteringw.lottie and I are doing a Halloween collab! My account is actually doing really well.

In the collab we are both writing the same quote and taking photos of the same things, but we're doing it in our own style.

I can't wait to see how her post turns out; we post at seven p.m.!

Sunday

I can't believe this is happening. I didn't mean this at all!

Everyone is commenting on Lottie's post saying that all I care about is getting more followers and that's why I collabed with her. Not only is that entirely false, but Lottie and I are becoming like friends now. I'm scared that she'll probably believe them and think I don't care about our friendship.

Monday

When I woke up, I checked my phone, and I'm so relieved, Lottie is not upset with me after all. She sent a DM and said, "I totally understand that gaining followers is not your intention. You're my friend, so I'd love to spread the love!" I feel like we've gotten a lot closer, and I realize our friendship is strong.

As usual, I go to Ms. Scott's class and she says from the screen, "Welcome, class, everyone who comes beyond this time will be marked late." Then she adds, "And, Charlotte, I do not accept nicknames for your name. Change it or you'll be marked absent," in a harsh, upset tone.

That's unusual . . . I look to see what Charlotte's name is, and my heart skips a beat.

"Yes, Ms. Scott, I'm sorry, I signed in to class with the wrong email," says Charlotte, like it is no big deal.

The time it took Charlotte to change her name was enough for me to read that it was @letteringw.lottie. All this time, I have been DMing the most popular girl at our school!

What do I do? Do I tell her? Do I not? What if she finds out? What if she already knows?

SUHA KHAN

YEARS AS MENTEE: 1

GRADE: Junior

BORN: New York, NY

LIVES: New York, NY

MENTEE'S ANECDOTE:

The idea of getting a mentor for the first time was nerve-racking, especially in an all-new virtual setting. Would it be painfully awkward? Difficult? Not at all. Though I still have yet to meet Vanida in person, meeting with her virtually every week has been a constant enjoyment in this rather unsettling year. She has led me to become a more confident and careful writer, and a more frequent one as well. Her knowledge and dedication are profound. I am immensely grateful to Vanida for her mentorship. I look forward to what's to come, especially with our joint work!

VANIDA NARRAINEN

YEARS AS MENTOR: 1

OCCUPATION: Corporate Attorney

BORN: Quatre Bornes, Mauritius

LIVES: New York, NY

MENTOR'S ANECDOTE:

Suha is a wonderful writer with so much potential and who demonstrated a lot of dedication to her work. It was amazing getting to know her this year and reading some of her pieces. Suha and I experimented with various literary genres during our sessions and had a lot of fun exploring screenwriting together for our project. She is a creative yet focused team player who never ceases to surprise me with her new ideas. I feel very fortunate for the opportunity to continue working with her and I cannot wait to discover more of her work!

Burn, Pine, Perish

SUHA KHAN

When a cold, unfeeling rejection appears at our doorstep, do we readily welcome it? Hardly. Alas, it makes its way indoors regardless, bringing along misery as a plus-one.

[I burn]

When blood pounds from the heart right up to the head.

Knowing all that could've been, all that should've been, was all that wouldn't be.

The heat bubbling, boiling, stirring counterclockwise inside my stomach.

The glow of the screen, etched into my brain.

Remembering the shirt she was gleaming in.

The one torn from my chest.

The screams of my silence in the midst of their cheers, still ringing in my head.

The pyretic embers of a burning log.

[I pine]

The treacly curse of the cut-and-paste strip: "We regret to
  inform . . ."

The shadows I used as stepping stones to see my way out.

Tears dripped before a sound could even surface.

Have you heard of the tree that fell in a crowded forest while everyone
  stood around?

No sedative for the surgery.

I tired my hand with a rubber eraser on ballpoint ink.

If only we could ignore wind like still air.

The yearn for indifference.

[I perish]

Like raindrops, like the ocean, and not at all like the sky.

Transparent, uncolored—yet tethered to blue.

My feet glued to the ground.

Autopilot.

Keeping my head afloat as I bob through the hallways.

Sinking but not drowning.

Afloat without any means to tread.

Flipping past but the crease still remains.

Holding my breath until I reach the surface.

What is left when all has left?

LUCIA KIM

YEARS AS MENTEE: 1

GRADE: Sophomore

BORN: Queens, NY

LIVES: Queens, NY

MENTEE'S ANECDOTE:

Kat is incredibly generous, talented, and funny. I'm so lucky to have a mentor who not only helps me with my writing, but who reminds me that anything is possible. Kat and I are very goal-oriented, and I feel that we make progress in every meeting. Of course, this doesn't take away from our time to update each other and talk about movies. Kat taught me the beauty of slapping things on paper, taking a break, then editing later. I've become a better author because of it.

KATRIN VAN DAM

YEARS AS MENTOR: 1

OCCUPATION: VP, Editorial, ViacomCBS Consumer Products Global Creative Group

BORN: Boston, MA

LIVES: Brooklyn, NY

PUBLICATIONS & RECOGNITIONS:
Come November

MENTOR'S ANECDOTE:

Lucia and I got matched after each of us had been ghosted by our original pairing. I'm so grateful to those other two people for dropping out! Every session with Lucia is a reminder of the power of saying "yes" to things. She is so enthusiastic about trying new things that I find myself opening up to possibilities I wouldn't otherwise even consider. Thanks to Lucia, I'm learning to be less rigid about everything needing to be perfect. Look, I'll show you: I'm not even going to bother coming up with the perfect closing sentence for this anecdote!

Full House (with the K.M.A.)

LUCIA KIM

My family and the K.M.A. are as tight as sticky labels on glass bottles: They're hard to separate, but they often look better together.

My mom is always the listener in a large group of friends. She doesn't need to brag or make people laugh to be recognized. She already has that aura: *I'm nice and everyone wants to be friends with me.* My dad, on the other hand, is the triangle in a symphony orchestra. Small but loud. He's about five feet, five inches, and he's the life of any party. He knows how to brighten the mood and pull a laugh out of everyone. We all want to sit at the same lunch table as that guy. But my dad doesn't quite have the same power within my family. My sister, my mom, and I formed our little squad. That makes my dad more like a mouse living in a house of three cats. My family runs itself as a democracy. We vote on issues, and whichever side gets the most votes wins. This is where our democracy is flawed, because my dad is always outnumbered. A typical day in our house sounds like this:

"Dad! We want to watch something on the TV."

"Whyyyy. I just started watching."

"Let's vote. Who wants to watch something else?"

The three of us are always on the same side, so we win the vote. We get dinner together when my dad goes out golfing with his friends. We cross our legs and snuggle them into my mom's blanket and have a girl talk. My dad is invited occasionally. But he'd much rather play golf.

My sister and I have a love-annoyance relationship. I'll say something, and then she gets annoyed. Or I'll eat something, then she steals from me, and I get annoyed. Our definition of love is watching YouTube "What I Do in a Day" vlogs, ordering food on Uber Eats, getting disappointed that the food is cold, then doing it all again the next day.

My favorite moments are when I get to spend time with my whole family. On a trip to Cape Cod, Massachusetts, we tried to memorize the song that's supposed to make you remember all fifty states in alphabetical order. We sang "Alabama, Alaska, Arizona, Arkansas . . . what was the next one?" for hours and hours on our way to lobster rolls, walks on the beach, and barbecues. You'd think this trip was just for the four of us, but it's not a family trip without my mom's closest friends, who all came with their families.

I like to refer to my mom's inner circle as the K.M.A. This stands for the Korean Moms' Association. It can also stand for what I want to yell so bad when listening to their conversations.

"Ashley, are you done writing your college supplements? Hurry up, why aren't you done? They're important!"

Kiss My Ass (K.M.A.).

"My son bought me a bag for my birthday. Let me show you. Hold on."

Kill Me Already (K.M.A.).

Luckily, my mom was different from her friends.

I've been to some of the K.M.A. meetings, mostly because they always eat good food. Moms gather in the Paris Baguette next to my church and grab their hot coffee with cream and sugar. The meeting's conversations range from cool dog facts they read on the Internet to their children's ambitions. As a high schooler, I appreciate my mom for not telling the whole Bayside Church about my goals and aspirations. I'm one of the lucky kids because the other moms are the epitome of oversharers. They brag about the 100s their sons have gotten on their math tests. They brag about their daughters and how they received recognition from their principal. They talk about how their kids will be dentists, doctors, and lawyers and how they are the perfect candidates for Harvard.

You'll know a member of the K.M.A. is bragging, but they'll never say it straight up. At times it's, "Oh, I don't think my son is smart, but his tutor says he's very quick at learning Mandarin and very fast at picking up new information." Or, "My son never told me college is tiring because he's not the type to complain, but the dermatologist said he has acne because he goes to Vanderbilt. It's a rigorous school." And sometimes it's, "My son never practices the piano. He's a boy, what do you expect? But his fingers are very flexible." These moms know what they're doing. They're sneaky.

My sister and I admire our parents and thank them for being different from the moms in the K.M.A. Our parents have never once said, "I don't think my daughter's talented, but her music teacher always tells me that she's good at expressing herself," or anything along those lines.

Even though the K.M.A. drives me crazy, they're like my extended family. They gossip, but they make me laugh. They rooted me in my Korean identity even though I was growing up as an American.

I forgot to say that K.M.A. can also stand for *Keeping Memories Alive*.

ALICE KRESBERG

YEARS AS MENTEE: 2

GRADE: Junior

BORN: Seoul, South Korea

LIVES: Queens, NY

MENTEE'S ANECDOTE:

Amelia and I have both learned new things from being part of Girls Write Now and have gotten to bond over our cats. We set writing goals and check them off as we write. We enjoy spending some of our pair sessions by listing possible topics we want to write about. We made jokes about how much I disliked writing poetry, and in the end, I wrote a poem for my submission . . . and enjoyed writing it!

AMELIA POSSANZA

YEARS AS MENTOR: 2

OCCUPATION: Publishing

BORN: Bryn Mawr, PA

LIVES: Brooklyn, NY

MENTOR'S ANECDOTE:

When Alice and I meet on FaceTime to write together, we are often joined by our cats. Alice's cat Lola loves to be picked up, and my cat Poppy is often snoozing in the background or knocking over a pen. Charlie, Alice's other cat, is rarely seen, though I hear he's overweight. The cats are a nice way to stay connected in this isolating time. And not only do they appear on screen—sometimes they also appear in our writing!

Where I'm From

ALICE KRESBERG

I was adopted from Seoul, South Korea, at a very young age. As an international adoptee, I've found it hard to connect with my birth culture.

Bustling streets surrounded by neon lights,
A foreign language which is music to my ears,
Harsh and soft sounds mixed together, coming fluently from people's
   mouths as they dodge others and make their way down the streets.

Stand owners calling out to you with friendly shouts,
Socks sold for only fifty cents each,
A slight fishy smell mixed with spiciness lingers in the air.

The stares and whispers,
The awkward moment of silence not knowing which language to speak,
The shame I feel when I can't understand something that's said to me.

A place I've been to two times—both very different experiences,
Once a carefree, unattached girl seeing Korea for the first time,
Another time, an insecure girl desperate to get closer to her culture.

A place I wish to explore,
A place I wish I could have another life to have grown up in,
A place which makes me cry,
A place I can barely call home,
Seoul, South Korea.

EMMA KUSHNIRSKY

YEARS AS MENTEE: 1

GRADE: Junior

BORN: Hoboken, NJ

LIVES: Bronx, NY

MENTEE'S ANECDOTE:

When I met Robin (via Zoom, of course) this fall, we hit it off pretty quickly, despite the challenges of the pandemic. We have a lot in common—from Eastern European Jewish heritage to poetry. She has introduced me to all kinds of amazing poetry and has been an unbelievable source of help and inspiration. I wrote more poetry this semester than I have in my life! She's an intelligent, interesting, and kind person and writer whom I look forward to many more weekly sessions with.

ROBIN MESSING

YEARS AS MENTOR: 1

OCCUPATION: Writer and Educator

BORN: Brooklyn, NY

LIVES: Brooklyn, NY

MENTOR'S ANECDOTE:

Meeting with Emma has been a privilege, a delight, and an inspiration. I'm inspired by Emma's thoughtfulness, deep engagement with our work, and brilliant gifts. What a joy, in the midst of this pandemic isolation, to read poetry and write together. Each time we discussed a poem, our conversation prompted new insights and understandings. Even through screens, we held a space for each other and our love of words. I am so moved by the work Emma has done in our pair project and by the initiatives she's taken. It's a privilege to know Emma more deeply through poetry.

Pandemic Letters:
The Wind or a Leaf Stuck to the Sidewalk

EMMA KUSHNIRSKY AND ROBIN MESSING

After reading the poetic correspondence between Natalie Diaz and Ada Limón titled "Envelopes of Air," we decided to write poetic letters to each other, which naturally interrogated our feelings and thoughts during a pandemic.

Masking & Unmasking

ROBIN TO EMMA

I've lived long & I can recall so much, yet some of the most crucial
moments are lost to me. Recollections aside, I've decided

not to hide anymore.

I mean shame. I mean rage. I mean loneliness. In a plague
the past feels present, the future eclipsed, the carnage

unfathomable.

Sirens have subsided & death
resumes elsewhere. Fall

has never been more beautiful

now that I'm married to ginkgoes, elms, & oaks.

I wonder what your youth

makes of isolation. In my early years

I refused to know what I knew. I wonder what
your loneliness might say. Snow

is on the way. I hope it will feel

like patience, that its silence will be soothing,
not a reminder of the cruelty

of power's inaction. Sometimes I wish

there were words for everything. *Dread*
isn't exactly right. *Pleasure* isn't sufficient.

I'm finding new ways to say

gentle, tender, helpless,
to free them from captivity.

Hiding in Plain Sight Like the Wind or a Leaf Stuck to the Sidewalk

EMMA TO ROBIN

I need the burning brightness of fresh air.

I don't know if I'm lonely.

Like this past summer I was
scrambling for words and

I felt inadequate, in my longing,

but there was youth.

Fun from a distance.

Up close there's the
tear-burning torture of everything

Being Dramatic.
doyouremember?

I liked the way the snow shoved cold down my
throat.

Made me feel solitary in good company.

and the island I'm on blows salt towards me
through me
asking me to inhale

I don't want to be hiding
either

but the salt wind hides in crevasses

To inhale something that hides
is an action of loving.

In the Wake of Immobility

ROBIN TO EMMA

I walk to the park every day now
a wedge against every repressed desire

for flight

inaction terrifies me sloth
an enslavement a knot

in a tree's heart

each twisted part craves
embrace each shame like your salt wind

meant for movement

& visibility I remember riding
my ten speed over asphalt feeling

myself fleeing

when I couldn't sense any other way
I finally understand the privilege

in motion you remind me

to love the paralysis of my past
that stasis can be bravery

as we wait

for this plague
to end

Me in the Context of Who I Was and Have Been Being

EMMA TO ROBIN

In a way it would be easier if
"the plague is upon us!"

Bell clappers against strike points.

Then we could scream to no end.
Scream ourselves hoarse.

I don't want to seem ungrateful for
the white sterility of .
the walls of my room.

But I guess I am.

I want to feel
movingsofast that motion is vibration.

Privilege in motion and immobility, where does it end?
Would it help to pound the pavement

with running feet?

I used to go barefoot everywhere.
Now my feet are calloused for no reason.

Why be calloused for wood floors?

I'm remembering the joy of flip-flops in rain.
Droplets warm and juicy.
Headphones sheltered under sheaves of hair.
Laughing by myself.

I seldom laugh by myself.
If you can make yourself laugh,
you are lucky.

There's a song called "The Waiting."
I am "The Waiting."

In Which I Try to Answer When There Are No Answers

ROBIN TO EMMA

Is it possible to make
our own luck? A laugh

hidden

like the sun's
presence even

in darkness?

I've witnessed more than one
personal plague

there was no returning from.

Sometimes sky or bush
makes being human

bearable.

Pam H. once asked: Can the Earth
give back what was taken

from me? Terror

the friend that never exits.
Drawn to gloom

as if to flame. I see that
hiding can be useful—

wintering birds

the same shade
as bark

imperceptible

if not for my attention.
Isn't awareness

one of the gifts

of being
with oneself?

Distortion of Reality Comes Easily Like a Wave or Exhale

EMMA TO ROBIN

Looking out the window

it could be
a moving picture
glued to the other side of the glass.

Who's to say?

How long of never-being-outside would
it take for me to believe
this is the only world that
Exists?

Once I was trapped in a bathroom for
Thirty minutes?
Forty minutes?
Could it have been an hour?

It didn't take long to start
trying to leave
by impossible means.

Before I yelled out I closed my eyes and
moved myself through the door.

I would go crazy *sofast*.

At what point are there no backsies?
I think never.
I think that we are never broken.

I'm going to be the cardinal in the snow.
If I can bear it.

LAUREN LEE

YEARS AS MENTEE: 1

GRADE: Sophomore

BORN: Brooklyn, NY

LIVES: Brooklyn, NY

PUBLICATIONS & RECOGNITIONS: Scholastic Art & Writing Awards: Honorable Mention; *Bopomofo* podcast; *The Stuyvesant Spectator*

MENTEE'S ANECDOTE:

Truthfully, I had never liked writing. I was told for most of my life that writing was just not my strong suit and I had convinced myself that math was the only subject I was good at. With Lillian, I was given a safe space to just write what I felt. I got to experiment with songwriting and poetry and found that I really love expressing myself on paper. When we tried songwriting together—which I think we did pretty well, considering the lack of experience we had—she was always so open and flexible to my ideas and opinions.

LILLIAN PATTERSON

YEARS AS MENTOR: 1

OCCUPATION: Freelance Writer, Editor, and Research Consultant

BORN: Jackson, MS

LIVES: Brooklyn, NY

PUBLICATIONS & RECOGNITIONS: *ARTpublika Magazine*; *The Broken Spiral* anthology; *Spontaneity*; *Litro*; *ViaNolaVie*

MENTOR'S ANECDOTE:

Lauren and I are both new to Girls Write Now, so in some ways we are still finding our legs as a writing pair. However, these last few months have brought a wave of creativity and inspiration that I did not anticipate. I am constantly amazed with the maturity and eloquence of Lauren's writing. Seeing her work has pushed me to return to projects I had left by the wayside. It has been a joy to work with her.

Butterfly 蝴蝶

LAUREN LEE

"Butterfly 蝴蝶" is an ode to my great-grandmother, who passed away a few years ago. On occasion, the butterfly of her spirit still flies by.

Bye-bye butterfly
It's time to fly away
You've spent some time on mother earth
But I wonder, how is it up in heaven?

Just know that I think of you every single day
You fill my mind with happiness
Hazy memories of my early years
Are held within a frame of you

Thoughts ingrained in my mind
Your words coming to me rapidly
Even when I couldn't understand you
Every time you spoke in Taishanese

Your hair was an elegant gray
Your perm was perfectly styled
But I never saw you leave the house
How did you keep it curled?

Remember when you made me
Chicken noodle soup?

Ladling it with those shaky hands
I never did say thank you

Watching the world pass by
You sat outside
Yet in all of those years
I never saw you in your own habitat
In your own room

I will never understand
How you sat for hours on the porch
With the sun on your face and wind in your eyes
You rested and watched, not even lifting a finger

Remember when you wanted me
To take your big old jacket
Every time you stuffed it in my arms
I wish I could take it from you now

I'll never forget your prickly moods
Your eyes heavy older person blues
But with me you laughed, your eyes wrinkling
With your warm husky chuckle

If I had known you would be gone
I would have studied harder
To understand your boring lectures
To keep you company in conversation

Born in a small village in China
Where the chickens run wild,
The oxen loiter by the water
And pigs rampant with fleas

You lived in Taishan
Where the houses are made of stones
No doors or running water
And the bathroom shared by everyone

The first in your family to leave and explore
The great new world of America
Looking back at it all,
Did you ever accomplish that American dream?

You did accomplish that American dream
That dream of a better life
That dream of happiness
I became that dream

Every life you planted in that great new world
We're thankful for the lives you gifted
Every opportunity ever given
Owed to you forever

Thank you for your butterfly
It has blessed me all this way
I know you are flying by me
Each time I catch the smell of thread

Hidden in your room
The thump of the machine
Each thread with its own smell
The warm aroma of textile fibers that fills the air

The smell of home
The smell of love
Even now when I walk into your room
I am sure I feel you flying by

Can you sew for me one more memory before you go away?
I wanted to say those words to you
But you were gone too soon
所以我说再见蝴蝶

RUTH LEE

YEARS AS MENTEE: 1

GRADE: Senior

BORN: Queens, NY

LIVES: Queens, NY

PUBLICATIONS & RECOGNITIONS:
Scholastic Art & Writing Awards:
Silver Key and Honorable
Mentions

MENTEE'S ANECDOTE:

Morgan has been such a saving grace in so many ways for me. She's helped me edit pieces from college applications to personal memoirs, attempts at fiction, and anything else I send her. Every week, she graciously sends me multiple links to articles, PDFs of books, and reviews to expand our knowledge. Our weekly sessions range from brainstorming ideas and editing sessions to therapy sessions. I am so grateful for such a brilliant and compassionate mentor who has sacrificed so much time and effort and given advice that has truly transformed my outlook on life.

MORGAN LEIGH DAVIES

YEARS AS MENTOR: 1

OCCUPATION: Freelancer

BORN: Sudbury, MA

LIVES: Brooklyn, NY

PUBLICATIONS & RECOGNITIONS:
Bright Wall/Dark Room;
Overinvested podcast;
The Daily Dot

MENTOR'S ANECDOTE:

Ruth and I spend our sessions talking about everything from her writing to current events, school, and more. I rarely need to give Ruth instructions for what to work on for our next meeting: She is brimming with ideas and eager to express them. Most of our sessions are dedicated to discussing how she can improve her pieces. Unlike most writers, Ruth doesn't get defensive when I offer constructive feedback on her work. Instead, she immediately begins thinking of new ways she might be able to express her ideas or different approaches she could take to making her writing stronger.

Flight 1004

RUTH LEE

She's finally ready to explore the physical world for the first time, but something is missing and it's the final piece to reconcile her two metaphysical worlds.

We romanticize things that we can't experience. Forgive my romanticization of the airport since I've never been inside one. Gray sweatpants loosely hang on my hips as I curl up on one of those big, blue chairs. I'm listening to Frank Ocean from my pirated Spotify playlist and taking Polaroids of the families going on their excursions.

There's a small girl planted on a pale blue suitcase giggling as her father rushes past me. Her brother strolls by while carrying their mother's purse. She playfully rolls her eyes, links arms with her son, and shares her croissant with him.

Sunlight shines through the ceilings and illuminates the marble floor. Hundreds of people pass by, adding to the rush of adrenaline that pounds through my blood.

I close my eyes and imagine myself in Italy, exploring my map of aqueducts and taking pictures of different cathedrals. My Italian is subpar, but I promise myself to figure that out once I get there. I walk through fields of dandelions, letting my sundress fly freely behind me. At night, I meet a curly-haired boy on the opposite side of the railroad tracks and he signs his number to me. We meet at the intersection and continue this exhibition of happiness together: jumping across rocks that lie on top of the pond, sharing a gnocchi dish we picked up at a corner restaurant, falling asleep under the moon with our hands intertwined, his stroking mine when we wake up. I untangle myself from him, grab my belongings, and continue on my journey alone.

Now I'm in Japan, visiting my brother, who's making cat-shaped onigiris. I haven't seen him in at least seven years, but it's like I've never met him in my life. The permanent creases in his forehead have disappeared, and his fingernails, once bitten down to the cuticle, are fully grown. He doesn't flinch away from my touch, and has a glint in his eye as he humbly boasts about this new life. He's finally accepted in this city of technology, surrounded by people who finally understand his speech impediment and preference of anime over social interaction. He reminds me to visit the Nomazaki Lighthouse, where I spend hours looking for the lock he signed when he moved here years ago.

As I climb up the stairs, I marvel at the never-ending horizon. There's a salty breeze, and the wind makes hollow sounds through my ears as I take in the scenery. Alone at the top, I try to compensate for the peace I couldn't have earlier.

My world was chaos. I considered days when there wasn't an incessant ringing in my ears or the constant screaming outside my muffled pillow, or days when I felt someone else's pain rip out a piece of my heart, peaceful.

I close my eyes and try to hear the ocean's song. The shining sun and refraction from the clouds cause phosphenes in the shape of anchors, and I open my eyes in confusion.

I'm standing in front of a small town house. There's an outdoor bath, and a patch of farm next to the house. In the distance, I can hear the honking of cars and can see the industrialized city of Seoul blooming in the background. This part of town, however, is abandoned. Outside of the wooden door, sitting on a rotting bench, I see a small child crying in the arms of her parents.

It's almost impossible to recognize them, but of course it's them. The frizzy, poorly box-dyed hair on my mother as she pushes her glasses closer to her face. The same Polo Ralph Lauren navy shirt my dad seems to be wearing in every single memory I have of him from my childhood.

This means that the baby they hold is me, but how can that be? The diamond under me turns into sand, which pulls apart and re-forms to create the one word: 희망. Hope.

I look back at my parents, who are significantly younger than they are now, and see an unfamiliar spark in their eyes. They've reunited in South Korea, speaking a language that they understand and sitting among people who understand them. They're college graduates who hold stable jobs, and are hopeful for a future that they can control.

I land right back at home. I sit up, hearing the conductor call for my flight. "Flight 1004. 14:35 to Identity."

I run with my suitcases clanging on the floor behind me. There's only one seat on the plane—the rest of the cabin is filled with photos of my past.

The image of the baby and my parents remains in the innermost corner of my mind, but I keep on moving forward. Our journeys have forked to two different realities. I've accepted that certain things are out of my control, including the power to change the family I was given. One day, we will reconvene in a happier place. For now, however, I gather all the moments and people that have made me who I am, excited to explore the destinations life has yet to take me.

CYNTHIA LEUNG

YEARS AS MENTEE: 1

GRADE: Senior

BORN: New York, NY

LIVES: Brooklyn, NY

MENTEE'S ANECDOTE:

My mind is restless—constantly looking for new sources of inspiration and finding places to fuel my ambition. At first, I didn't know what I wanted to write for my project, but the opportunity to brainstorm and hash out ideas vocally usually provides the most productive results. I'm so grateful to have the opportunity to chat with Alison about my love for *Normal People* by Sally Rooney, and to just generally meet another person who searches for perfection with semantics.

ALISON LEWIS

YEARS AS MENTOR: 1

OCCUPATION: Literary Agent

BORN: Boulder, CO

LIVES: Brooklyn, NY

MENTOR'S ANECDOTE:

I love it when Cynthia and I start talking about whatever is on our minds—be it existential thought, ecstatic experiences of nature, or Britney Spears—and end up with rich fodder for writing. I also love when we just sit together and write for ten or fifteen minutes, and all the usual barriers of fear and procrastination and perfectionism fall away.

Internalized Misogyny

CYNTHIA LEUNG AND ALISON LEWIS

Through the discussion of pop culture, we will be examining the prevalence of the patriarchy in certain aspects of our psyche.

CYNTHIA LEUNG: This piece of fabric is my pride and joy. A tag on the back of the neckline displays a generic logo. The shirt's a little oversized, but it's the perfect lazy-day throw-on. On it, a large image is stretched across from the middle. It's Britney Spears. Ever since I was a young girl, I'd move my feet with every beat of her songs. The nasality of her timbre became a normality when processing sound in my head. Sadly, she truly wasn't appreciated enough in the earlier years of her career. Alison, could you describe what '00s critics thought of her?

ALISON LEWIS: When I was in elementary school, it was very cool to hate Britney Spears. We were, I think, all wrapped up in the media narrative (also our parents' narrative) that she was "inappropriate"—too sexy, scandalous, self-objectifying, and "crazy." She "set a bad example" for girls and women. We were supposed to value ourselves for our brains, not our bodies. It was a strange mix of what felt like very conservative, Puritan values around how women should dress and behave, and some kind of Second Wave feminist anger at how women had been reduced to sex objects for so very long. I wonder how all of that thinking strikes you now, growing up in a very different era?

CL: From an etic perspective, it's quite apparent that this notion that Ms. Spears is detrimentally sexualizing herself is an explicit example of internalized misogyny. The best example to describe this phenomenon would be to use *Legally Blonde* as a microcosm to reflect this idea. Despite being placed in a pedagogic environment, in which most women were most likely aware of the misogynistic nature of academia, many other female students at Harvard used attribution error to diminish any form of academic credibility that Elle Woods may have had, based solely on her flamboyant wardrobe and bubbly disposition. I feel that the '00s were probably the height of the prevalence of internalized misogyny, even though it's still existent to this day. Many films and media ascribed certain characteristics to female figures to create a stereotype (don't get me started on how film uses stereotypes of Black, Indigenous, and characters of color to invoke some humor) that certain women were noncomplex. They were either dumb and ditzy or smart and "not like other girls." Do you have any experiences in which you felt intimidated by the environment you were in based on your ascribed characteristics, Alison?

AL: Yes, definitely, although there are always so many layers! In middle school, I wanted to wear makeup and short skirts in order to be seen as "pretty" and "cool," and was conscious (and constantly nervous) that I wasn't playing the part quite right. At the same time, my friends and I (who were not especially cool) looked down on the popular girls who we thought dressed too provocatively, in their miniskirts and band-aid dresses. I am sure we were, in part, secretly jealous—and, at the same time, judging them by the misogynistic standards of the time, where women were supposed to be pretty, but not too *sexy*. Do you find yourself thinking about how you dress or present yourself in similarly complicated knots of internalized misogyny, Cynthia?

CL: I feel that the ways I perpetuate internalized misogyny are rooted in my own insecurities, for sure. My tendencies to be self-critical are very explicitly transferred onto my own desire to fit into a cookie-cutter image of "the perfect woman"; therefore, I would unknowingly criticize other women to convolute my own feelings of unhappiness. It's a self-destructive and lethal process, but this mentality is so normalized, to the point at which even someone who doesn't identify as being a man can employ the "male gaze" in their everyday lives.

AL: I agree. I'm so curious what "the perfect woman" looks like to you, or, more broadly, to your generation? And, on another track, I wonder what you think we can do to combat internalizing these kinds of misogynistic standards toward ourselves and other women? Is the first step, maybe, as in therapy, just to recognize it and begin to talk about it with other women in our lives?

CL: Unlike finding superficial traits that dictate attractiveness (which are usually influenced by Eurocentric beauty standards that perpetuate anti-Blackness, colorism, contingent racism, ableism, transphobia, and other systems of oppression) beautiful, I find that the most attractive women are those who make other people feel beautiful, who can make others happy, and who give more than they receive. I still don't definitely think that I'm beautiful, but I don't necessarily think this is a destructive mind-set to have, because I always want to find ways to improve myself internally. To combat internalized misogyny, having an open dialogue that is inclusive and invites all self-identifying women, could be a step toward progress. Obviously, we should argue that the only method to alleviate this issue is to completely dismantle all oppressive forms of social stratification, but in the meantime, we can prioritize a method of discussion to participate in inclusive feminism.

CAITLIN LEVY

YEARS AS MENTEE: 2

GRADE: Junior

BORN: New York, NY

LIVES: New York, NY

PUBLICATIONS & RECOGNITIONS:
*The Speakeasy Literary Magazine,
Aster Lit, Hypernova Lit*

MENTEE'S ANECDOTE:

I met Leah during a difficult time for me—one in which her wisdom and unwavering compassion helped me through. Not only has she helped me discover who I am as a writer, but she has also believed in me. That is the greatest gift. Above all, Leah is loving, in every sense of the word—and I am so lucky to have found her.

LEAH GUTTMAN

YEARS AS MENTOR: 1

OCCUPATION: Clinical
Psychologist

BORN: Greenwich, CT

LIVES: New York, NY

MENTOR'S ANECDOTE:

How can I describe my writing relationship with Caitlin? Only this: You had me at hello. You had me at hello! Working with Caitlin has been more rewarding than I could have ever imagined. She is the type of person who makes your jaw drop. Not least because of her passion. Caitlin's exuberance for life, and for the beauty of language, is deeply felt in her poetry. Our meetings mostly involve me sitting with my mouth agape, marveling at how she creates magic with words. It's an exhilarating, if not slightly drooly, hour. Hats off to you, Caitlin, and thank you.

Haiku Series for Erik and Lloyd Ocean

CAITLIN LEVY

This piece is inspired by Erik Simpanen and Lloyd Mullings, both of whom I read about in The New York Times. *They were married in September 2020 and changed their last names to Ocean.*

I. I saw two hands in
the paper, masked lips//each
man Mr. Ocean.

II. No name could hold both,
surname encoded by hand,
by sway of tide, O

III. fraying ocean swells//
by moonlight—from ocean comes
flesh, such fire, their name.

IV. They were born before
the sun could trace the black sea,
as a dark sky rang

V. 'Mr. Ocean, hear!'
Lend me your light, life-giving,
& I will give you all mine.

VI. The clouds mourn their sea—
rain held in two lips, in skin
soft against the sky

VII. Imagine two eyes,
wet by blossoms, salt, its scent,
bursting at their necks . . .

VIII. two men, through deserts,
thirst for a droplet-cool tongue,
come upon ocean

VIIII. Lapping waves, their joy,
the life-giving water and
life breathing beneath.

X. Picture their long hands
sweeping against water's back,
a soft reminder—

XI. You are found in light Brush of darkening sea, we— They
    swallowed the big

VII. Sun whole in love//We wrote a new history, earth, Earth,
    Mr. Ocean.

WINNIE LIANG

YEARS AS MENTEE: 1

GRADE: Senior

BORN: Brooklyn, NY

LIVES: Brooklyn, NY

PUBLICATIONS & RECOGNITIONS:
National Merit Scholarship
Finalist

MENTEE'S ANECDOTE:

It would be a lie if I said I wasn't nervous during my first pair session. I entered the breakout room and said hi, and Caroline said hi, and we struck up an easy chat—and my worries melted away. We clicked, and I never could have asked for a better mentor. As she's pushed me to improve, I've learned more than I could imagine (including about terrifying southern insects). We write together, laugh together, and talk together—sometimes as a mentor-mentee pair, but more often as friends. It's a relationship that I hope one day we can extend beyond a screen.

CAROLINE WRAY

YEARS AS MENTOR: 1

OCCUPATION: Assistant Editor

BORN: Atlanta, GA

LIVES: Brooklyn, NY

PUBLICATIONS & RECOGNITIONS:
Gulf Coast Online Exclusive

MENTOR'S ANECDOTE:

From my first encounter with Winnie's writing, I've been astonished by her ability to blend the contours of emotion with gorgeous descriptions. When she shared this story's first draft, I could see that something exceptional was afoot: even as the material is singed with longing, it carries the reader off into a rainbow-colored sky. I treasure the specific pandemic intimacy that Winnie and I share—it's funny, being so familiar with her bedroom wall while never having been in the same building—and I can't wait to watch it continue growing over time (an ice-cream outing is absolutely in our future)!

Your hand is light in mine.

WINNIE LIANG

A dreamlike meditation on loss and love.

Your fingers are cold, colder than I remember. You trace a pattern on my skin, skimming the surface, trailing ever so softly. I think that if I try hard enough, I can feel it.

It was in April that we began. A yellow-white month, not with the sharpness of gold, but the fragility of plumerias. Fragrant, five-petaled flowers with a custard center and a snow cradle. You picked one off a tree, even though we weren't supposed to go over the fence, and told me it looked like an egg. We twined together with the same ease that its yolk melted into its whites.

I am in a place that feels like home, and you are here, so it must be true.

But the sky is getting purple and I am getting red. You laugh, full of sunshine cheer, and drop your heart in my waiting hands. You wrap your fingers around mine. They're white, cold, but I think they should be orange, warm. Orange, fire.

I think that for you, I would burn.

"I thought you were going to cut your hair," you say.

"My mom likes it long," I respond. I am half-hazy, and the world is silver, but you are here and the world is baby pink.

"If you were your mom, we wouldn't be here, would we?"

I am quiet. "No," I say. You twirl fingers into my ever-growing hair, wisping mist blue beside it. "We wouldn't."

We are changing.

Once, you were lit with life. You, a burning tea candle, cherished, beloved, unwavering in your faith. I, a sputtering oil lantern, searching for freedom but afraid of the risk. Should I be freed, I would only ever send smoke in the sky. You laughed when I said it aloud, and called me a romantic. You said it again when I denied it.

Now, you are colder. Smaller. The wind was quiet as it snuffed you out, leaving my fingers to curl around smoke. But it roared as it knocked me over, and I set our city alight. As we watched our home fall, I lost you somewhere in the blaze.

"Mint."

"Chocolate."

"Mint!"

"Chocolate!"

The chill of the ice cream shop is a welcome respite from the sweltering summer heat. I wanted to go back home, but you wanted ice cream, and the electric excitement sparking in your eyes leads me helplessly along.

We sit on the boardwalk, my feet idly kicking up sand. Ice cream drips over our sticky fingers, and my face is aglow with joy. Its taste is a bubbly peach lemonade, which lingers fruit-sweet and pleasantly tart.

"Do this again sometime?" I need to ask, hesitant, because I had fun, and I think you did too, but if not—

"If you promise to pick a better flavor." My expression must be so indignant that your mirth is irrepressible, flowing like cream and honey, and your laughter echoes in my head for the rest of the day.

It is evening, and you stand at my side. A cloud of spun sugar, trailing threads in a blooming-rose sky, is the sole witness to our story.

You are soft against a gentle sun. On your face is a smile that has been absent since the sunrise-pink days of our youth. I tell you this, and you make it brighter.

It's cold.

"Give me your hand," I say, and you oblige, your smile now morphed into gentle yellow. I think I might say I'm scared, because you soften. And when the rest of me goes black and purple and blue, I follow the glow where my fingers meet yours.

MENGNAN LIN

YEARS AS MENTEE: 1

GRADE: Senior

BORN: Fujian, China

LIVES: Queens, NY

MENTEE'S ANECDOTE:

I really enjoy writing, creating, and sharing with Selena. Starting from brainstorming around the thoughtful prompts that push us to dig deep inside ourselves for a truthful response to the actual writing process where we allow our creativities and emotions to take the lead, Selena and I have built a strong, trusting bond that motivates us to be creative and unlimited during this tumultuous time. I appreciate the established mutual trust and understanding during our writing process.

SELENA BEAUMONT

YEARS AS MENTOR: 1

OCCUPATION: Literary Agency Assistant

BORN: Syracuse, NY

LIVES: New Rochelle, NY

MENTOR'S ANECDOTE:

I love that the writing exercises that we were able to do were hopefully able to build confidence and connection. Sharing writing can be a vulnerable experience and I'm glad that we were both comfortable to be able to do so.

Me in the Eyes of 2020

MENGNAN LIN AND SELENA BEAUMONT

Two perspectives on 2020, a year of change, growth, tragedy, and conflict.

Mengnan

I'm not a perfect student who
Can sit still in front of the never-tired computer for 24/7
And be on top of every assignment

I'm not a perfect friend who
Has a thousand different ways to
Cheer my friends up when they are in great sadness

I'm not a perfect older sister who
Has endless patience to
Cook every meal with different recipes
Answer every question which might not have an answer
For my also vulnerable little sister by myself at home

I'm also just not a perfect human being who
Has growth mindset embedded in their body
And can be optimistic
Whenever a challenge pops up

I'm weak
I try to be strong, act strong

And tell myself that I am strong, but
I AM WEAK

I'm a child of silence that
Makes me a fairly good listener
Who is empathetic to embrace
All the smiles and the scars

But not this time
Because when I close my eyes and listen
I hear tremendous noises from every corner of
the world crying, screaming,
begging for hope and changes

"I hate 2020!"
"Grandpa! Grandpa! Please don't go!"
"Mom, I want food."
"Is there any more masks left at home?"
"I'm sorry, but I really can't lose this job!"
"When can I go back to school?"
"I promise I will pay the rent as soon as I get a new job!"
"2020 is full of disasters!"
. . . . . .

SHUSHHHHHHH
I open my eyes with tears and
Cover my ears with all my force
"Jie Jie, what are we eating for lunch?"
My little sister comes into the room and
Sees me trembling
She doesn't ask anything, but just
Runs to my side and hugs me tight
"It's okay, it's okay."

It is not okay, baby
But it's okay to be "not okay"

It's okay to have missing assignments
As far as you catch up with them
It's okay to not know how to console your friends
As long as you are spiritually by their sides and support them
It's okay to lose your patience with your siblings sometimes
As long as you give yourself a little more patience and love
It's okay to be imperfect or temporarily pessimistic
As long as you are still looking forward to tomorrow
To the beautiful, hopeful things that will happen tomorrow
To the beautiful, better self that you will become tomorrow

Don't worry,
You are ON TIME.
You are ON TRACK.

Selena

The men in front of me are white. This is important in the story I'm about to tell.

I go to the deli at six a.m. while the sun debates whether it will rise to find two people ahead of me where there should be none in the crevices of early morning. Two men three times my size, identical in a way that doesn't matter to me with strangers, similar enough that I notice the way the slightly younger one examines the older one with the same mimicry with which a child looks at their parent. I say that I am a person who cares about the details that make another person, but not before the caffeine stakes my heart. In the turn of the giant fabric of our collective story, these men would mean little to me, as many of them do, but they open the thin lines of their mouths and out comes an accent so Frankensteined, my head threatens to snap from my neck. It is an accent that, beneath the patchwork of racism, is the accent of the echelons of my family. It is the accent of the five men who work behind the counter, men who have watched me grow up over the decade, between cups of French vanilla, who crow my name in chorus upon entry in that beautiful accent, chittering away in Spanish while I stand on my toes to shove dollar bills into their tip jar. It's the same accent that sharpens across the stove in the back while it weaves through distorted orders—"Turkey and jam on rye; mini-bagel scooped out toasted two shades darker than you," one lady says. It is an accent in the mouths of these men that sounds like a nasally secret, not meant to be heard, the skittering laughter that follows turns my hands to stone, and I will the rage inside me to be silent.

My mother says that I have enough anger to burn down a forest, that my birth and the sign that defines it embedded in the sun was destiny, that my words unfettered could kill the soul of a person, so I learn the grooves of the top of my mouth, sentences dying behind the seam of my teeth, while the men in front of me straighten their faces, placing their order with a cool ease that hollows out my entirety, stepping out of one body and into another. This is a poem about the consistent hum of such consistent people in the narrative of my life that keep it stitched together. This is a poem about the many women who live inside of me, begging in moments of conflict to scream.

SIENNA LIPTON

YEARS AS MENTEE: 1

GRADE: Sophomore

BORN: New York, NY

LIVES: New York, NY

MENTEE'S ANECDOTE:

Michele is a great mentor and friend. She is understanding and willing to talk if I need it during our meetings. I always appreciate her guidance, whether it's about writing or anything else. We always have something fun to talk about, and I look forward to spending more time with her in the next few months.

MICHELE KIRICHANSKAYA

YEARS AS MENTOR: 1

OCCUPATION: Writer

BORN: New York, NY

LIVES: Brooklyn, NY

MENTOR'S ANECDOTE:

Sienna is a lovely young woman and a lovely young artist. An avid fantasy fan, Sienna is always thoughtful and engaging and comes to each session ready to write. As a first-time mentor, I feel I have been learning from her as much as I hope she has been learning from me. During our time together, we have touched upon the art of storytelling, speaking about the importance of representation in books, and the magic of words, both those already written and those we get to create. I wish her nothing but the best in her hopefully bright future.

Love Letters to the Seasons from a Statue and a Student

SIENNA LIPTON AND MICHELE KIRICHANSKAYA

As the title says, "Love Letters to the Seasons from a Statue and a Student" is an ode to the elements from two very different pairs of eyes.

In the fall, I watch families heading to the playgrounds, friends shouting and laughing together, everyone trying to soak up a last bit of warmth before the cold sets in. Knitted mittens and woven scarves are abandoned, discarded on benches, hidden under trees, forgotten as people hurry to escape a sudden storm.

The school semester just started, so I'm trying to savor my last window of freedom while it lasts. Kids shriek with laughter as they play on yellow-green grass, red cheeks framing their gap-toothed smiles. I burrow into my plush scarf, grateful not to be the person who left theirs behind on one of the wooden benches lining the path. The trees glimmer overhead in ruby, gold, and amber, a last bit of life before the season dies.

During the winter, ice covers my arms and head, like the jackets and hats the masses wear to enjoy the first fall of snow. It is usually still and quiet, except for the coldest days, when the children come in waves, dragging their sleds to enjoy the steepest slopes of the park. I spend more and more time in the quiet company of the soft moon. Lights are strung across the trees, even the blistering wind's not enough to discourage the crowds who arrive every year. I can never quite tell what they are doing.

Christmas in New York. The off-key carolers are giving me a headache, but I have to admire their enthusiasm. It's easy to get jaded in this exhausted city, especially this time of year, when gray slush covers the ground after all the pretty white snow melts away and it feels like the sun forgets your name. But watching the kids sledding downhill, the love-birds dragging their terrified partners around Wollman Rink, the park getting bathed in a shower of silvery feathers, you have to beam, taking the holiday cheer where you can.

In the spring, the animals are first to return, tentatively braving the rainy days. The humans come after, eager to rush into the seasons, baring more and more skin. A young woman wanders around, her hand in that of another young woman. It must be love. Young infatuation is everywhere. I miss the feeling. Soon everyone walks through the park's paths together. I try to imagine what it's like to be truly warm, in the company of others, in the company of the sun.

As my girlfriend slides her hand into mine, I try not to blush like the secret sappy mess I am. When you spend so long watching other people—straight people—fall in love spring after spring, the sweet air feels like it wasn't meant for you to breathe in. The sun is out, and so are her freckles, a million stars painting her brown cheeks. For a second I'm so jealous of them, so close to her skin, when she looks at me, her smile the sun, pulling me in for a kiss that tastes of warmth and the salty pretzel we just shared.

In the summer, the sun glints off my polished skin. I cannot smell the sweet breeze, but the air breathes alive with the joy of a hundred children, finally free from the confines of the classroom. Sticky fingers on sticky hands leave their ice cream residue on my metallic body, evidence that I have become the next victim of a horde of climbing bodies. Gaggles of families and friends, slightly less burdened by their usual workload, enjoy one another's company, as well as the company of the grass and the trees. The young woman is back, this time alone. She sits down, leaning against me, and begins to read. I know I cannot move, but I try to convey extra warmth in my frozen expression, hoping to communicate my joy at her presence.

While the rest of the city boils like the smelly armpit of a subway rider, the breeze coming through the bright green trees makes you forget all that, can make you imagine you're in an entirely different world. A different time already gone by, where people spoke a different way and wore strange clothes. Like the metal guy I'm leaning on, though he's kind of quiet, so I have no idea what he would sound like. The park is filled with statues of old dead white men, some who deserve the commemoration more than others. I look up at his face, at the smile that rests on it, bronzed for eternity. Maybe it's just me, or maybe it's the summer sun warming his frozen expression, but I can sort of imagine that maybe, just maybe, the sweet expression he has on his face is meant for me. I don't know whose statue I'm leaning on, but his smile as he looks down on me is nice, so I hope that he was the type to deserve one.

MAI LISTOKIN

YEARS AS MENTEE: 2

GRADE: Senior

BORN: New York, NY

LIVES: New York, NY

PUBLICATIONS & RECOGNITIONS:
City Dreams, Quaranteen Newspaper, Beacon Ink

MENTEE'S ANECDOTE:

Emily and I love sharing humorous and compelling anecdotes about our lives as New Yorkers, and often exchange human interest stories with each other. This collaboration many times manifests as entertaining written pieces sprinkled with vivid imagination and colors. It is my personal delight to have discovered a literary partner in crime, from whom I can learn the patient persistence required as a writer. Emily is a constant inspiration to me as a passionate and successful author, as she guides me through the winding and complex road of editing, and skillfully demonstrates effective and objective self-critique.

EMILY NEUBERGER

YEARS AS MENTOR: 2

OCCUPATION: Writer

BORN: Long Island, NY

LIVES: Brooklyn, NY

PUBLICATIONS & RECOGNITIONS:
A Tender Thing

MENTOR'S ANECDOTE:

My relationship with Mai has been one of the bright spots in this trying year. Every week when we sign on to Zoom for our pair session, she inspires me with her positivity and her consistent work ethic. The pandemic twisted her high school experience into something no one expected, yet she faces her work and challenges with a brave face, eager to learn more about the world. Writing with her is a joy, and taught me that inspiration should not depend on the right conditions, but rather a flexibility to record the changing world around us.

Of Pyrite and Men

MAI LISTOKIN

A kindhearted, eccentric gentleman is hoodwinked by his naïve ges-
ture and a glittering gem in a dusty New York shop.

Mr. Watson seldom had company. Equipped with his personal calculator, the eager salesman was frantically punching digits, frowning in deep
concentration. As I walked into the gem shop, he was escorting around
a strange tall fellow dressed in the finest pink-and-green plaid suit and a
pair of round spectacles. As it appeared, he was showing him every un-
earthly specimen around. The customer had a thin mustache and a genuine curiosity on his pale face, reminding me of a character from an
eighteenth-century British series I once followed. It was of no surprise,
therefore, when my dear shopkeeper Mr. Watson, with familiar formal-
ity that matched his apparel, approached him as "Mr. McAllister" when
he suggested yet another fossilized lizard embedded in a shell.

Now, Mr. Watson and I are not strangers. I can honestly attest that
he is a most devoted geologist, whom I often chat with on my way home
from work. We sometimes discuss the formidable display of incredible
rocks from Madagascar, rare minerals from extraterrestrial meteorites,
prehistoric fossils, and luminous crystals. As it turns out, this shop does
not suffer the blessing of rush-hour shoppers and bustling crowds fighting their way in. The high-price ticket might be the reason this lovely
shop is usually quiet, which selfishly I enjoy all to myself. But today the
commotion inside drew me in!

"How about this impressive fossil, Mr. McAllister?" Mr. Watson exclaimed with one part confidence and one part careful hope. "It dates back twenty-five thousand years ago and can be undoubtedly described as one of the earliest salamander specimens discovered in the western hemisphere."

It became obvious to me that Mr. McAllister had no visible interest in the salamander. "I'm afraid I am looking for something much more dramatic, as it is a personal gift to a dear friend," he declared out loud to an invisible audience. "I fancy something shinier that will summon a gasp." To my dread, he was mindlessly leaning on a glass shelf heavy with precious stones. Disaster was looming.

Mr. Watson anxiously leaped forward to stabilize the tilting shelf, catching the falling rocks in his open palms. A golden sheen in his hand caught Mr. McAllister's piercing eyes.

"Behold!" he ordered in a deep baritone voice, halting the nervous salesman abruptly. "Show me the golden rock in your left palm. I believe we have detected a contender."

I silently held my breath as the spectacle unfolded. Perspiring, Mr. Watson opened his palm to reveal a rather large multifaceted rock in a shiny golden hue. Mr. McAllister caught me standing stunned in the middle of the store. He purposefully removed his spectacles dangling from the bridge of his nose, while his right eyebrow rose inquisitively.

"What do you think this stone is composed of?" he asked me in a tone lacking any acceptance of failure.

The stone glimmered, but not as bright as true gold. "Hmm, I think it might be pyrite," I offered in a hesitant voice, nervously glancing at my fellow expert Mr. Watson, who seemed quite on edge, with the calculator trembling in his other hand.

Mr. McAllister's eyebrows lifted momentarily in an impossible arch of disbelief. Mr. Watson's anxious voice filled the silent abyss. "We teach them well, sir," he said and shrugged. Was Mr. McAllister sweating under his mustache? I couldn't quite tell.

"But what do you believe it is coated with?" Mr. McAllister pressed. This time I didn't reply as swiftly.

"Gol—" I began, but he swooped in and finished the thought for me.

"That's right! Solid twenty-four-karat gold!" He continued almost breathlessly, "And I will be gifting it this very afternoon."

I began to feel as if I was participating in a bizarre quiz show and looked around at Mr. Watson, who was busy rearranging the already neat amethysts on the shelf. "What a very lucky recipient," I responded vaguely.

"I shall deliver this brilliant gift to my very *best* friend, Pete," he exclaimed resolutely. My puzzled expression was no impediment to this headstrong customer.

"Pete . . . ?" I waited for some description, drawing a blank.

"My dear friend Pete lives in Central Park, not far from Belvedere Castle, in fact," McAllister explained. "He is dressed in rags, and resides on the third bench from the hot dog stand. I shall tell him, 'Pete! If you are ever down on your luck and need to liquidate your assets, just head down to the diamond district in Midtown and exchange it for a handsome sum of money.'" I nervously eyed the price tag on the box—was it truly that expensive?! I swallowed at the figure: $2,000. Plus tax. For a rock?! I felt light-headed.

Before I could think twice, Mr. McAllister was at the front desk, signing paperwork with Mr. Watson, who was enthusiastically sealing the deal. The salesman was bursting with excitement at the prospect of relaying the news to his boss. The cash register opened with an unfamiliar yet satisfying ding.

Mr. McAllister buttoned his plaid jacket and strode purposefully out the door, gift bag in hand.

WILLOW EDIDIN LOCKE

YEARS AS MENTEE: 1

GRADE: Sophomore

BORN: New York, NY

LIVES: Brooklyn, NY

MENTEE'S ANECDOTE:

Our meetings began with a writing prompt and some creative writing. The first few times we met, we brainstormed possible topic ideas. We discussed writing about racism in hospitals, reproductive rights, etc. We worked together to find information on the topic we landed on (systemic racism and the prison system) and educated ourselves through articles and books. We pulled quotes that we found meaningful from outside sources and then began to write. Sometimes the writing flow came more naturally, and sometimes it took us discussing our ideas for it to come. After many fun meetings, we finished the piece!

CLAIRE McLAUGHLIN

YEARS AS MENTOR: 1

OCCUPATION: Book Publicist

BORN: Grand Rapids, MI

LIVES: Brooklyn, NY

MENTOR'S ANECDOTE:

Even though we weren't able to meet up in person this year, Willow did an amazing job pursuing her interest in journalism and social justice this fall. She reached out to and interviewed a subject for her opinion piece, and we were able to listen to that interview together over Zoom and incorporate some of the most meaningful quotes into her piece. It was wonderful to watch her writing project evolve from an early idea to the in-depth, researched, and thoughtful piece it is today.

Prison Through the Eyes of a Former Inmate

WILLOW EDIDIN LOCKE

A look at the US prison system through the eyes of someone who has lived through it.

Imagine you are twenty, fresh out of high school, and thrown into the prison system. You are told you are going to spend ten years at Rikers Island and will spend the majority of your time in a maximum-security facility. Regardless of how you ended up in this position, you are still practically a child, and now, instead of navigating adulthood like your peers, you are navigating the empty cells of prison alongside a number of grown men you don't know. You might feel a sense of panic and fear.

Regardless of the emotions that are coming up for you, it is likely that your identity plays a key role in your feelings surrounding the criminal justice system. To understand your reaction to the scenario mentioned, let's take a closer look into where the law enforcement system started in the first place. This is a huge factor in the way the system works today—we see time and time again Black people being disproportionately targeted by police officers and then being in jails. Considering the history of the prison system, this really isn't all that surprising.

In the 1700s and the 1800s, due to the fear that slaves in the South would rebel against their masters, slave patrols were formed to catch runaway slaves and make sure slaves were doing what they were told. The slave patrol that was founded on oppressing Black people evolved into the police force—and therefore the criminal justice system—that we have today, which continues to perpetuate the oppression of Black and Brown people. According to the Pew Research Center, in 2017, while Black Americans made up only 12 percent of the adult population, they made up 33 percent of the sentenced prison population as a whole.

The racist history of law enforcement has threatening implications on the real lives of people of color. Looking beyond the statistics, to understand the impacts of racial disparity in prisons, we must hear from the people who have experienced it firsthand. I will bring you along as we take a closer look into the life of former inmate Peter Roman. I came across Peter, who had been incarcerated for ten years, and found his story particularly profound. I got to hear firsthand from Mr. Roman how he got to prison, what his time there was like, and the impact it will have on his future.

Peter grew up attending what he described as an "overcrowded" public school in New York, where he received his early childhood education. Throughout his childhood, he had family and friends who were incarcerated. While describing his relationship with law enforcement previous to being incarcerated, as well as during the time he was in prison, he said, "I've never seen police officers as friends or allies." He graduated high school and received two additional years of college education, before being charged with attempted murder at the age of twenty. Peter was in jail from ages twenty to thirty, missing out on a significant part of his early adulthood. During Peter's time in prison, he describes the relationships between prison guards and incarcerated people as if there were two teams, one being the police, and the other those punished by them, telling me, "It was really like war."

In addition to tensions with the staff, mental health issues contributed greatly to the hardships faced by those who were incarcerated. Peter used his time in maximum-security prison, where he was let out of his cell only one hour of the day, to read books and work out. While this might be a productive way to spend time, keeping sane was not always easy. Some prisoners left in a worse mental state than they had come in with, which Peter says is due to a lack of mental health resources.

We are told that the goal of prisons, and other forms of punishment by law, is to keep us safe, hence the name "justice system," but what if the system that is supposed to protect all citizens is actually doing the opposite? This leads to the question: Is the prison system actually effective in reaching its goal? As someone who's been through the system as a person of color, here's what Peter had to say: "I lost out on a lot. It definitely did not serve me for the better." When it comes to law enforcement specifically, after his time in prison he said, "I still don't feel like they're there to protect us." This means law enforcement really does not have its supposed desired effect.

What needs to happen in order to make a more effective "justice" system is often debated. Here's my answer: A system that was literally founded on the oppression of Black people cannot also be used to protect them. For a system to be truly just, the foundation must be built on mutual aid, equity, and justice. The current system is not broken, it was meant to work this way, and the only way to stop it is to take it down entirely.

PILAR LU-HEDA

YEARS AS MENTEE: 3

GRADE: Junior

BORN: New York, NY

LIVES: Brooklyn, NY

MENTEE'S ANECDOTE:

My third year writing with Girls Write Now and my mentor Catherine has been truly amazing. I love getting to work on new writing with her, and as my recent project is longer than usual, I am so pleased that I have received her support and feedback. Catherine is a fantastic writing partner and always offers creative solutions when I feel out of ideas. Writing this chapter with her was exciting and rewarding, and I am so glad that we get to share it with others.

CATHERINE SANTINO

YEARS AS MENTOR: 3

OCCUPATION: Writer

BORN: Albany, NY

LIVES: New York, NY

PUBLICATIONS & RECOGNITIONS: *LADYGUNN, BuzzFeed, Insider*

MENTOR'S ANECDOTE:

Pilar and I immediately bonded over our love of theater and the arts, and this has been a through line in both our friendship and our writing relationship. This year, Pilar embarked on writing a novel and I could not be more proud to see how she has progressed as a writer and as a young woman. She's always filled with amazing ideas and concepts, and the eloquent writing she brings to our sessions astounds me. I'm so glad we got to work on this special project together and that she is sharing a portion of it with the Girls Write Now community.

The Deception of Roses: Chapter Four

PILAR LU-HEDA AND CATHERINE SANTINO

This excerpt picks up at the start of chapter four. Our two main characters, Winifred and Bernie, are departing from their train and must run separate errands around the city of Manchester.

Part of me didn't want to part ways. The thought of going to Luella's alone now seemed daunting. I had maps and my journal and her letters, but something made it seem scarier than I was willing to admit out loud. We stopped just behind the archway and off to the left to avoid the commotion of exiting passengers. I pulled out a railroad map that I had taken from the school library, trying to balance it in its half-unfolded state, while closing the unruly carpetbag and snapping the clasp closed. Bernie looked over my shoulder. "Myrtle and Union?"

"Yes, my friend's family owns a dressmaking shop and that was the address they last used. Why?" He traced over the map next to the penciled circle around the corner of Myrtle and Union, a few blocks over, and stopped over the wavering blue line.

"River Irwell. My father took me to the riverfront as a boy, we used to have picnics there while my brothers were at school. It also happens to run right next to the library, see?" He pointed once again at the map, this time stopping over the fine print that read "Chetham's Library, est. 1853." He turned toward the doorway. "We can go together!"

I twisted to my side to fit out of the grand doors, as people were still all around us and there was little space to be had. I half-skipped to reach him before walking in stride with him. "What makes you think I don't want to go alone?"

"Oh. Do you want to go alone?"

"I think I could manage."

"That does not answer my question."

"Do you know how to get there?"

"I haven't been before, but I used to pick up sweets for my sister on Myrtle. It should only be two blocks west."

"Lead the way, then." I realized he must have been doing that since we stepped out of the station, because I was still a step or two behind him, following without questioning. Carriages rambled by as we ambled on, each block looking more or less the same. The road was divided into lanes, but it was quick and chaotic. I opted to walk on the inner side of the street, away from the foul-smelling puddles and whirring metal rims of wagons. When I realized we had been going on for quite some time I asked, "How much longer do you think?"

"Thirty minutes to the shop maybe, but ten to the library."

"Oh." I pretended I remembered or understood at all that the library was closer to the station than Luella's shop. *Was I holding the map upside down?* "Well, would you like to visit the library first?" He looked surprised by my question, and I realized that perhaps the intention all along was for us to split ways once he got to the library, but my question implied we were visiting together . . .

"Sure. If that's all right with you. I just have to pick up my father's book from the reserved section; it should be brief."

Now was probably best to ask. "Should I come with you? I can wait outside, or walk the rest of the way to the dressmaker if you prefer."

"Well, you're welcome to come. I used to visit with my family when I was younger; it's beautiful inside."

"I think I will. Thank you."

Bernie pointed to a narrow road up ahead. As we crossed the street and joined the bustle of the city, I couldn't help but be proud of myself. I had a long journey ahead, but the first step was complete. No matter what happened, at least I knew I finally had left Griffith Hall, something that had been a fruitless dream for years.

Bernie stopped in front of a sprawling rosy brick structure, curving around the road and towering with its colored windows. The library.

It looked like Griffith's, only awake. The doors looked as if the very breath of life had blown them open, inviting scholars and academics into the arched rooms with their rich mahogany shelves and endless volumes of fabric-bound books. The smell of warmth and parchment was faint in the foyer, reminding me of Briar's room at home. I wondered what she would think of the library now. I stood by the glass display cases, idly reading the pamphlets tacked up beside them. "Help Wanted, Experienced Young Writers Needed." Or "Skilled Carpenters Wanted," something about ship work. We had passed by the bustling docks at some point, and the burning smell of fish and sewage stinging the air was still vivid in my mind.

"Rose*?" Bernie's voice cut through my thoughts.

"Yes. Sorry." I really had to get around to telling him my name.

"I'll just go over to the desk and ask for my book."

"Okay." It seemed so personal, what Bernie was doing. It struck me that he was truly picking up the last of his father, that he was piecing together the bits of his family, starting with this book. "I can stay here."

---

* It is Bernie's belief that Winifred's name is Rose, since she introduced herself under that pseudonym in chapter two.

SOPHIA LUO

YEARS AS MENTEE: 1

GRADE: Sophomore

BORN: Staten Island, NY

LIVES: Staten Island, NY

MENTEE'S ANECDOTE:

I've had so much fun working with Amy! During these weird times, it's hard to meet up with people in person and working on Zoom can be a little strange and it's hard to get to know someone. However, we got to know each other and warmed up to each other super quickly. We are very productive together and explore many different topics and characters.

AMY PARLAPIANO

YEARS AS MENTOR: 1

OCCUPATION: Editor, *The Athletic*

BORN: New York, NY

LIVES: Brooklyn, NY

PUBLICATIONS & RECOGNITIONS: *Sports Illustrated, ESPN The Magazine*

MENTOR'S ANECDOTE:

Sophia is creative, funny, and a wonderful young writer. She is teaching me new things all the time, whether it's how to pull off a great twist ending (she surprises me with them every time!) or how to best navigate Book TikTok. Sophia is always excited to explore writing and the world in different ways, and there's no one I'd rather dissect Taylor Swift lyrics or write poems based off of Jane Austen novels with.

tears fall

SOPHIA LUO

A short story about tears.

tears rolling down our cheeks.

it's interesting how tears travel down our faces. each one takes a unique path, sliding down our cheekbones and making their way down our chin. sometimes they don't reach our chin, wiped away quickly by the backs of hands or brushed away softly and tenderly by the fingers of others. tears from a scientific standpoint are droplets of water mixed with salt, fatty oils, and other proteins. each ball of water, transparent and made of H_2O, rolls down our skin by the force of gravity. but in reality, they're much more than drops of water. they're fueled from happiness, despair, sadness, or anger. each tear has a cause or a purpose. tears have a backstory of their own.

LORENA MACA GARCIA

YEARS AS MENTEE: 3

GRADE: Senior

BORN: Bronx, NY

LIVES: Bronx, NY

PUBLICATIONS & RECOGNITIONS:
Scholastic Art & Writing Awards:
Honorable Mention

MENTEE'S ANECDOTE:

Through everything that has happened, I can honestly say that Candace stuck with me and has been a constant person in my life for the past three years. She is everything I wanted and didn't know I needed in a mentor and became much more to me than that; she became my best friend. Candace and I have really grown into such confident people ever since we first met and we continue to grow and support each other whenever, or wherever, we may be. There are no words I can say, or write, to thank her for being my mentor.

CANDACE CUNARD

YEARS AS MENTOR: 3

OCCUPATION: High School
Teacher

BORN: Laguna Beach, CA

LIVES: New York, NY

MENTOR'S ANECDOTE:

After almost two years of café meet-ups and bookstore wanderings with Lorena, it's been tough to stay apart, but in many ways our relationship has only grown as we've shared our struggles and strategies navigating quarantine. There's a new kind of vulnerability and compassion required to move through this scary world, and I'm so grateful for all the ways Lorena and I have been able to do this together, whether through writing or talking or sharing about what our pets are getting up to! I'm so proud of how much she's grown, and so hopeful for her next steps.

I'm Happy

LORENA MACA GARCIA

A piece that has been waiting too long to say what needed to be said, out loud and to the world. Regardless of everything that has happened this year, I'm happy to be alive!

Writing has been difficult to do even physically, as if my hand has forgotten what to do. Typing seems like all I do, even in the barest details I have to type to communicate, inform, and even to say I love you. Nothing is ever how it once was, and I preferred to look at my own world before me, with nice rose-colored glasses and a cup of iced coffee. Now change is set and it keeps turning, a wheel of events spinning to see what's next. All the while I stay trying to keep a smile on my face and in the shelter of my own home, one I used to detest. I grow scared of the outside world, the lack of memory installing itself with just everyday routine going on autopilot. I don't want routine, I don't want big changes, I want simple little acts of nonsense and inexpectancy. I want to know how to laugh out loud again without being shamed into being quiet when others are in "a meeting" or "days are too rough." I want to smile at the simplest of things, like when my dog lies down next to me or when I smell my newly lit caramel candle. I want to be there for friends when times are hard and uneasiness sets in but keeping them and their families safe will always come first and everything impeding that is shamed upon even into submission. Writing is what I am doing by typing on a simple Chromebook laptop, something that is not my own, but what I need to use for my now-everyday occurrences. To be a simple teenager will be gone in a few months' time and the expectations of adulthood will follow me from that point on. The future, change, and even feeling anything is scary and yet we choose every day to move forward with the smallest of steps. Moving alongside time in tune with a melody no one seems to know the lyrics to, but continue to dance along without a care in the world. I'm happy, I'm happy to be alive.

WAGIHA MARIAM

YEARS AS MENTEE: 1

GRADE: Junior

BORN: Bronx, NY

LIVES: Bronx, NY

PUBLICATIONS & RECOGNITIONS:
Scholastic Art & Writing Awards:
Honorable Mention

MENTEE'S ANECDOTE:

This was our second piece, after my short story where I wrote a somber piece about a father coping with an honor killing that he did. This second piece was also a third; I challenged myself by making this piece more lyrical, immediate, and sensory. I used a third-person narrative instead of a first to make it more subjective. I used a lot of Brigid's feedback about mood and tone, showing and not telling, and especially having a unique and consistent voice. I think my character is very real and definitely has her own distinctive story to tell.

BRIGID DUFFY

YEARS AS MENTOR: 1

OCCUPATION: Copywriter

BORN: Brooklyn, NY

LIVES: Brooklyn, NY

MENTOR'S ANECDOTE:

Wagiha has an incredible appreciation for language, and her thoughtfulness extends beyond spoken English. She has found unique ways to communicate with her grandmother, who does not speak English, and she started a sign language club at her school. Our conversation around innovative ways to express oneself via limitation inspired a new question: What is the experience of a colorblind painter? Answering this very question, Wagiha created a third-person narrator who immerses the reader in a celebration of color in the face of its very absence.

What's your favorite color

WAGIHA MARIAM

This piece is about a colorblind painter who is navigating her way in an art piece before a deadline. She cannot see a single color but has to finish the piece using her senses.

Checking over her shoulder, she mixes the colors in her palette.
Unsatisfied
at the infinite hues in her canvas, she looks up at the portrait.
The white villas she painted on top of a cockeyed hill,
the violet trees that stood awry from the land around it.
She stepped back focusing on what was surrounding her instead,
Inhaling the smell of solvent on her fingertips and mineral spirits in
    the air.
She exhaled harshly.
She looked around her at unfinished pieces,
rectangular reminders of rude stopping points that begged to be filled.

In piece number one, a vilified ballerina.
She chose to paint the hems of the skirt pink.
Pink was the floral scent when you walked into a flower boutique.
Or the smell on the florist's apron,
raising a brow as she handed her rotten Lotus flowers.

"Are you sure you would like to buy these, Miss?"
She was not sure, but she bought them anyway.
Lotuses were supposed to be easy, less complicated.

But pink on her ballerina looked out of place. She could not put a finger on it. *It* was confused. Or was *she* confused?

In another work, an oil painting of a sunset.
The sky was a fiery, golden orb that rose up from the horizon while the clouds melted into oranges, then reds, and then blues.
Why *orange, then* red, *then* blue? she thought.
Why not red, *then* orange, *then* blue?

She heard the door shut behind her.
"Hey!" She looked to see her friend entered exasperated putting a bobble hat and a tote bag on her stool.
"How's your piece going? It looks really good so far." Her friend rocked on the heels of her sneakers gazing at her piece.
"Oh." She paused thinking about what to say. "I don't know yet."
"Why don't you maybe add a little yellow there, for the sky," her friend asked.
She picked up her liner brush to make futile strokes on the painting.
"Why would I paint the sky yellow?" she asked.

"Why not? Is there even a difference for you?"
She frowned, the blues and yellows *did* look similar to her.
She crossed her arms and didn't respond.

She looked at her friend who pulled two apples from her bag.
Apples she recognized from the street cart with the green umbrella outside her studio.
(green? red?)
"I don't feel like painting fruits. I told you to get me resin from the department store."
"They aren't for you to paint. Here."
Her friend extended one arm to her. When she didn't step forward to grab it, her friend wiggled her arm.

"I gave you the yellow one. Or *opal* as the vendor says." Her friend bit into her apple.

"What am I supposed to do with this?" she asked standing with the apple awkwardly in one hand instead of a bristle.
"Eat it, obviously. Try this too. It's a *winesap* one."
She placed one apple in each hand, forcing her to look at them and remember how to distinguish them.
She took small bites out of both.
"How does it taste?" her friend asked.
That was a dumb question.
It was almost as dumb as when she was asked what her favorite color was.
Flavors don't translate into words.
When you bite into an apple, it's just a spectrum of sweet to tart.
She had no idea what her favorite color was either, and if she did, it would change every five minutes,
like every other bite of an apple.
"It tastes the same," she said.
Her friend leaned back into the stool, her chin dipping into her chest.
It was the same look of disappointment from every face that anticipated an answer from her that matched theirs.
"Well, if you were to paint these apples, how would you differentiate between them?"
She scrunched her face.
"I would paint one red. And paint the other yellow."

Her friend's lips were pressed tight. She was quiet for a moment.
"Achromatic, is that how you *see* movements? Is it how you *hear* sounds and *feel* feelings? Just because an apple is red doesn't mean you have to paint the apple red. Who's stopping you from painting it purple?"

Her friend sighed and threw her bag over her shoulder.

"Well it's getting late so I'm gonna go home. Good luck submitting it
   by tomorrow. Keep the apples."

She was alone in her studio again.
How does she define yellow?
For a moment, she closed her eyes.
Yellow was when she looked up at the sun,
couldn't see the color, but was blinded with intimidation.
Yellow felt achromatic like a mix of black and white,
Yellow was the astringent opal apple compared to a red winesap one.
The warm bubbling laughter of her friend when she handed her rotten
   lotus flowers on her birthday.
She breathed in.
She picked up her paintbrush and painted the sky,
breaking into an amber smile.
She exhaled, put down her brush, and went to the kitchen for a snack,
Maybe a bite of red or blue with a white drink.

ISABEL MARKS

YEARS AS MENTEE: 1

GRADE: Freshman

BORN: New York, NY

LIVES: New York, NY

MENTEE'S ANECDOTE:

Elena comes into every meeting with so much vision. In a few of our meetings, she's come prepared with a PowerPoint of art and poetry and writers I've never heard of. Most times, I would come in late on Tuesdays, uninspired and ready to sleep, but end up producing something I loved. Anyway, my point here is a much larger one about how much Elena has taught me about what it means to be a writer—her dedication, her drive, and the energy she brings to writing reminds me how much of good writing is work and willpower.

ELENA NICOLAOU

YEARS AS MENTOR: 1

OCCUPATION: Journalist

BORN: Ridgewood, NJ

LIVES: Fair Lawn, NJ

MENTOR'S ANECDOTE:

Once, Isabel and I collaborated on a short story. She'd write a sentence, then I would. Each round, I was surprised and delighted by the places she had taken the story once it was returned to me. It was as if I'd push the story an inch ahead and she'd send it tumbling off a cliff, where it would promptly land on a roller coaster whirring by. You get the drift. Ever since, I've been in awe of her imagination and am grateful I get to learn from all the places her mind goes.

Headache

ISABEL MARKS

Here's the only poem I've ever written that is good but not about someone I still talk to. Enjoy!

are you too polite to tell me that I'm crying?
my cheeks are so flushed that I see pink
when I stare at my reflection in the window
behind you.

your lips are parted just enough for me to
see you biting your tongue. be careful, that
will hurt like a motherfucker if it starts bleeding.
poptarts and the hemorrhage, please,
and all of my poems are about you.

forget all the poems, all the paths lead to you.
i am in a fucking maze where it's you or a
blockade, baby, and even though we haven't talked
in a year, your ghost gives me headaches.

i'm still angry but i don't know how to do that.
add that to the list, teach me righteous
indignation and clean logic? i have to stop
buying child advil. because no, i still can't
swallow pills.

MICHAELLE McCASKILL

YEARS AS MENTEE: 1

GRADE: Senior

BORN: Queens, NY

LIVES: Long Island, NY

MENTEE'S ANECDOTE:

Lennox fuels the ideas and I write them out into full stories—we make a great team!

LENNOX McGRAIN

YEARS AS MENTOR: 1

OCCUPATION: Social Media Associate

BORN: Chicago, IL

LIVES: New York, NY

MENTOR'S ANECDOTE:

Kai writes with such conviction and confidence, and I always look forward to hearing her ideas when we write together. Her creativity paints the most beautiful stories into all of her writing pieces, and I look forward to seeing where her skills will take her in the future!

Negativity Is Destruction

MICHAELLE McCASKILL

We face our obstacles with the perception that we can't be scarred, but we have to remember that a glow stick has to break before it shines.

As individuals, we seek curiosity. Our minds are the most mendacious part of our bodies. We create scenarios that add to our own pain. We don't face our actual truths. We pretend to be ready for the obstacles we face so we never have to try. We hide behind pain, desires. Some take their problems head-on, and others choose to turn away, but what we have yet to see is, we are obstruction to our own pain, we are the monsters to our own pain. We cling on to the pain like broken relationships or broken homes. No love, no peace, no sanity. Or broken families where sons grow up without fathers and daughters without mothers.

Hurt people hurt people.

Karma.

Pain.

God doesn't like ugly.

We don't look nor call onto Him because we're afraid to be judged. As people we don't think we deserve to be forgiven. We are alone. We are in pain. We are angry. We perceive the deception to the pain into our own minds. We are hypocrites, selfish, liars, angry . . . Monsters, but maybe if we looked up to Him, we could fly. It's heartache, it's heartbreak. It's the overwhelming feeling in your chest as if your windpipe can't release oxygen through your lungs. But some love the pain, and others hate it. We feed into it like it's a drug addiction. We have no control over it. The voices inside our heads that slip in our minds like tides on the ocean floor. It's like experiencing a nightmare that you can't wake up from, until you're up at one a.m. and you've arrived at the realization that you think you are alone. I tend to believe that at night, we have the undeniable truth that we think that we're alone. The pain at night becomes unbearable, heavy, but if we called onto God He'll draw you closer to Him, He has His arms open wide and maybe just maybe, He'll bring you home.

KIARA McLARTY

YEARS AS MENTEE: 1

GRADE: Junior

BORN: Bronxville, NY

LIVES: Bronx, NY

MENTEE'S ANECDOTE:

I first met Caroline when Ariah put me in a breakout room one October day. I remember that I wasn't paying attention and was completely confused about who this was and what we were doing. Despite my early aloofness, Caroline has been able to give me insight on the aspects of adulthood—whether it's what college is like or the actual importance of high school. Caroline has helped me find ways to communicate with other people easier just because she is such an open and honest person.

CAROLINE K. FULFORD

YEARS AS MENTOR: 3

OCCUPATION: Digital Librarian and Technology Researcher

BORN: Ridgewood, NJ

LIVES: Brooklyn, NY

PUBLICATIONS & RECOGNITIONS: *Indiana Review* Fiction Prize; The Center for Fiction NYC Emerging Writers Fellow

MENTOR'S ANECDOTE:

Though I have yet to meet her in person, Kiara brings such an energy and openness to our remote pair sessions that I hardly feel the lack of face-to-face connection. She sees her world with a bright and perceptive eagerness to which I can only aspire. Participating in our discussions about her future, her ambitions for her fast-approaching time at college, and the power of her own unique voice has been my privilege and my honor. All semester, speaking with her has been the highlight of my week.

Once Upon a Very Dirty Borough

KIARA McLARTY

*The Princess of New York City struggles to literally find her voice
and come into her inheritance—a stutter, and the power to speak.*

Once upon a very dirty borough,
Upon a very not-so-quiet neighborhood,
And upon a definitely rhythmic reggae household,
Lay a forgotten princess trapped in a castle.

This princess, not like the others, had a curse bestowed upon her.
This curse was passed on from generation to generation
And for if she doesn't break this curse, she will not be able to seize her
  throne.

For this curse prevented her from speaking.
Her vocal cords would rattle and she would grip her tiara to push the
  words out
Clearly unable to rule her kingdom, according to the peasants.

Complaints after complaints pervaded the town.
They sought a new monarch after the death of the king four
  months ago.
They needed a leader, and they needed one now.
Leaving the princess feeling trapped for she was the king's only heir
Causing her to stay in her tower to avoid the verbal harassment.

The princess lay in her royal bed and contemplated her options,
She could step up and claim herself as the king's daughter and lead
    her city
Or she could stay hidden in her tower and mourn the loss of her father.

She knew she would be a great leader for the kingdom.
She breathes through the aroma of taco and halal trucks.
She walks on the beat of the music of the streets.
She understood the dirt under the fingernails.

But what could she do with no one giving her the chance to speak?
How do you speak for the oppressed when you're oppressed yourself?
How do you empower the powerless without a voice?

After days of contemplation, she sought advice from her royal adviser,
    her mother.
Her mother who understood this curse more than anyone.
Her mother who, herself, had a stutter.
A stutter she was able to overcome due to the love she had for her city.
Her mother advised her to imagine what her father would have wanted,
    and left the princess alone to ponder.

The princess lay restless in her gold fortress and thought about what
    was stopping her.
This curse, passed on from generation to generation
It was not a curse, but indeed a blessing.
She held not only the right to speak, but the power to change the world.
The power to make her kingdom into a better place
And the power to do so with her voice.

Once trapped in her castle,
She now breaks free, and reigns the day.

MYRA MICHEL

YEARS AS MENTEE: 1

GRADE: Junior

BORN: New York, NY

LIVES: Bronx, NY

MENTEE'S ANECDOTE:

I have never written a poem with another person. It was fun to explore writing with someone with more literary experience and maturity.

RENIQUA ALLEN-LAMPHERE

YEARS AS MENTOR: 1

OCCUPATION: Journalist

BORN: Paterson, NJ

LIVES: Bronx, NY

PUBLICATIONS & RECOGNITIONS:
It Was All a Dream; TED Talks;
The New York Times

MENTOR'S ANECDOTE:

I thought it would be hard to write with somebody else. But it was easy and a lot of fun to share our common experiences.

Melanin Tears

MYRA MICHEL AND RENIQUA ALLEN-LAMPHERE

A young girl born to immigrant parents trying to fit into American society. She realizes that she is uncomfortable with herself and the nation.

"What
are you?"
What am I?
How do I go about
answering that? Black as
night, bright as day. Freckles
scattered everywhere. "She's different,"
I'm told. Well, I'm not your mold. Glossed
platter-sized chocolate eyes, A button nose, and
two pairs of lips so bare. The upper brown, the lower pink.
It's not discoloration. Kinky oily coily hair that I have *no choice* but
to wear. They are tied into two tough puffs. "Ouch!" I shout. They are tightly
bunched together, resembling inky irises. "Ciara, *nice* hair," they say. "It's quite
exotic." Exotic I think not, maybe chaotic. I have curly hair everywhere, bet it'll reflect through my
silverware. Insecure, quite unsure. Conflicted you may have predicted. Cheeks
moist and tender, coated with a glaze of warm chocolate drops. *Drip-Drip-Drip* they go, from
my cheeks to lips they melt—felt from a state of confusion. But what am I, America?
I love me. But maybe you don't. I am an immigrant. Citizen. Status unknown. Black. Brown.
I am democracy and I am a demon you say. I am your hope, your dream, your past, your present.
Your plague. Crying into the everlasting night. I am your pain, your promise,
your slave, your President. I am your foreigner, your future. I am your tears,
your joy, your blood-stained reminder of your new world run amok.
I am me, I am you, or maybe I am nothing at all.
No, I am something. I am your
contradiction.

DEWOU GLORIA MINZA

YEARS AS MENTEE: 1

GRADE: Sophomore

BORN: Lomé, Togo

LIVES: Bronx, NY

MENTEE'S ANECDOTE:

Writing with my mentor has allowed me to feel less insecure about my work and more willing to share it with others. I've also learned about multiple rules/ways of writing that I didn't even know existed before!

NICOLE MARIE GERVASIO

YEARS AS MENTOR: 5

OCCUPATION: Nonprofit Literary Festival and Public Programs Manager

BORN: Trenton, NJ

LIVES: New York, NY

MENTOR'S ANECDOTE:

My mentee and I share a lot of uncanny similarities. We are unflinching nonconformists—the feminists who can appreciate *A Clockwork Orange*. We have overactive imaginations and dark senses of humor. But possibly my favorite discovery has been that we share a fondness for a very random literary device: anthropomorphism. She laments the abject existence of her shoes; I hear the curtain whispering. It means we see life in everything, and that is a very special gift to share.

[Entries from a Not-So-Muggle Muggle]

DEWOU GLORIA MINZA

Finding yourself waiting for your Hogwarts letter to arrive? Poppy is here to tell you all about her muggle problems!

I was in the therapist's office today—a new one who claims her name is Dr. Jiko—and you'll never believe what she said to me! The nerve of some muggles. The conversation bothered me so much, it just kept replaying in my head. It's fascinating how my memory becomes laser-sharp when I want to forget something, but I can't remember squat when it comes to this form of torture muggles seem to enjoy . . . *calculus*.

Anyway, like all the unsuccessful souls before Dr. Jiko, she couldn't "cure" me of my "identity crisis."

To me, a muggle is not someone who cannot use magic, but someone who doesn't care for the possibility that there's something more than what we are taught to believe in. It's that sense of apathy—that lack of interest in anything other than the uniformity of everyday life—that has me trying to revive Voldemort. Well, okay, maybe not revive. In all honesty, while I do not condone Voldemort's bloodlust, he knew what he wanted and how he would get it—how far he would need to go, and how many sacrifices he would need to make. Any of that ambition would be better than the dead-fish-eye look of muggles (they're bland to the point where it should be considered sinful).

Note to peeping eyes:

As delirious as I sound, I assure you, dear reader, I have not recently escaped from an insane asylum. Now, put this diary down before my spidey senses start tingling and I find you.

With all these thoughts churning in my mind, I arrived at Dr. Jiko's office, hoping that this cognitively superior being would be able to put the jumble of emotions I felt into something more than the incoherent, fragmented phrases that escape me whenever I try to explain my thoughts to others.

Hope crushed. The woman introduced herself like so: "Hello, Poppy. Today, I am Dr. Jiko." *So much for cognitive superiority.* She stumbled over a simple introduction with a clumsiness that would have made English teachers blush, as if she didn't know her own name from one day to the next. She seemed to have caught on to her mistake though.

SUSPICIOUS DR. JIKO: "Good morning, Poppy! It's nice to meet you!"

When she realized that I wasn't going to respond, she continued.

QUESTIONABLE THERAPIST JIKO: "Keeping quiet is all right. I understand this must be a new experience."

ME: *As new as the other five therapists,* I thought. To my self-pronounced therapist, I only nodded.

DR.(?) JIKO: "Your mother tells me that you are currently going through an identity crisis. That sound about right?"

ME: *As right as the sky is pink.* I nodded to her once more. I didn't feel like this therapist (can someone confirm that fact for me?) was going to understand me *at all.*

LEGALLY LICENSED(?) THERAPIST JIKO: "Tell me what you see when you look at this image." She passed me a paper with several inkblots.

ME: *The default therapist move. A bit early in the game though.* I so wanted to answer her with: "Well, if you want me to be literal, I see the results of someone who decided they weren't fond of pens anymore and did away with the writing tool rather violently. If you want me to be metaphorical, I see a muggle ignorant of the world beyond their comfort zone, content to feast on whatever new form of a heart attack the world has conjured up." Her reaction would have been worth it. Outwardly, though, I only pretended I was in deep thought before shrugging my shoulders as if I were disappointed to come up empty.

AUTHORIZED(?) DR. JIKO: Smiling, she took back the paper without comment and continued with her questioning. ~~The doctor~~ Jiko asked, "What is it about, er, *muggles*"—I could see her making mental notes to wash her mouth out with soap later—"that has you upset?"

Of course, I didn't answer her. I let her wait as long as her psychoanalytical senses advised her to before she would need to ask her next question. While she waited in expectant silence, I pondered her last question.

ME: *It's not them that's got me upset; it's the fact that they don't mind being muggles. I mean, if you could give rise to your wildest dreams, wouldn't you want to search for that possibility? Instead, the halfwits just walk about, refusing to be anything but grounded. I've tried rallying people who shared similar ideas to storm Hogwarts and demand our letter be delivered, but that only got as far as step one: finding people to—*

THE LION, THE WITCH, AND THE AUDACITY OF THIS THERAPIST: "What if I told you there was no such thing as Hogwarts and magic or anything of that nature?" She was letting her impatience creep into her words. "There have been no known records of . . . 'muggles' going to magical schools or witches and wizards using magic. Any form of supernatural activity would've made headlines."

Of course, you would neither see someone walking their pet dragon in Central Park, nor a billboard advertising extendable ears. She looked at me as if I had stolen one too many prescriptions from the local pharmacy. Her condescending tone let me know that I was done listening to any more of her malarkey (she dismissed me, mumbling about soulless eyes—which, to me, was pretty ironic, considering I was clearly the one with the broader perspective on life).

I've had enough of therapists. The next time I write, I'll be in the middle of single-handedly storming Hogwarts . . . once I find it. Still haven't given up yet! Keep fighting!

TOA MOHEMED

YEARS AS MENTEE: 1

GRADE: Senior

BORN: Alexandria, Egypt

LIVES: Queens, NY

MENTEE'S ANECDOTE:

Stephanie Bok and I have a very supportive and collaborative writing relationship. She provides many resources for me to draw inspiration from and expand on my work. Even through my periods of writing slumps, Stephanie has been patient and helpful in order to support my process as not only a writer but a human being experiencing the duality of creation and of life itself. This writing process has revealed a lot of my personal traumas in a beautifully imaginative way, which has been aided by Stephanie every step of the way.

STEPHANIE BOK

YEARS AS MENTOR: 1

OCCUPATION: Theater

BORN: Valdosta, GA

LIVES: Brooklyn, NY

PUBLICATIONS & RECOGNITIONS: Host of the original writers' cabaret "Write Night @ Frank's" in Brooklyn for ten years; facilitator of the Modern-Day Griot Theatre Company's playwrights' lab for five seasons; writer/producer/director/performer with the popular sketch comedy group American Candy since 2010

MENTOR'S ANECDOTE:

Toa has been actively working on her poetry through a process of trials and tribulations that is familiar to any writer. I have witnessed her mind at play through our conversations and many attempts at writing and brainstorming pieces. This piece brings everything home. It is an accomplishment of Toa's adolescence.

A Life of Comedy and Tragedy

TOA MOHEMED

This is a piece on the regurgitation of trauma from the perspective of a young girl transitioning into her authentic self through reflection.

little girl, why do you weep and wail?
your cries behold truth that those stricken by your light cannot see
in your eyes, they see an angel, a saving grace, God
but still, you cry
and cry
and cry . . .
a tiny heart ridden with the blues
born in sorrow & pain
only to live a life in vain

the arms that cradled you and eased your fears
become foreign to you throughout the years
baba's at work & mama's crying cause she's stressed
the blues residing in your heart are no longer suppressed
here comes the chaos & the puppeteering
on goes your mask,
the sock & buskin

blood! sin! shame!
this is womanhood, little girl
your life will never be the same
cause little girl, you are not so little anymore

but ain't it funny?
the blood of your womb which carries man
is deemed "bad blood," abominable, impure
you are disgusted of your own flesh & blood
bend your knees and pray—repent! repent! repent!

they tell you lower your gaze,
cover yourself, you're a woman now
don't laugh too loud, you cackle like a witch
you talk too much, won't you be quiet?
this box is suffocating
here you are, kicking & crying like a newborn child
in the chambers of your mind, you yell—i want out! out! out!

let me free!

let me free!

let me free!

a spirit anchored by the fearful & fretful mind . . .

KAYLA MORGAN

YEARS AS MENTEE: 1

GRADE: Junior

BORN: Brooklyn, NY

LIVES: Brooklyn, NY

PUBLICATIONS & RECOGNITIONS: Scholastic Art & Writing Awards: Silver Keys; opened for Cicely Tyson in Conversation with Whoopi Goldberg event; performed at Upright Citizens Brigade Theatre and Five Angels Theater; chosen for Public Declamation at The Brooklyn Latin School

MENTEE'S ANECDOTE:

Stephanie has been an impactful force in my journey to a radiant future. One of the biggest goals we had as a pair was to get my poetry recognized. Inside and outside of our meetings, we would develop our understanding of poetry and edit my poems to be even more potent. She has encouraged me to push through rejection and to follow my dreams, knowing that my day would come. And soon, it did. My words and poetry started to be recognized by large audiences, which exceeded my expectations with Stephanie by my side cheering me on.

STEPHANIE COHEN

YEARS AS MENTOR: 1

OCCUPATION: Editor

BORN: New York, NY

LIVES: New York, NY

MENTOR'S ANECDOTE:

One of my favorite parts about working with Kayla is discovering unexpected commonalities. Whether it's music we both enjoy, our shared love for animals, or our taste in poetry, we've discovered we like similar things but we also get to teach each other about our own unique interests. Something special about embarking upon this mentorship with Kayla is seeing her hard work recognized by her school, peers, and the creative writing community. I was able to watch her do a live virtual declamation on a performance I got to help her with, and I was so proud of and happy for her!

My Mother's Allegiance

KAYLA MORGAN

"My Mother's Allegiance" focuses on the essential factors that encouraged my mother to flee to America, and the assimilation and racism often present in the experiences of an immigrant.

My mother had recited the pledge
'til her throat bled of eternal loyalty,
hand on heart devoted to the land of liberty.
Ancestral faith in future days,
binded to her words,
had presented Uncle Sam with a salute.
Bittersweet tears for salvation,
the hollering of heartbeats,
and longing for a sanctuary,
had settled in her eyes like a refugee camp.
She bleached the Patwah* off
her tongue, intertwined English
with freedom.
Silk pressed† the kinky coils
out of her Africana strands—
she lost her roots,
earned a savor of privilege.
Echoes of "I surrender," ascending

---

* Jamaican Creole.
† A technique used to straighten curly/coily hair.

from her Jamaican wounds on one hand.
Prayers: knee on ground, head down,
Bent to the red stripes on the other.
My mother couldn't hear the barking:
barbaric, uncivilized, savage—
spewing like saliva, emerging
from Uncle Sam's "peace" treaty.
Her frantic footsteps fleeing
to the white stars
were too thundering.

MERIL MOUSOOM

YEARS AS MENTEE: 1

GRADE: Senior

BORN: New York, NY

LIVES: Queens, NY

MENTEE'S ANECDOTE:

I remember the first time Judy and I met, it was so hard to get work done because we kept chatting with each other! That's when I realized that we were a perfect match.

JUDY ROLAND

YEARS AS MENTOR: 7

OCCUPATION: Ghostwriter

BORN: Oceanside, NY

LIVES: New York, NY

MENTOR'S ANECDOTE:

Meril and I really enjoy visiting and writing together—always so much to talk about! We have very different approaches to writing—Meril tends to tackle more serious topics and I like to use humor—so we really complement each other.

A Room of My Own

MERIL MOUSOOM AND JUDY ROLAND

Join me on this four-year journey to become the Meril I am now.

I'm balancing three plates at once, wearing my Salwar Kameez, struggling to serve food to the men at the table. The upcoming protest needs all hands on deck—the hands of men, as per Bengali custom. Intuitively understanding I don't belong, I exit the men's room.

My Salwar Kameez grants me entry into the kitchen, the women's room. Amid the family party preparations, I'm surrounded by a sea of aunts and grandmothers, whose dresses, like mine, have thousands of embroidered sequins in true Bengali fashion. Yet, I feel like an imposter. The women around me have walked the well-worn path of child marriage, dropping out of high school to become housewives.

I'm dressed like them, but I dream of transcending the confines of the two rooms. I want to be with the men. Not as a server, but as an organizer. To be seen as a capable mind, not a beautiful dress. My mouth opens, yearning to bring politics into the women's room.

"If I was your father, I would have married you off already!" an auntie interrupts. "You look beautiful in your Salwar Kameez," she adds, scanning my prepubescent body. Here, I'm just another woman, and I can't hide my shame. My mouth closes and my cheeks redden. I remain silent, despite the voice inside screaming, "This is not who I am." I struggle to find someone—anyone—like me. But if I'm not a woman, what am I?

******

A year later, I'm closer to figuring that out. I'm balancing three pamphlets at my gender justice advocacy program. While I took the job to support my family, I'm devouring articles about gender identity.

As the meeting starts, I look around the room. At thirteen, I'm the youngest of the dozen high school– and college-aged women of color. Among the drab beige walls of the conference room, their colorful conversation and personalities perk me up. But in a room of inspiring activists, I feel like an imposter once more.

A few weeks and many pamphlets later, with the group's support, I'm emboldened. I start speaking.

Everything comes spilling out: worries about graduating high school, escaping child marriage, forever being relegated to the women's room. The applause and affirmation that follow my story make it clear that activism is the space for me. The canyon between the rest of the room and me shrinks as I discover that I belong here. I can make change like these women of color.

The next four years certainly proved it. My passion for equity has brought me in front of the NYC chancellor of education, lobbying him to address school sexual assault; into the pages of *The New York Times*, covering the plan I created with peers for an inclusive pandemic school reopening; and onto the Zoom screens of classmates whom I'm mentoring on how to testify for the citywide Panel for Educational Policy. I have even founded an organization, PoliFem, to educate young people on local politics.

This passion brought me to the thing I'm the most proud of. After many meetings with a state senator, a petition, and a town hall I organized, I convinced him to support a bill—helping ensure its success— that funds New York State schools by an additional $4.53 billion annually.

I also finally found the word that describes who I really am: nonbinary.

******

Fast-forward to fall 2019; I'm at a police-free school protest I planned. I wear something I used to despise: my Salwar Kameez. I face the crowd of thousands, fully inhabiting my first-generation-nonbinary-Bengali-American skin. The host misgenders me, assuming that I am a "girl." I correct them, "Dresses weren't made just for girls, I wear this because I'm Bengali."

I realize that the personal is profoundly political. I have not settled for bringing politics into the women's room. I have made my own room, for nonbinary people of color and others with intersectional identities.

MAYANNA MUELLER

YEARS AS MENTEE: 1

GRADE: Sophomore

BORN: Seattle, WA

LIVES: New York, NY

PUBLICATIONS & RECOGNITIONS:
Soups On Competition—Best
Borscht; *Bardvark Literary
Magazine*

MENTEE'S ANECDOTE:

Meeting Lyz for the first time was nerve-racking. I would refuse to turn my camera on for most of the time. But little by little, I was able to connect with her, realizing how alike we are, and be myself. It's a pleasure to meet with Lyz every week as I finally would be able to share my ideas with someone like-minded.

LYZ MANCINI

YEARS AS MENTOR: 1

OCCUPATION: Freelance
Copywriter

BORN: Syracuse, NY

LIVES: Jersey City, NJ

PUBLICATIONS & RECOGNITIONS:
Pitch Wars Mentee 2020; *Slate*;
Man Repeller

MENTOR'S ANECDOTE:

My work with Maya has been so incredibly inspiring and fun—it is truly the highlight of my week to spend time talking about writing, storytelling, identity, and YouTube series that I never would have found on my own. I am very grateful to have met Maya.

The Ice Cliffs

MAYANNA MUELLER

The themes in this poem sparked from an adventure in Lake Placid when I was visiting with my family. We went on a frozen nature walk and saw these gigantic ice cliffs.

On the peninsula of Mirror Lake, Lake Placid,
Daylight spreads over the frozen forest.
And the fingers of the thousand-hand giants tower over me,
Hardened thick with frost.
"Hello!" I say.
Nothing. No response, just silence.
They bow over like withering flowers crushed
By an invisible weight.
They communicate silently between each other. Nobody could
    interrupt.
There's no loneliness like theirs.
And the light breeze moves the old sheets revealing the new
    underneath.
There,
In that moment, I realized that if
I stay any longer, I will break into ice.

MAIESHA MUNTAKI

YEARS AS MENTEE: 1

GRADE: Junior

BORN: Saidpur, Bangladesh

LIVES: Queens, NY

MENTEE'S ANECDOTE:

Before I used to be unconfident about the stories I used to write, but getting encouragement and praises from my mentor on my writing has changed my confidence level for writing. I enjoy collaborating and learning from my mentor. The writing prompts that I wrote with my mentor were fun to write as well. Moreover, talking to my mentor about careers and college has helped me learn something new that I didn't know before: writing with my mentor about careers and college has helped me learn what I want in the future.

MARÍA ALEJANDRA BARRIOS VÉLEZ

YEARS AS MENTOR: 1

OCCUPATION: Writer

BORN: Barranquilla, Colombia

LIVES: Brooklyn, NY

PUBLICATIONS & RECOGNITIONS:
Flash Fiction Fellow
SmokeLong 2020

MENTOR'S ANECDOTE:

Maiesha teaches me about empathy and attention to detail in each of our sessions. Her contemplative personality inspires me to slow down in my practice and to pay attention to my surroundings. I love her stories, her humor, and how, even though sometimes she's hesitant, she tries every idea or prompt I bring her. Her bravery is contagious.

Silent Neighborhoods Across New York

MAIESHA MUNTAKI AND MARÍA ALEJANDRA BARRIOS VÉLEZ

A poem about our two neighborhoods in New York and our experiences inhabiting the city through our own particular lenses.

Corona Avenue

If I were to tell you about my neighborhood
I would tell you about my dad,
Before moving to the neighborhood
I could see him being so cautious
I learned
I don't need to know every neighbor
I used to think a neighborhood is supposed to be a community
But maybe I had the wrong idea
It's not all that bad
There's not always talk among the neighbors
The least bit of words we exchange with each other
Are the "goodnights" and "have a good days" in the elevator
There's a large park right next to my apartment
Its spaciousness isn't its only specialty
There are trees all around in order
and the center of it is the big circular field
even if it's only human-made nature
it makes me feel serene
with that there's even a pool
that comes to life during the summer

everyone, including kids, swim there
But I always wished the pool wasn't coed
with that there's a space for soccer, basketball, and tennis
The kids would sometimes quarrel over the game
or cheer for scoring
Been to this park a couple of times
Saw new faces every time
Probably because I can't ever get to familiarize
The faces that pass me by.

My favorite place in my neighborhood
Is the library where
I borrow my favorite graphic books
There are stores in front of my building
But I've barely gone to every one of them
I had this thought that kids in a neighborhood became friends
    easily
But after moving to this neighborhood I realized
It's the opposite
Been here for four years
But never have I made a neighborhood friend each year.

It's safe to walk around the neighborhood at night
But I remember my mom being cautious
while walking through the dark streets
While walking through my neighborhood's streets
Most are walking and minding their business
Few men are listening to Spanish music and chatting
The beautiful roses in the summer are always vibrant
If a Muslim is passing by
I would receive an instant *salam*
That I barely get to reply back
Few balconies are bright, shiny, and sparkly around Christmas
giving out the message that it's time for celebration.

During summer days
along with bearing the heat
I'd hear the kids from my room
every summer day
I like my neighborhood the way it is
I might not see the attachment to my neighborhood
But all the little bits and pieces
I know of my neighborhood
are just what makes living here
comforting.

I wish my neighborhood was more of a community
Where
Neighbors know each other well
They celebrate together
They cope together
The silence wouldn't be so encompassing,
What I wish for the most is
a big family neighborhood.

Fort Greene

If I were to tell you about my neighborhood
I would tell you about the trees:
Old, wise, resilient with great deep roots that stick to the land never to
    let go,
I would tell you about the wind that hits the window on sleepless
    nights
and the car sounds, music, sirens, reggaeton that wakes us up—
The moving trucks, the recycling trucks, and the infinite glass-
    shattering sounds,
I would tell you about loneliness,
about walking and not knowing,
about walking and not talking,

no questions, no curiosity,
no one to talk back and no one to listen,

I would tell you about the wagging tails of dogs and
the children sledding on hills on the rare day of snow,
I would tell you about their kindness,
and I would tell that no one is as lucky as the trees,
people with roots in this neighborhood and in this land,
are forced to go,
are forced to leave behind,
are forced to look away,
are told to look away,
although they can't,
although they dream to return,
although this neighborhood my neighborhood,
might become a place they don't recognize,
If I were to show my neighborhood,
I could tell you about all the places that feel mine,
at least for now.

AMARI MURRAY

YEARS AS MENTEE: 1

GRADE: Senior

BORN: Brooklyn, NY

LIVES: Bronx, NY

SHARON MESMER

YEARS AS MENTOR: 1

OCCUPATION: Professor of
Creative Writing at NYU and the
New School and Writer/Poet

BORN: Chicago, IL

LIVES: Brooklyn, NY

PUBLICATIONS & RECOGNITIONS:
*American Poetry Review, New
York* magazine, *Posit*

MENTOR'S ANECDOTE:

When Amari and I got together for our first one-on-one meeting on Zoom, she said, "I'm going to read you a poem, and you tell me if you know what it's about." At about the third line, I knew exactly what it was about—an epileptic seizure. I have temporal lobe epilepsy, and while it's not the same form Amari has, I recognized certain similar features. When she was done I said, "It's about epilepsy!" She said, "How did you know?" "Because I have epilepsy too," I laughed. And then we both looked at each other, like "How did Girls Write Now know? Did they know? What a coincidence!" We've had a lot of talks about this since then, and about how it impacts our writing and social lives. During that same meeting we also discovered we'd both been bullied. It was kind of a match made in heaven.

Epileptic Born

AMARI MURRAY

*Have you ever known someone with epilepsy? Or ever wondered
what happens when someone is having a seizure? Well, let my words
of my health introduce you to the world of being a victim of epilepsy.*

Loss Consciousness.
Lights out.
Listen as my body hits the floor.
I become numb with no movement whatsoever.
Need assistance as quick as possible.
Am I okay? What's gonna happen?
Help me understand what just happened to me.

Wake up multiple hours later confused.
Was it the heat? Stress? Flashing lights? Idk.
Prescribe my medication so my health can stay on track.

It sticks with me life long and year-round.
Can happen any moment, anytime, anywhere.
Just gotta make sure I have someone with me.
When alone who knows what's possible.

AMANDA E MUSMACHER

YEARS AS MENTEE: 1

GRADE: Senior

BORN: Queens, NY

LIVES: Queens, NY

MENTEE'S ANECDOTE:

While I looked back into my childhood for this piece, Kat wrote from the perspective of their teenage life, a time from when they were my age. Both being queer, young individuals, with many overlapping experiences due to these identities, navigating how to reflect upon younger versions of ourselves was something that was very inspiring for me. As I am able to look at Kat as an older peer, as someone who has made a living off of their love of writing, I've seen that there are futures for queer kids, and those futures are not so far away.

K. A. JAGAI

YEARS AS MENTOR: 1

OCCUPATION: Executive
Assistant at Alloy Entertainment

BORN: New York, NY

LIVES: Brooklyn, NY

PUBLICATIONS & RECOGNITIONS:
Electric Literature, Frontier Poetry, Publishers Weekly

MENTOR'S ANECDOTE:

Being Amanda's mentor has been an honor. It's been amazing to see how the experience of being a young queer is both the same and radically different, all of which obviously defines and informs our work in different ways. Gen Z is so much more on top of things when it comes to gender identity and queerness, and it's so inspiring to see how engaged the new generation is. I'm delighted to be a part of their journey as they discover who they are, both as a person and as a writer. I look forward to watching them grow.

childhood archeology / Teenage Fever Dream

AMANDA E MUSMACHER AND K. A. JAGAI

These are two poems that reflect back on our younger selves.

childhood archeology

their limbs bounded together by plastic,
the small, hard, creatures
were lined up, feet digging into the wearing carpet,
the carpet carrying the fur of my cat, the dirt of my mother's shoes,
the secrets the walls kept enclosed in one room.
i was a paleontologist at age 5,
marching my dinosaurs to the bathtub on the opposite
end of my apartment. they were going to drink
the infected waters, dirtied by grime, rust,
the taste of a decaying home.

i dream of myself, sweeping the small
brush across the dust, digging up
sediment, burying the dead
bugs, my friends.
scooping the dirt out of my landlord's flower plots,
and leaving the reminiscence of my memories—
pebbles i had found on my walk home from the bus,
letters i wrote to my father, the paper ripped
from the pictures i drew of him,
scratched x's across his eyes.

how i found serenity
in the dimly lit alleyways, throwing lighters
at the concrete wall.
the pop would be startling,
but the puff of grey smoke that arose
reminded me of the exhaust that clouded my mother's lips
as she exhaled.

there was no product to be seen on tv
to alleviate how much my mother had to scour the countertops,
her acrylic nails lifting, turning yellow
from the suds and her cigarettes,
but could clean up the
mess
we always found ourselves in.
despite her attempts at scrubbing the checkered tiling in our kitchen,
there were stains that never went away,
crumbs never sucked
into the vacuum machine, leaving small lines of feasts
for the roaches to munch on
when we turned out the lights for sleep.

the sounds of the neighborhood's inhabitants kept me awake—
the nest of newly hatched birds taking shelter in my wall
chirping at any hour of the day.
the windows were large, displaying
wet tar on the empty street,
as the nighttime creatures crawled out
of their slumber for the day.
awake and ready to navigate the dark, to find
a scurrying roach to devour as a midnight snack.

and when i would awake in the dead of night—
scared to let the monsters in—

my dinosaurs came to life,
nibbled on my toes,
and kept the cockroaches away.

Teenage Fever Dream

We're half-awake on Houston
and it's 3 a.m., so you tell me
just stay the night, come on. No one's
home. Cold metal under bare toes
etches the mark of the fire
escape into the calloused skin
on the bottom of my feet.
There's a burn in my lungs from the bright cherry
lingering at the end of your death stick
and the sound of the radio echoing up from
the street below: skateboards and screaming
and an empty soda can kicked
into the gutter by an errant foot of wind.

You and every stupid kid wants
to live forever—buoyed by the drugs or
the drink or the sex or whatever
it is that keeps you up at night
pulse screaming in your veins so
loud you can't even hear yourself
trying to count the headlights
scrolling past the buzzing ceiling fan—
but we know nobody lives forever.
Not us, and not the beautiful people
and not the ageless leather-crusted
denizens of St. Mark's. Even heroes
have got to die, sometime, even if they
come back shiny and new and

the same as they ever were, but not
quite. Not yet, anyway—now
every window is bright and the sky
is dark and the night is warm
and breezy and the city
roars its life like a living creature.
More than anyone, She knows the score—
She's been reborn fourteen times
and will be again and still She has it
in Her to scream—*smile, baby. Isn't it grand?*
To be young and alive and in enough pain
to know for sure that you're living.

SUE NAJM

YEARS AS MENTEE: 1

GRADE: Senior

BORN: Brooklyn, NY

LIVES: Brooklyn, NY

MENTEE'S ANECDOTE:

Working with Caitlin has been one of the best experiences. Before Girls Write Now, I was scared of applying to colleges, being out in the real world, and getting to know myself as a writer. Caitlin helped me with that. She's open and honest. It was very easy to communicate and ask for advice. She pushed me and encouraged me when I needed it most, especially when applying for colleges. When I got into school recently she was the first person I wanted to call. She's genuine and always excited for our calls. I couldn't have asked for a better mentor.

CAITLIN CHASE

YEARS AS MENTOR: 4

OCCUPATION: Creative and Content Strategy Consultant

BORN: Syracuse, NY

LIVES: Brooklyn, NY

MENTOR'S ANECDOTE:

The first thing one notices about Sue is her boundless enthusiasm. Every call, every week, Sue tells me with elation about something that made her laugh, or a triumph of hers, or a film she fell in love with. These moments may be small. But they speak to something much bigger: Sue's determination to live life fully and with purpose. In challenge, Sue has an uncanny ability to see a path forward. We often speak of how she hopes to change the world as a storyteller and filmmaker—and I believe, if anyone can, Sue will.

As a Woman

SUE NAJM

*In New York, there are many times I've been catcalled on the train.
I wrote this poem to release my bottled-up anger about the constant
catcalls and times I was seen as an object.*

As a New Yorker, I'm used to the constant stares. The looks given from afar and maybe a couple of glares.

"What in the world is she wearing?" "Is that her real hair?"

As a New Yorker, I've had my fair share of being driven to fear I'd be snatched. Or was it because I'm a woman and I was out without a man?

As a woman, I'm used to the word *slut*.

"That slutty dress she had on, of course she was asking for it."

Asking for it was written on his lips. When *no* was all over hers. But no, it's okay to touch, isn't it? That Fashion Nova dress said to dig your filthy hands in her panties.

Wait. And her shoes said too, *"Have her scream saying no."* But her dress said *"yes."* Right? Her slutty dress said yes, right?

As a woman, I understand what it's like to walk down the street in fear a man would not take no as an answer. I live in fear that there wouldn't even be a question. Just take it. And smile after.

As a woman, when I walk down the street I hear men telling me how I'm supposed to feel.

"You need to smile more," says the man who drinks beer at two p.m.

Wonderful, I'll smile more.

As a New Yorker, taking the train is stressful as it is. Which one is my stop? Jeez, I'm lost once again.

As a woman, the train is where he is. In a crowded car full of those who look for a miniskirt to come and grab.

"You look lost, let me help you find your way," he says with his hand in his pants.

But I have common sense. I keep my head down. Don't look him in the eyes, that'll give him the right to come and pry.

As a woman, I'm told that it's our words against theirs. They said it didn't happen, or maybe I was drunk and forgot my consent.

"What were you wearing?" "Did you flirt with him that night?" "You looked like you had a lot to drink. Are you sure?"

Rape? That's the word we don't say, right?

Rape? What's that?

Isn't that when a woman accuses a man of assault to get his money? Or maybe she said this to get attention.

"I always knew she wanted attention."

Rape? Well, we aren't really taught that word. But, hey, in case a bad situation comes, here's a whistle. Blow when you can, no one will hear you 'cause he'll have his hand over your mouth. But, hey, here's your whistle, maybe this'll help.

As a woman, I'm told to keep my mouth shut. *Rape* is a word you barely use, because sex for you is a game you chose. You say when and where. You say the words that I do not want to hear.

As a woman, I'm ashamed of the way we view others. We throw around the word *whore*. How could you let these men take you down, then take down another woman?

"She waited ten years to say he raped her?"

She didn't wait, she was broken, and tried to heal. In those ten years, she still couldn't breathe. So she spoke up in a courtroom full of men.

"Rape? What is that? Didn't you consent? Wasn't he your boyfriend? Wasn't it YOUR bed?"

But she said no that night, he hit her twice. No one seemed to believe that.

As a woman, I'm scared.

ELAINE NG

YEARS AS MENTEE: 1

GRADE: Junior

BORN: New York, NY

LIVES: Brooklyn, NY

MENTEE'S ANECDOTE:

Anne is a very supportive mentor; she encourages me to submit different works and helps me edit them. She inspires me to create prose describing different scenarios that occur in real life, strengthening how I write and my grammar. She enjoyed my poems and helped me decide which I should submit to the anthology. I love working with Anne and how we interact over writing.

ANNE C. LEFEVER

YEARS AS MENTOR: 1

OCCUPATION: Lawyer

BORN: Edmonton, Canada

LIVES: New York, NY

MENTOR'S ANECDOTE:

My writing relationship with Elaine is inspiring. She has a natural curiosity that prompts her to see mundane events in a very creative light—for example, the experience of watching a bee carry out its tasks. She also has a natural humility that lets her be very vulnerable and self-aware in her writing. As someone whose profession requires her to write nonfiction materials, I enjoy exploring Elaine's perspective and the topics she chooses to focus on in her poems. In turn, I think my perspective helps Elaine branch out from traditional styles of poetry to explore more free verse.

Bee

ELAINE NG

On a warm spring's day, I walked down the street and I saw a bee.
I wondered what other functions it had besides pollinating.

It buzzes around the flower
And I freak out.
I start to wonder, what could it do at this hour?
It mumbles and bumbles as I start to doubt.

Bees are known for honey and stings.
I edge closer to the flower and I almost flinch.
Believing that I could disturb, away I start walking.
I don't want a pinch.

It works away, literally a busy bee.
I wonder why it chose this job.
Why can't it decide to swim at sea?
Do they even have the right to sob?

We, as humans, can swim at sea.
We, as humans, have the right to sob.
We, as humans, can choose to be lazy.
We, as humans, could even choose our jobs.

The bee's job has never changed throughout the centuries.
Like any other animal, it has a given role.
They won't need to visit any cemetery.
And they do not need to do what is told.

VICTORY OGUNNAYA

YEARS AS MENTEE: 1

GRADE: Senior

BORN: Brooklyn, NY

LIVES: Queens, NY

MENTEE'S ANECDOTE:

Kaley is a great mentor and friend. I know I can count on her whenever I'm feeling down, and her advice has helped me through challenging times. As a writer, the help and advice she gave has made me a stronger and more consistent writer. She is a very helpful person and I appreciate her very much.

KALEY ROBERTS

YEARS AS MENTOR: 1

OCCUPATION: Freelance Writer and Director's Assistant

BORN: Niantic, CT

LIVES: Brooklyn, NY

MENTOR'S ANECDOTE:

Victory is such a thoughtful, considerate young person. She sees the world in a special way, and is eager to contribute goodness to it. In a year that sometimes felt unexplainable, Victory and I had several chats that made it feel simpler.

Why I love you

VICTORY OGUNNAYA

This piece is all about love and how it blinds us. It's a beautiful thing that we all experience in our own way. This is just a window into another love story that will warm your heart.

You asked me once, what a kiss was like, and I was confused.

This was after your fifth girlfriend and my second boyfriend. I honestly thought you were insane.

I wasn't trying to shame you, I just thought it was interesting. You, the experienced one, had never been kissed before.

And I said, "I don't know."

Honest to God, swear on my dead mother, I had never been kissed before. And then you thought I was crazy. Honestly, I wanted to kill you for doubting me, but it was a beautiful day and the sun was out, the trees in the park were just big enough that the shadows covered your face and your eyes glistened, so that your smile was so big I thought you were gonna leap out of your body so I let it slide.

I wasn't surprised that we hooked up after prom. We both agreed we'd never talk about it again, but I could never get rid of that feeling that something was growing between us. We graduated, I was valedictorian, you screamed your ass off when I was onstage and I almost yelled at you to shut up. But I was so excited and fucking nervous and it was nice that day, the lights in the auditorium were big and flashy and the smile on your face was so big I thought you were gonna leap out of your seat so I let it slide.

I remember you talking to me about your parents and how they could've made it so big if they followed their dreams but their parents didn't let them. So you promised me and yourself that you would never let that happen to you. "I gotta follow my dreams," you said, cradling my face in your arms in that nice way, so that your hand was stroking my cheek. I said something about supporting you and you joked about how great it would be if we were together. I thought it was dumb but the night was cool and warm, and the smile on your face was so big I thought you were gonna leap out of your body so I let it slide.

You told me you loved me yesterday. I said I just wanted to be friends and you knew I was lying. You knew. There was no way we could be just friends. You wanted to call me out on my bullshit but you didn't. You were so upset and I couldn't stand it. I turned away from you and you said you were gonna be leaving for a while. I asked when you were gonna be back. You said you didn't know. I said okay. You said we'd stay friends then and you left. I'm writing this now as I realize how much I need you. You know that just as well as I do, and I hope you can forgive me. And even if you can't, I'll understand. I love you.

MAYA OLIVO

YEARS AS MENTEE: 1

GRADE: Junior

BORN: New York, NY

LIVES: New York, NY

MENTEE'S ANECDOTE:

I could not have asked for a better mentor to work with every week during this program. Rachel has taught me how to get outside of my comfort zone in experimenting with different forms of poetry. I've had so much fun working through challenging poetry prompts and sharing our work with each other. We definitely got to see a glimpse of each other's inner writer and the amazing things we can put out with our words combined.

RACHEL FELTMAN

YEARS AS MENTOR: 1

OCCUPATION: Executive Editor, *Popular Science*

BORN: Vineland, NJ

LIVES: Jersey City, NJ

MENTOR'S ANECDOTE:

Maya writes such beautiful poetry, and she's made me realize how much I enjoy writing poetry myself! I was worried I'd have nothing to offer a poet—I'm a journalist and a sometimes-fiction-writer myself—but having someone to talk about poetry with has been so much fun. I'm excited to see her portfolio continue to take shape this year!

Versions of our selves

MAYA OLIVO AND RACHEL FELTMAN

These are poems we wrote, together and separately, while reflecting on the theme of transformation—these poems are about all the different versions of ourselves we hold at once.

Versions of myself

RACHEL FELTMAN

My favorite version of myself is always roughly two years younger
That's how long it takes
For me to forget
How much I hated her
How her voice wavered
How her flesh wobbled
How her hair frizzed and her bones ached
I can only love her when I've had time to make myself believe
That I've lost everything I see in photographs of her
Just in time to start sowing seeds of self-love for the girl I am today
That I'll reap some twenty-odd months from now
Flowers to arrange prettily for the loathsome woman I'll become

Teddy Bear

MAYA OLIVO

I wish I were a teddy bear
Filled to the brim with secrets

You can toss me around and even
Then I'll wear a sewn-on smile

I wish I were a teddy bear
A stranger to the concept of romance,
Body dysmorphia, sleeping through dance
And watching past friendships
Harden like old playdough

Still dancing to the mundane
Symphony of the day by day
Nine to five hours
Of stepping on the scale
Smacked in the face by smothered subconscious mind waves

How to walk only for the sake of walking
And wave at people,
At past mes
At future yous,
Hoping our mistakes won't trail along behind them
Still, keep waving
At people, and people, and more people

I wish I were a teddy bear
Filled to the brim with stuffing
I can't tear the stitches on my own
In here there's enough stuff in
Even if I crack and need to cry at my home
Okay, maybe I need your help

All the nonsense arguments with mother
Her breath tumbles into
My unused body
Knees wobble in misaligned chaos

Muscles strain to lift sentences that
Somehow always outweigh the room

I wonder if they would still exist
If my crayons weren't in the garbage
I wonder if they would still exist
If I still allowed myself to eat pancakes every day

I wish I were a teddy bear
Why?
Toys can't play or scream
Can't speak or dream
Nobody wants their crayons clothed in
Dust from the retirement home

Home is my weakness
Even before I had to I couldn't leave it
Playing video games in my brain
Pancakes vs. pounds reaching 108
Innocence vs. a dance I really hate

And then,
A whistle
A knock
On the door
The wood bruises your knuckles
My stuffing falls to the floor
You giggle
Sun absorbing your whole face
I shiver
Like I'm surprised I still can keep standing
"It's time," you say
"It's time to go."

For the eyeing of my scars

RACHEL FELTMAN

I keep trying to get her out
But she's stuck in my throat
The last remaining ash
Of the fire you set in me
She's the dark muck you left over and I, I, I
I know that one day she will try to rise
Up out of my gullet

I would let her stay if she'd just settle
I don't think I'd have much choice
If she'd just settle
She could make a home in my gut
Hook a single claw into the meat of me
And I would have to claim her

But she'll claw her way out
Lash my tongue with her red hair
And she'll fight like the devil but I, I, I
I will choke her back down
Mangled and digestible

Why is it that men
Fill our throats with the specters they've made of us
Leaving us to nurse them and bear them
And kill them
And love them

ladybug pimples

MAYA OLIVO

i can feel your fingers tug at my sleeve
i can hear your keys a-jingle when you're 'bout to leave
do you care to look up from your work
and call me your distraction for as long as you please

i know my trash can's getting bloated
from all the poems i feed it at night
and i know that you're not worth it
you can call me your distraction every night of your life

compassion is a color i will never wear
your face
your body
your nose
your hair
my feet stay gliding with the tunnel of boredom
my eyes
my lips
i wish
i cared

how do you feel that your name's in the bible?
what did you think after my choir recital?
i'll pour my lip gloss in your morning tea
you belong with the dogs but i don't want you to be unhappy

pitter patter
rain drops dive into your pores
i'm the beetle in your bedroom that's so hard to ignore
my classmate keeps a list of everything you've done

your fight for the white army and my fight for the sun
nobody has won

i pretend like the play's so simple
pray for makeup to cover my ladybug pimples

ALYSSA OLMEDA

YEARS AS MENTEE: 1

GRADE: Junior

BORN: Jersey City, NJ

LIVES: Bronx, NY

MENTEE'S ANECDOTE:

Even though we've been working together for only a short period of time, Carina and I have been able to bond over our love of journalism, and quarantine lifestyles. Whether it's debating whether we should write about polar bears or climate change, there are always endless possibilities of amazing stories and ideas we can come up with. Our conversations are always thought-provoking, and we leave our meetings already anticipating the next.

CARINA STORRS

YEARS AS MENTOR: 3

OCCUPATION: Journalist

BORN: Tallahassee, FL

LIVES: New York, NY

PUBLICATIONS & RECOGNITIONS: *Elemental*, New York Academy of Sciences, Lasker Foundation newsletter

MENTOR'S ANECDOTE:

Alyssa and I just started working together this year, when nothing in the world was normal, and I was afraid that it would be hard for us to bond over FaceTime. Quite the opposite! Alyssa has such a warm and calm demeanor, and our conversations have flowed easily and happily. It's been uplifting to talk about the weirdness and challenges of our pandemic lives and put our experiences into writing. I'm especially excited that Alyssa wants to explore different genres this year—she's such a talented (and speedy!) writer and I can't wait to see where it takes her!

A Harvest of Memories

ALYSSA OLMEDA

Hi, I'm Alyssa. I'm excited to be able to present my work to you! I love nature, and I hope this piece is able to transport you all to the countryside with me.

It was a crisp fall night, and there was a chill in the air. The leaves were already changing into warm shades of reds and oranges as they littered the city ground. I got into the car with my brother, and we greeted our grandparents. We drove upstate in the blackness of the night that hugged every corner of the earth. After three hours that involved music, snacks, and frequent gas station stops, we arrived at my great-uncle's house. It stood tall and welcoming. Compared to the city, the air here felt light. I looked above me and stared at the millions of stars that shone in the night sky. As I walked toward the entrance of the house, the sound of nature rang in every direction. Crickets harmonized in the grass, owls with their occasional hoots, and the footsteps behind me stepping on the gravel. When I got inside, I was met with the comforting smell of wood. I drifted off to sleep and awoke to birds chirping, as the sun beamed through the windows. The warm glow of the sunlight kissed my face and I started my day. As I drank my coffee and sat on the back porch, I saw red cardinals flocking in the sky, eventually perching themselves on tree branches. A deer with her fawn warily ate grass in the nearby field, sensing my presence. As I observed this moment, all my worries eased away. My shoulders relaxed, my jaw unclenched, I closed my eyes and breathed in the crisp morning air of autumn. We spent our Saturday evening playing board games and sitting out on the deck, laughing and telling stories into the night. Sunday morning it was time to go home. I often dreaded these moments, as the drive back to the city felt longer than the drive upstate. But alas, I rolled out of bed and my nose jubilantly met with the smell of coffee. I got dressed, packed my things, and headed downstairs. I went to sit on the back porch and turned my gaze over to the shrubs that were aligned behind the garden rocks. A chipmunk rustled through the bushes. My coffee mug kept my hands warm as the brisk air whipped all around, causing the tree branches to dance mighty and high. Taking the final sips of my coffee, I started walking toward the car. Traveling back to the city felt like the final moments of a vacation. You know it's going to end, and you're leaving paradise to return to your daily routine. Looking out the window, I took in the bare trees with the red and orange leaves littering the side of the highway. Those trees would soon be replaced with houses, and then eventually buildings that reached toward the sky. I could feel the air getting denser as the smell of gasoline and exhaust settled in. The car slowed down, and we slid even farther into our seats as we sat in traffic. Eventually, we arrived in the Bronx, and it looked exactly as I had left it. I looked up at an empty sky, carrying the stars only in my memory.

KAILEE ORTIZ

YEARS AS MENTEE: 1

GRADE: Sophomore

BORN: Brooklyn, NY

LIVES: Brooklyn, NY

MENTEE'S ANECDOTE:

I'm so grateful to have such a patient and kind mentor such as Shyanne. I will be honest and say that I was a bit nervous to have such a soft-spoken mentor online, as communicating normally already is hard enough, but she has proved me wrong time and time again. I truly respect Shyanne as a mentor and hopefully a friend, as her listening ears and open heart truly let me be myself with her, which is something I really needed right now. Every time I hear her writing, it motivates me greatly to work harder to become a better writer. It's this kind of beauty that I've never experienced before that just makes Shyanne more of a shining star. I can only wish to shine as brightly as her one day.

SHYANNE BENNETT

YEARS AS MENTOR: 10

OCCUPATION: Poet, Teaching Artist

BORN: Brooklyn, NY

LIVES: Brooklyn, NY

PUBLICATIONS & RECOGNITIONS: *Green Mountains Review, The Acentos Review, Oversound*

MENTOR'S ANECDOTE:

Kailee is enthusiastic, curious, caring, thoughtful, and ridiculously talented! In addition to her writing endeavors, Kailee is formally training as a singer, exploring photography, learning to sew, and studying Korean. Kailee's creative ambitions, and desire to grow and experiment, shine through her writing. When Kailee first showed me "Cerulean Summer," I was struck by her vivid, precise images and authentic emotion. Even more impressive, she wrote the whole poem as pantoum, a strict Malay poetic form. Even though I'm a professional poet, I've struggled to write in this form before, so needless to say, I was blown away.

Cerulean Summer

KAILEE ORTIZ

If you've delved into the addiction of nostalgia these days, you can relate to this recurring poem and its story of two children spending their last summer together.

Cloudless skies of cerulean sheened over our fits of laughter.
Our smiling star beamed brightly in the empty sky, giving us a hello.
Child laughter and hot metal that smelled of burnt plastic, scalding our
sensitive skin.
Our garden of Eden, my life-sized snowglobe holding the memories of
when we were young.

Our smiling star beamed brightly in the empty sky, giving us a hello.
In our Eden, the prickly grass smelt of butter popcorn; the giant stones
were used as thrones.
Our garden of Eden, my life-sized snowglobe, holds the memories of
when we were young.
Our backs left rosy pink, my toes feeling rough against the flaring
summer concrete.

In our Eden, the prickly grass smelt of butter popcorn; the giant stones
were used as thrones.
I miss the days when we screamed to our hearts' content, and no one
thought we were crazy.
Our backs left rosy pink, my toes feeling rough against the flaring
summer concrete.
Because being a kid gave you the privilege to be so-called crazy.

I miss the days when we screamed to our hearts' content, and no one
    thought we were crazy.
Where hot sweat dripped down my back, baby hairs sticking up on
    my neck.
Because being a kid gave you the privilege to be so-called crazy.
I was so out of breath my heart felt as if it were about to explode outside
    its chest.

Where hot sweat dripped down my back, baby hairs sticking up on
    my neck
I felt the blood rush through my veins, a fire spreading across my cheeks.
I was so out of breath my heart felt as if it were about to explode outside
    its chest.
I felt more alive than I have in the past four years combined.

I felt the blood rush through my veins, a fire spreading across my cheeks.
No worries about boys or girls or do I like boys and girls.
I felt more alive than I have in the past four years combined.
No thoughts of being a good student or daughter, but how much longer
    do I have left with you?

No worries about boys or girls or do I like boys and girls.
Wonders spinning inside my head, will we chase one another again?
No thoughts of being a good student or daughter, but how much longer
    do I have left with you?
My eyes still look for you in the city, my heart waiting to race once
    again.

Wonders spinning inside my head, will we chase one another again?
I miss your shadow alongside mine; I wish I never pushed you away
    like I did.
My eyes still look for you in the city, my heart waiting to race once
    again.
Our pinkies intertwined with a kiss at the fist to seal our deal.

I miss your shadow alongside mine; I wish I never pushed you away
like I did.
Scared of the world surrounding me but scared to face you no longer,
Our pinkies intertwined with a kiss at the fist to seal our deal.
I want to be free of these regrets I've made in memory of you.

Scared of the world surrounding me but scared to face you no longer,
4,000 miles of space is reason enough to forget about each other.
I want to be free of these regrets I've made in memory of you
It is not my fault we grew so far apart.

4,000 miles of space is reason enough to forget about each other.
Yet, I miss the laughter and I miss our thrones, our baby crushes, and
dancing onstage with you.
It is not my fault we grew so far apart.
I miss my grandma's house, near our school; now who begs me to even
call and say hello?

Yet, I miss the laughter and I miss our thrones, our baby crushes, and
dancing on stage with you.
I miss when things were so simple, and how my life didn't have to rest
on my palms.
I miss my grandma's house near our school; now who begs me to even
call and say hello?
I'm trying to live again, even all alone. I want to live, grow old, and
happy without a shard of regret.

I miss when things were so simple, and how my life didn't have to rest
on my palms.
I certainly never want to regret you.
I'm trying to live again, even all alone. I want to live, grow old, and
happy without a shard of regret.
Maybe we can see each other again one day when I am brave enough.

I certainly never want to regret you,
Or the child laughter and hot metal that smelled of burnt plastic,
    scalding our sensitive skin.
Maybe we can see each other again when I'm brave enough to face you,
Where cloudless skies of cerulean sheen over our fits of laughter.

MARIA OSORIO

YEARS AS MENTEE: 1

GRADE: Junior

BORN: Medellín, Colombia

LIVES: Queens, NY

MENTEE'S ANECDOTE:

When I joined Girls Write Now, I didn't know what to expect, I had never had a mentor, and I have never shared my writing, but working with Barbara has made it easy, enjoyable, and a learning opportunity with each meeting. I wouldn't know what specific moment to choose, but something constant in our relationship is how she is always listening to me and including me in all the decisions we made for our projects. In all the activities we do, she is honest and always thinking about how we can improve and be better with each piece we write.

BARBARA VICTORIA NIVEYRO

YEARS AS MENTOR: 1

OCCUPATION: Communications and Multimedia Producer

BORN: Buenos Aires, Argentina

LIVES: Brooklyn, NY

PUBLICATIONS & RECOGNITIONS: Buchwald Editorial, NYXT.nyc

MENTOR'S ANECDOTE:

When I met Maria I was nervous; it was my first experience as a mentor. We engaged easily because we are both from South America and we wanted to explore environmental justice and Latin American poets. We decided to communicate in Spanglish and she surprised me because she has a strong critical thinking process. Even knowing that she is shy—as she describes herself—she has the courage to share her emotions and ideas through her work. I cannot choose a specific moment; it is the process of learning together, being committed and laid back, that makes our mentee-mentor relationship so enjoyable.

Chatty Seagulls

MARIA OSORIO

"Chatty Seagulls" is a poem about making every second of your life worthy.

Until completing the cycle of my existence,
I will not give up my dreams,
I will live my life like there was no tomorrow,
I will try new things,
I will leave a legacy.

I will jump from a plane and fly like an eagle,
I will touch the clouds in the sky and feel the freedom,
I will travel across the world and meet new people.

Definitely try to find love,
if that even exists.
Find someone to share the good and the bad,
someone to share a soul with.

Until completing the cycle of my existence,
I will see the beauty around me.
On a normal day,
I will look at the sky,
listen to the sound of the sea,
the waves hitting the rocks.
Chatty seagulls flying through the sky.

I won't complain about how cold or hot the days are,
I will take them as a gift from Mother Earth.
She is waiting for me to go back to her,
when my existence is complete.

Listen to the beat of my heart,
bump bump, bump bump.

JULISSA OZUNA

YEARS AS MENTEE: 1

GRADE: Sophomore

BORN: Bronx, NY

LIVES: Bronx, NY

MENTEE'S ANECDOTE:

My writing relationship with my mentor, Jordan Davidson, was very beneficial and informative. During this process I was able to learn how to expand on my writing skills and vocabulary. Jordan allowed me to learn how to deliver my main message in an effective way. I enjoyed our writing relationship and I am confident that I will continue learning more with Jordan's guidance.

JORDAN DAVIDSON

YEARS AS MENTOR: 1

OCCUPATION: Journalist

BORN: Queens, NY

LIVES: Jersey City, NJ

PUBLICATIONS & RECOGNITIONS:
Elemental, Bitch Media

MENTOR'S ANECDOTE:

Julissa is incredibly driven and unwavering in her mission to empower others to prioritize their mental health. We take her passion for mental wellness and workshop different pieces to convey the message she wants to share. Whether it's poetry or a short story, we work together to break down the type of writing she wants to do and discuss how we can use each part to spread a message about the importance of putting your mental health first. I can't wait to see what incredible things she does next—both as a writer and as a mental health advocate.

Lost Souls

JULISSA OZUNA

When you put others before yourself, your oxygen masks will be lost. You cannot feign your own happiness, therefore you need to learn how to love yourself.

Those who cannot love themselves suffer the cost,
And feel pain,
When their oxygen masks are lost.

When the way you feel is tossed,
It can feel as though you're going insane,
Those who cannot love themselves suffer the cost.

Shedding tears that turn to frost,
Hoping that you're not to blame,
When your oxygen mask is lost.

Trying to keep everyone happy at any cost,
You try to feign
happiness knowing that those who cannot love themselves suffer the cost

Stop letting yourself be bossed,
By people who aim
to keep you from loving yourself because those who cannot love
    themselves suffer the cost,
And their oxygen masks have already been lost.

SRIHITHA PALLAPOTHULA

YEARS AS MENTEE: 1

GRADE: Junior

BORN: Fremont, CA

LIVES: Fremont, CA

PUBLICATIONS & RECOGNITIONS:
Scholastic Art & Writing Awards:
Gold Keys, Silver Keys

MENTEE'S ANECDOTE:

Before meeting Yvette, I was nervous. Afterward, however, my anxiousness disappeared. Yvette is so kind, welcoming, and funny. In our time together, I have learned so much about writing. My greatest takeaway is that I don't have to rush with my words. Yvette has given me unwavering support with everything. She has been there to celebrate my successes and to help me face failure. Our time together has been invaluable and always goes by too fast. I am extremely thankful to Girls Write Now for pairing me up with someone as incredible and inspiring as Yvette.

YVETTE CLARK

YEARS AS MENTOR: 1

OCCUPATION: Author

BORN: Huddersfield, England

LIVES: New York, NY

PUBLICATIONS & RECOGNITIONS:
Glitter Gets Everywhere

MENTOR'S ANECDOTE:

I consider myself incredibly lucky to be Srihitha's mentor. From our first meeting, her talent and dedication were evident. I am so proud of her recent achievements in the Scholastic Writing Awards—I danced for joy when she shared the news! Srihitha has a unique voice and a beautiful, brave writing style which will inspire others. She certainly inspires me.

I was a good Radha

SRIHITHA PALLAPOTHULA

"I was a good Radha" revisits the relationship between the protagonist—a young girl—and her mother while she faces a critical life decision.

Trigger warning: Drugs, death, suicide

Your name is **DIE**syllabic Radha,* after a writer whom your mother Loved, *L* for Love as in lust and lies; you don't need to remember that.

Your mother was a sad, stoic woman, used to freeze up like hail, rain dismissed to ice. Your father SHUT your mother up; you don't need to remember that.

Your mother said things like I was once a girl, I was once a girl who was loud, I was once a girl who was loud and laughed. I was once a girl who was loud and laughed and looked like a heroine, say, Savitri,† I was once a girl who was loud and laughed and looked like a heroine, say, Savitri, pearls and string and tresses fluttering, I'd devour creamy butterscotch ice cream by the bucket; then your mother's eyes would lick bitter, green okra off her husband's dirty floor, like a servant, and whisper "I am now a lady"; you don't need to remember that.

When your mother swallowed, she did so out of compulsion, as if her

---

* In Hindu mythology, Radha is considered to be the god Krishna's dearest companion. There are cases in which she is depicted as his wife. Radha is loyal, sweet, kind, pure, a symbol of virtue.

† Savitri is the Queen of Telugu cinema. Though she passed away long ago, her legacy lives on through her movies and a biopic, *Mahanati*. She struggled with addiction during the later years of her life.

soul demanded the glassy, colored pills that laced her tongue. Desperation took shelter in her eyes, her body caved into itself. You need to remember this.

You need to remember how your mother swallowed because after eight years of marriage accompanied by your now-dead husband, a return gift from this party called society, you've discovered a massive stash of pills stuffed into a rich chest labeled "surprise for my wife (to be delivered shortly after I die), From: Your Dead Husband, To: Woman I've brought up from nothing to Something." You need to remember how your mother swallowed because the police are swarming your nest, like venomous bees; they'll sting you all over if they find you. You need to remember how your mother swallowed because you don't remember your dead husband's name or face, don't remember what he did, don't remember a single moment in the eight years you were married, don't know what the something he died of was. You need to remember how your mother swallowed, so you can pretend you're dying while her ghost possesses you, so you can down eighty bottles of pills before the bees reach you, so the dark skin that wraps around your neck can learn to stretch, thin, then sag with your weight. You need to remember how your mother swallowed, so you can mold yourself into the Radha you are expected to be: pure, so you can, for once, when the police arrive, feel like a Queen. Snarl "you won't find anything here" with authority you have no right to as you put yourself to sleep no better than a vet would a bitch. You need to remember how your mother swallowed, so you can suck the life out of your body before the bees do. You need to remember how your mother swallowed, so you can protect a man who means nothing to you, a man you've never loved.

You know then that you've been a good Radha.

SHREYA PANDIT

YEARS AS MENTEE: 1

GRADE: Senior

BORN: Queens, NY

LIVES: Queens, NY

PUBLICATIONS & RECOGNITIONS:
Presidential Volunteer Service
Award: Finxerunt Policy Institute;
Senior Editor of School
Newspaper, *Veritas*

MENTEE'S ANECDOTE:

I have really enjoyed working with Lane! She has improved my writing tremendously, from making easy-to-understand guides to informing me more about journalism as a whole. My favorite writing exercises are the open-ended contemplative ones that are comparable to journal entries. I am not much of a creative writer, and these prompts have definitely allowed me to reflect and challenge my writing. Another exercise I liked was crafting ledes based off a short prompt, which was great practice for articles, since I have never done anything like that before!

LANE FLORSHEIM

YEARS AS MENTOR: 1

OCCUPATION: Staff Writer, *The Wall Street Journal Magazine*

BORN: Milwaukee, WI

LIVES: New York, NY

PUBLICATIONS & RECOGNITIONS:
The Wall Street Journal

MENTOR'S ANECDOTE:

I had so much fun working with Shreya on our article about TikTok. I don't usually get to write articles with other people, and collaborating with her on it was a great learning experience. She's so knowledgeable about TikTok and the ways her generation uses social media and participates in activism, and to be honest, I hope she learned as much from me as I did from her. Throughout the semester, we've also done writing prompts and worksheets, and on everything we do, it feels like we are in sync, working well (and efficiently!) together.

What Does It Mean That TikTok Users Are Getting Their News from the Platform?

SHREYA PANDIT AND LANE FLORSHEIM

Social media is revolutionizing the way we receive information, from beauty hacks to geopolitical conflict. Why misinformation can spread this way—and how to minimize consuming it in your own reading.

Rahib Taher, a high school student and avid TikTok user, initially downloaded the video-based social media app to watch political memes, but soon found himself watching videos that gave him news in real time too. He says he admires the platform's ability to include a diverse range of voices: "I think most news conglomerates are pretty center- or right-leaning, and I like platforms where there's a wide range of public involvement like TikTok."

Social media is revolutionizing the way we receive information, from beauty hacks to geopolitical conflict. However, its influence can also vastly affect the spread of information—and misinformation—even potentially altering elections. In 2019, NPR reported that Facebook says Russian operatives may have reached up to 126 million people on its platform ahead of the 2016 US presidential election. In addition to Facebook, Twitter has long been a news source for its users, and even Instagram has taken on this function—the 2020 Reuters Institute Digital News Report found the use of Instagram for the news had doubled since 2018. TikTok is the latest entrant.

There isn't as much data available on TikTok as there is on other social media platforms. However, the nonprofit organization Media Matters, which fights misinformation online, cites recent research that found Tik-Tok to be a rapidly growing platform with the largest percentage of users between the ages of sixteen and twenty-four. Media Matters researcher Olivia Little also cites a recent Pew Research Center report that found about half of adults get their news "often" or "sometimes" from social media.

"So while there is limited data available that explicitly shows how many TikTok users are getting their news from the platform, we can all see that the app is used to intentionally circulate and sometimes explain current events to young people," says Little. She cites examples including Black Lives Matter organizers using TikTok to broadcast information about the movement, as well as creators who used TikTok videos to brief their followers on the Georgia senate runoff elections that took place in January.

Users can benefit from this content. Says Little: "TikTok users often create content breaking down difficult concepts or events, making them accessible to users of all ages. TikToks can be fun and funny and also add critical details and perspectives that might be omitted from mainstream media narratives." However, like any social media platform, Little adds that a major drawback to getting your news from TikTok is that misinformation can go undetected or unmoderated, making it look like it's reliable when it's not. "Reliable news outlets thoroughly fact-check reports prior to their release, but individual creators on TikTok don't have editors like a newsroom would and are not faced with that same review process before posting."

This is the process of social media users like Amy,* a high school student in New York. Amy uses TikTok for entertainment and news, even making some of her own videos. "I get a good amount of my news from social media . . . [but] if I find something interesting, then I go off TikTok and onto Safari, and I look up stuff on my own."

Another issue, as Amy put it, is that "social media is an echo chamber." The app's algorithm picks up on your specific tastes and what topics you may interact with the most. Because of this, the news you get is chosen specifically for you, not completely diversifying the opinions you interact with—potentially preventing a more comprehensive overview of a situation.

Although Gen Z makes up the majority of TikTok's users, millennials are also getting their news from the platform. Noah,* twenty-nine, a New York–based editor, has been a TikTok user since 2019. Although he joined the platform primarily to watch comedy, the algorithm regularly shows him videos about politics and current events.

A recent example he points to is learning from a TikTok video why his stimulus check had been delayed. "A lady made a video after she had spoken to TurboTax and it turned out that [for] anyone who had filed their taxes with a certain method on TurboTax, last year's stimulus checks were delayed," he says. "A day later, I got an email from Turbo-Tax saying everything that she said. But I found it out on TikTok first."

He says the best part of getting some of his news from TikTok is the way it's sandwiched between pieces of entertainment. Others, like Rahib, admire TikTok's accessibility too: "I think that the format is just way better than some other social media sites. It is more user-friendly."

While TikTok and other social media apps were not created with the circulation of news being their primary function, there is no denying that they now have a large effect on our consumption of the news. And while the COVID-19 pandemic has made activism more challenging, apps like TikTok and Twitter allow for a more accessible way to make your voice heard. Apps like these are a good way to expose yourself to events going on, but take what you see, hear, and read with a grain of salt and always remember to fact-check.

---

* All names followed by an asterisk have been changed.

NAYEON PARK

YEARS AS MENTEE: 1

GRADE: Junior

BORN: Jeonju, South Korea

LIVES: Queens, NY

PUBLICATIONS & RECOGNITIONS:
Scholastic Art & Writing Awards:
Gold Key

MENTEE'S ANECDOTE:

Through our weekly meetings, Tingting has inspired and motivated me in so many ways that I have never thought was possible through an online medium. From her expertise in digital storytelling to our shared appreciation for city vermin and animated films, Tingting helps me explore passions in ways that are so gratifying. The hour-long calls seem like a short catch-up with a friend and a way to experiment with our talents outside of school and work. In so many more ways than writing and reading, she has taught me personal growth as a woman, friend, and, of course, a mentee!

TINGTING WEI

YEARS AS MENTOR: 1

OCCUPATION: Senior Graphic Designer

BORN: Suzhou, China

LIVES: Brooklyn, NY

MENTOR'S ANECDOTE:

Nayeon is one of those young leaders you meet and think, "The future will be a brighter place." Nayeon's creativity and sense of humor have brought this year light and laughter. Despite her gentle demeanor, she's one of the hardest workers I know. Her art is heartfelt, down to earth, and the subjects she cares about both diverse and inspiring. She doesn't shy away from experimentation and questioning. Her curiosity is contagious! Most awe-inspiring is her integrity toward her ancestral history, which will no doubt inform her works for years to come. I am excited to watch her journey unfold.

Banana Bread and Lemon Glaze

NAYEON PARK

Short story about code-switching and living between two worlds.

I am both a lemon and a banana. A lemon is citrusy and sharp, while a banana is soft and sweet. When I speak Korean, my tongue stays behind my teeth, articulating edged consonants. I must do this when I ask my mom what is for dinner tonight. "*Sampgyupsal* and *Gge-nip*," my mom says among the clattering of plates and chopsticks. I then go to my brother, who has called America home his whole life, to see what he thinks of pork belly and roasted garlic at eight p.m. My tongue suddenly softens up, creeping out of my mouth to touch my lips.

"Yeah, that sounds good," he murmurs.

I open the door to his room wider: "Did you want a bowl of rice with that?"

At that question, he furrows his eyebrows in disgust: "No, also make sure there is a fork available." I shake my head slightly and laugh at the irony. How could someone with such dexterity with a gaming keyboard still not understand how to use chopsticks? But I keep my thoughts to myself. After all, though I am an expert at the art of chopsticks, I still convulse at the smell of string beans and fermented soy paste.

My father always teases me, claiming that I am a banana—yellow on the outside, white on the inside. Almost every Korean kid in America has heard this common and relatable joke, this playful jab at their identity that implies that although I am Korean, I often have Americanized mannerisms and speak in a perfect English tongue. However, I would also describe myself as a lemon—the same both inside and out. What my father doesn't see are my friend's bugged-out eyes when I mention that I was born in Jeonju, South Korea. They are fascinated by the fact that I am bilingual and ask about how Korea was when I lived there. I am then treated a bit differently—not necessarily in a bad way, but as though they finally understand why I have a "very slight accent" or "an unusually strong work ethic."

Another term to describe this fruity phenomenon is *code-switching*. I've trained myself to switch seamlessly, both in speaking and in mannerisms. My code-switching dexterity means the range of my voice undulates at Olive Garden. While I speak a dainty and quiet Korean to my aunt about how salty and fatty the chicken alfredo is, I suddenly change into a deeper and bolder English when the waiter asks how the food is. "Absolutely delicious! We love it," I say in a loud, saccharine voice. My aunt glances at me, finding my double identity both dumbfounding and hilarious. We laugh together as we both agree: Raspberry sorbet for dessert is truly delicious, or *masshi-suh*, as we say.

Throughout my life, two versions of myself flow from one to another. Many people often say that they feel conflict with their two cultures—their parents' country versus the one that they are currently immersed in. To them, I would like to introduce banana bread with a lemon glaze. I learned that if you eat a banana under the hot summer sun, you might experience a heavy stomach. To alleviate that discomfort, a dash of lemon juice will soothe it right up. From the outside, it may seem like my two cultures are separate from each other, but I see it differently; I am able to live in both worlds, aware of the beautiful contrast of each culture, and, sometimes, finding brilliant harmonies between the two. I pride myself in the ability to tell my grandma about my Olive Garden dinner, someone who lives thousands of miles away and does not speak a lick of English. My cousins text me, and it is obvious they are a little envious. They, too, wish that they had sampled the amazing raspberry sorbet I ate with our aunt. And it's in moments like these that I am proud to be both a lemon and a banana.

MARIELLA PARMENTER

YEARS AS MENTEE: 1

GRADE: Junior

BORN: Las Vegas, NV

LIVES: New York, NY

MENTEE'S ANECDOTE:

Writing with Adrian has given me a lot of confidence in my work and my abilities. She is genuine when we work together to create writing that depicts who we are, and I deeply appreciate the guidance she has provided me in the past few months. We have had the best time getting to know one another, and I can't wait to further our relationship. She is a really talented writer, and role model that I look up to. She's the best!

ADRIAN HORTON

YEARS AS MENTOR: 1

OCCUPATION: Journalist

BORN: Chicago, IL

LIVES: Brooklyn, NY

MENTOR'S ANECDOTE:

Ella comes across as one of the most humble people you'll meet, but she's a force of many talents revealed over time. Once, in the middle of workshopping our free-write poetry, she mentioned that she had made a video audition for a talent show that combined two other interests: singing and baking. She layered harmonies for a song from the musical *Waitress* while preparing sweets in the kitchen. I watched the video in awe (and shouted into my webcam). The attention to detail, creative ambition, and eye for fun felt true to her and our sessions, even on Zoom.

Selected Poems

MARIELLA PARMENTER

Writing poetry has served as an outlet to relieve stress during this anxiety-filled year. I've poured many of my feelings into these poems, some of which are selected here.

Weave of compassion

An unfamiliar pull of emotion embraces my mind.
Is this the result of our social landslide or new corners?
Unaccounted knowledge, strain, and cries are defined,
As an expectation that just brings more mourners.

Sometimes love moves too fast for you to get to know it.
And it feels like a journey to receive.
Remind me that I am a member of humanity with grit.
And that compassion is my weave.

Overwhelming binds of difficulties and smiles create a collection.
A weave of existence.
Holding on to a silly hope that one can be shown affection.
There is persistence.

Collect the trinkets of your memories that you lived through,
To string each thought into a piece of art for your debut.

Look again

Real treasures never flaunt.
They are humble, and considerate.
Although they may haunt,
The things they do are deliberate.

Should I be searching?
Or will it fall in my lap?
Dangerous people are lurking,
When you don't have a map.

Inherent and cruel may these places be,
Constantly brewing ways to keep you wee.
Wishing to learn the path to be free,
Alone, or with someone, should I just plea?

From the outside I see how I am blind,
With an internal storm, I stay resigned.

Can something go my way?

My eyes bore into nothing.
Again.
Does everyone have to?
Explain?

Lists and endeavors cover my pages,
Ideologies, rules as well.
Explanations of dark ages
And how my heart has lost its swell.

I used to care about big things,
Going my way.

Looking for a hairbrush is a pain.
I can't convey.

Wishing my face held a forever frown,
Because it feels comfortable.
No matter what, my certainties worn down.
Existence is insufferable.

VIKTORIA PAVLOVA

YEARS AS MENTEE: 1

GRADE: Junior

BORN: New York, NY

LIVES: Staten Island, NY

PUBLICATIONS & RECOGNITIONS:
Scholastic Art & Writing Awards:
Honorable Mention

MENTEE'S ANECDOTE:

Writing gives you the ability to look beyond yourself. Anything is possible in your stories, and anything you create is completely yours. Writing is an escape from reality, because it lets you create your own world.

NEVIN MAYS

YEARS AS MENTOR: 1

OCCUPATION: Editor

BORN: Landstuhl, Germany

LIVES: New York, NY

MENTOR'S ANECDOTE:

Viktoria was ready to roll from our first meeting. She doesn't shy away from a challenge, a fact that has sometimes intimidated me . . . What could I offer this ambitious and talented young person? It's been a pleasure to share her journey as a writer, watching her explore new techniques, conquer emotionally and artfully difficult revisions, and readily take on leadership roles in addition to her ambitious personal projects. Buckle up, world, because Viktoria is in the driver's seat!

Now I See You

VIKTORIA PAVLOVA

Going blind at the age of ten was his worst nightmare come true, until he began to see in color.

My biggest dream from ten to thirteen wasn't to become an astronaut or an entrepreneur. It was to be able to see again.

Going blind, ironically, was the most eye-opening experience I'd ever had. At nine, I'd been diagnosed with a sinus mass that was pressing on my visual nerve. Since the problem went untreated, by ten, I lost 50 percent of my vision. By the next Christmas, I lost my vision entirely. I was depressed after that, and peevish.

On my thirteenth birthday, my dream to see came true, well, partially. Every time I met or spoke to someone new, I saw a color in my mind. My parents were green, which meant they were good people. My sister was blue—she was joyful. People I had a bad feeling about, depending on how they talked or acted, I saw in red. It became easier for me to get in tune with my surroundings afterward, because I'd gotten some of my life back. I focused on my other senses: smell, touch, and sound. I'd begun to feel hopeful.

But going back to school as the blind boy was not how I imagined middle school. I was homeschooled after I lost my eyesight, but once I could walk around the house, and learned braille, I went back to school with the assistance of an aide.

Now at fifteen, I roamed the halls alone with only my walking stick.

"Mom?" I called as I dragged my hand along the wall and avoided the dining room table. I smelled pancakes in the kitchen.

"Lucas! I'm making breakfast," she replied. I heard her wipe her hands on what I assumed was her apron.

"Do I look okay?" I asked.

"Your hair is silky and brown, and your eyes are mesmerizingly blue. If only you could see them."

"If only I could see a lot of things." I sighed. "How about my outfit?"

"You have blue joggers and a red shirt on." She laughed.

I groaned, disappointed that in two years I hadn't gotten my clothing system down, feeling the fabric and the tags of my clothes to try and decipher them.

Back in my room, I rechecked my pant tags until I found a pair I thought worked better. I sensed my sister Hannah's blue shadow at the door, and she told me my outfit was presentable—black jeans, red shirt.

I grinned at her sheepishly, grabbing my walking stick from its place at the foot of my bed, and followed Hannah back into the kitchen.

School was a dreadful task, the whispers in the halls, the people avoiding me. Although I've been able to wander the halls alone since freshman year, it's difficult to navigate my giant school. Walking through the crowded corridors, the colors of students stood out, each dazzling and distinct. It was almost as if I could see the people themselves and not just their voices.

School dragged on, but I finally made it home. However, two hours later I picked up my walking stick and joined Mom inside her car.

We arrived at my ophthalmologist's office and sat down. I'd gathered from the gasps and hushed whispers that I was the only blind person in the room. I could smell the perfume and baby powder of the parents and children.

"Lucas Whitman?" called my usual nurse. I heard everyone's shoes sliding against the carpet closer to their chairs as I walked through the waiting room.

The exam room smelled subtly of isopropyl alcohol and hand sanitizer. I recognized the sterile smell instantly, having been exposed to it for years.

Today we'd find out if I was approved for an experimental surgery to bring back my eyesight. Mom had fought for years to get this surgery, and each year was rejected.

The doctor walked in and I followed his green outline across the room to my mom's green one. The nurse's blue stood vibrantly next to them.

"Lucas, how are we today?" asked Dr. Robinson.

I shrugged. I stopped listening as he dragged on, but tuned back in when I heard Mom beginning to cry. The aura in the room changed, and their colors started to shimmer. My knee stopped bouncing and I became more in tune with my surroundings. The ticking of the clock, the clacking of computer keys from the front desk, a toddler laughing had all become more prominent.

"You were approved!" Mom exclaimed.

My body froze.

"Lucas," said Dr. Robinson, "if all goes well, you'll have your eyesight back." I could practically feel the smile growing on his face.

But as I looked around the room and saw the excitement, I thought about how I can hear and feel things that most people can't. I can see vibrant colors, rather than dull ones that don't make you feel anything. I can memorize the layout of a room by walking around it once. I'm not sure if I want to lose that, if I want to be like everyone else. I'm not Lucas, the blind boy who everyone pities.

I'm Lucas, the boy who sees in color.

AMBER N. PERSAUD

YEARS AS MENTEE: 1

GRADE: Sophomore

BORN: Queens, NY

LIVES: Brooklyn, NY

MENTEE'S ANECDOTE:

Rachel Prater and I have been working beside each other for a short time; however, she is humorous and we clicked instantly. She gave me ways to grow in my writing and has encouraged me every step of the way. While writing my stories I keep Rachel in mind and always make sure that it would be a piece she is proud of!

RACHEL PRATER

YEARS AS MENTOR: 3

OCCUPATION: Production Editor

BORN: Dayton, OH

LIVES: New York, NY

MENTOR'S ANECDOTE:

Amber and I hit it off from the first moment we met, virtually. Virtual meetings can be difficult. Not with us, luckily. We instantly discovered we have a lot in common and that foundation has built a quick and easy mentor-mentee relationship between us. Amber is smart and hilarious, and I've been proud to watch her unlock her creative side. She has a story to tell that is hers alone, and I'm excited for everyone to hear it! The world is truly at her feet, and I'll be cheering her on, every step of the way.

Resplendent at Dawn

AMBER N. PERSAUD

*My life has come with many struggles, but throughout all of them,
the cold blue of the morning has always brought comfort. This is my
way of sharing said comfort with you.*

The brightness of daybreak shows against the open blinds,
The sun has not yet risen and the cold blue surrounds me,

In most cases, blue is associated with sadness,
But right now,
while the world is still asleep and I hear the faint cries of the birds
    and wind,
I feel glee.

At this moment, for the first and last time for that day,
I will feel free and unattached to any negatives from the day prior.

At this moment,
I will open up a window and take a breath of fresh air
that takes me to a place like no other.

In which my head is filled with nothing but, well, nothing.
In times like these,
it feels like bliss and a blessing to have nothing on my mind.

Of course, the feeling will fade as it did the morning prior,
and before that.

But I shall not worry about that now.
I'll sulk in the feeling,
lay back down into the warmth of last night's struggles, and close
my eyes.

And as the morning fades and the blue finally dissipates,
I'll begin mourning the feeling,
And chasing the high that was.

BRITNEY PHAN

YEARS AS MENTEE: 2

GRADE: Junior

BORN: Bronx, NY

LIVES: Bronx, NY

MENTEE'S ANECDOTE:

Though I spent most of last year mainly stuck in my own room, my mentor, Lindsay, helped keep me company through weekly meetings where we formed a two-person book club to read and discuss *One Hundred Years of Solitude* by Gabriel García Márquez. As I slowly watched the autumn pass in tandem with the events of the story, I began to feel inspired by both the characters of the book and the fantastical style of the author. Without Lindsay's help, I wouldn't even have an idea as to where to start my story, so I am immensely grateful for her.

LINDSAY ZOLADZ

YEARS AS MENTOR: 5

OCCUPATION: Music Critic

BORN: Washington Township, NJ

LIVES: Brooklyn, NY

MENTOR'S ANECDOTE:

This year, my mentee Britney and I started one of the most rewarding projects we've undertaken together: a book club. We'd both always wanted to read Gabriel García Márquez's *One Hundred Years of Solitude* but had never gotten around to it—no better time than now! For several months, we met virtually each week and discussed the latest happenings in the Buendía family. Britney was so inspired by the novel that, for her lyrical anthology piece, she reimagined the fates of two of the book's female characters. Reading together was a perfect way to weather our one year of solitude.

The March of Yellow Butterflies

BRITNEY PHAN

Two women talk as the world comes to an end.

The old woman possessed an inclination unlike anything else on Earth, which had made her astutely clairvoyant of the final, all-consuming storm that would soon destroy the town. As she sat in her favorite wicker rocking chair, Pilar recalled the history of the village that she had always known as Macando: full of men who hailed from fantastical legends and women who had brought them down with just the single barrel of their guns (years later, she'd come to interpret the lifetimes of their descendants across paper cards adorned with mystic symbolism); and in the brothel where she stayed, awaiting life's last few moments, they were revived in brief glimpses of her memories as she looked to the sky ahead, feeling strange and supernaturally perceptive in the room that she both lived and died in, thinking nothing but that it was only the natural course of life. So she knew with a psychic conviction. This was the end. But this was also the beginning.

Through the window, the faint smell of rain was just starting to gather. An omen, no doubt. A warning. It rarely rained in the small village where summers seemed to bleed into sweltering decades marked by the merciless strike of the sun. Ursula, newly sprung into life and armed with great truths that went beyond the realm of living, found herself alive among the cockroaches seeking solace between the cracks of the brothel's walls, and was overwhelmingly filled with the nostalgic urge to discard them. "Must these people leave everything to rot?" she asked to no one in particular, and Pilar cracked a small smile, but decided not to say anything.

Of course, it would be by some cruel twist of fate that the spirits had brought them back here again, joined together for a greater, unexplained purpose, left to pick at the pieces which everyone else had left behind. Ursula faced the other woman for the first time since she had woken up, marked with an unmistakable determination that once halted wars and had outlived the remainder of the Buendia family. "I never understood what my sons saw in you," she told her truthfully, and like that, got up to place her hand above Pilar's rocking chair. The winds began to blow stronger. "I know," Pilar said, lifting her frail hand to catch any semblance of the breeze, "but we've done a good job here, haven't we?" There was nothing now except for the storm, and then the town that would be ravaged by it. This was supposed to be their second opportunity on Earth, abandoned by their creators and left to their own devices, they found a paradise in each other.

Ursula scoffed. "You fool."

TORI PHELPS

YEARS AS MENTEE: 2

GRADE: Sophomore

BORN: New York, NY

LIVES: New York, NY

MENTEE'S ANECDOTE:

When I first met Laura, I felt shy and nervous. But after talking to her for a bit, she seemed as if she was one of my old friends. Her kind, warm smile mixed with her soft soothing voice made me feel at ease. Laura has helped me come up with amazing, weird stories, with prompts she has pulled from her writing workshops, her book, or just something she saw online that she thought I would like writing about. I like how we have similar taste in books and how I can feel comfortable enough to share my tastes in music.

LAURA GERINGER BASS

YEARS AS MENTOR: 5

OCCUPATION: Author

BORN: New York, NY

LIVES: New York, NY

PUBLICATIONS & RECOGNITIONS: *New York* magazine and Bank Street School of Education Best Book of the Year for *The Girl with More Than One Heart*; American Library Association Best Book of the Year for *Sign of the Qin*; American Library Association Notable Book of the Year for *A Three Hat Day*

MENTOR'S ANECDOTE:

I've had the pleasure of seeing Tori blossom as a writer this year. I'm happy we met last year when it was still okay to go to Alice's Tea Cup together for an after-school treat and an in-person meeting of minds. Now I see Tori in front of her virtual backdrop of the Golden Gate Bridge, picturesque but not as tasty. There are advantages to the wonders of Zoom though. How else would I have made the acquaintance of Tori's talkative dog, Chance? He had lots to say the day we discussed Hawthorne's *The Scarlet Letter*.

Growing Up

TORI PHELPS

This is the story of Alani, an abused girl who is taken away from her mother by Child Protective Services and finds herself in a "living hell." To get by, she lies.

I'm in this situation again. I lied. I ate all of the cereal. I felt stressed and binged. My mom was furious, so furious I got scared and a lie slipped out. Eventually, I told her the truth. She went crazy and said things she probably never meant to say. Or maybe she did.

Living with my mom is a living hell. She's not my real mom. I haven't seen my real mom for years. Okay, my not-real mom provides food, clothes, and an education. So I guess I can't complain, but honestly, the lie I told wasn't a big one. She didn't have to say the things she said.

I don't know why I lie. Crazy, right? My not-real mom thinks it's my past. She thinks it's because I want to do whatever I want whenever I want. Who knows? Maybe that's it, maybe it isn't.

My name is Alani Johnson. I'm fifteen years old, and I'm in the tenth grade at a preppy, predominately white school. Not my choice. If you had known me in first grade you'd say that I had a troubled past. My therapist tells me that the things that have happened to me have led to the way I am now.

I was not bad. I was never bad.

Let's start from the beginning. I was born at the Brooklyn Hospital Center on May 30, 2005. My real mom was there for all the big baby moments, but she was nowhere to be found when I started to get older. No, she did not disappear.

She did not leave me on the doorstep of some random house. She sent me to live with my grandmother. She stopped calling to check up on me. She stopped coming to visit me.

I was hurt.

When I was two, it was just me and my mom going everywhere and doing everything together. When I turned three, everything changed. My younger brother, David, was born. I was no longer the star of the show.

My brother was really heavy and he cried too much. He actually did take away all of the attention. I'm not being melodramatic.

I didn't like being a big sister. I helped change David's Pampers. I helped feed him. I slept with him so if he cried in the middle of the night I would be next to him to comfort him and give him his pacifier.

One day, I was playing with my dolls when my brother took one of them. "Hey! David, gimme back my doll!" I yelled and he started to cry. I tried to apologize. "Shhh! David, I'm sorry, you can have my doll. Just stop crying . . . please!" That was the first time I got into trouble. I had to stand in the corner until my punishment time was done. It was a long time.

When I was four years old, we moved to my grandma's house. I don't remember why. I asked: "Why did we have to leave Dad? Will we come back to see him?"

"We have to leave," my mother said. "He's dangerous. I don't know if we'll see him, Lani, just stop asking so many damn questions!" I could see why he might be dangerous. You will see it too, later when I tell you more.

I went to pre-K right across the street from grandma's house. After three years, I got accepted to an all-girls charter school a couple of blocks down from where we lived. Honestly, it was hard making friends there because I was known as the "throw-up" girl. Long story short, I ate some breakfast and threw it up. Yeah, not so fond of that memory.

Fast-forward to the middle of first grade when all hell broke loose, and when I say hell . . . I mean HELL. One day I got in trouble for something—I don't remember what. My mom lashed out and I had to go to school with a black eye. I thought my eye would hurt like crazy. It didn't, but I couldn't open it and when I did the lights were too bright. I couldn't see.

I had been hit before, but never this hard.

If my mom had only kept me home and called in and said I was sick, the school probably wouldn't have called Child Protective Services. I was shut up in a room with someone who kept asking me questions. I lied.

"So what happened to your eye? . . . Do you like your mom? . . . Who do you live with at home? Do you and your brother fight . . . ?"

I did what my mom told me to and said that I slipped in the bathtub and hit my head. That was new for me. For the first time, I had to lie to protect my mom. I don't remember how they made me spill, but they did, and I don't *want* to remember what happened after.

FLORENCIA MICAELA PINTO

YEARS AS MENTEE: 2

GRADE: Senior

BORN: Queens, NY

LIVES: Queens, NY

PUBLICATIONS & RECOGNITIONS:
Taking Our Place in History: The Girls Write Now 2020 Anthology

MENTEE'S ANECDOTE:

When I met Maddie for the first time I remember being afraid of her. I thought that we would not have common ground and this thing wouldn't work out. Looking back, I realize how wrong I was. Maddie is one of the few people with whom I have come to feel a genuine connection. Thanks to her, for the first time I tried different writing styles, from fictional stories to poems. But beyond improving my writing skills, I opened up about my experiences and received support during vulnerable times. Maddie, more than a mentor, has become a friend and confidant.

MADELINE McSHERRY

YEARS AS MENTOR: 2

OCCUPATION: Communications Manager, Amazon

BORN: New York, NY

LIVES: Kingston, NY

PUBLICATIONS & RECOGNITIONS:
Cambridge Review of International Affairs; The London School of Economics Review of Books; Foreign Policy Rising

MENTOR'S ANECDOTE:

Over the past two years, I've come to admire Micaela's bravery, willingness to explore, and desire to grow. Last year, after focusing on personal essays, she boldly ventured into fiction. So I wasn't surprised when she began this year by telling me, "I've never written poetry. I want to try." We started in a structured way, working through prompts, focusing on form and style. When that didn't stick, we tossed aside the exercises, and I asked her to focus on feeling, to write from heart to hand. As usual, her intuition and daring brought her exactly where she needed to go.

These Days

FLORENCIA MICAELA PINTO

This is a piece about how it feels to deal with the struggles that grief may bring. And about trying to move forward by taking one day at a time.

Some days are worse than others: I wake up, repeat the same routine, brush my hair, brush my teeth. I get stuck in time, carrying a heavy weight, repeating over and over in my head things I said, things I regret, things I wish I had said.

Some nights, the storm comes. Pain and fears creep in me again, I can't sleep. You keep coming back to my head: our long car rides, trips to the beach in summer, your awful but funny jokes, the way your eyes got lost in the room whenever you were thinking too much. And the inevitable happens: I cry and cry and ask myself what I did wrong, why didn't I try harder, what would've happened if it was me and not you. I'm drowning. I can't breathe, I muffle my cries. Pretend I'm fine.

But some days, I wake up with a smile and want to try again. I open the curtains, let the sunlight in. I dress, braid my hair, put on perfume, I look at myself in the mirror, wash and change my bedsheets. In the kitchen, I pour flour on the table, add water, knead the dough, add the butter. Let it sit, and knead again. Good days don't happen every day so I make them worth it.

On good days I like to think of my future, the endless possibilities. Moving away far from home and starting all over again: cutting my hair, buying a house, falling in love. These days you're on my mind, but in a good way. I hear your voice, telling me to keep going, follow my dreams. Like you did when you were here.

Days like this, I know things will get better, that eventually I will be fine.

ONNAH PLUMMER

YEARS AS MENTEE: 1

GRADE: Freshman

BORN: Newark, NJ

LIVES: New York, NY

MENTEE'S ANECDOTE:

Ashley has become someone who I can trust and rely on. I can also have a lot of fun with her. Since we've met, we found a lot in common with each other. We both love sports, talking about mental health, food, and even podcasting. I learned so much about her through the podcast we did on athletes' mental health. Even though I've never met Ashley in person, through the screen I can tell how great of a person she is. Hopefully I can eventually meet her in person so we can continue growing our relationship!

ASHLEY LOPEZ

YEARS AS MENTOR: 1

OCCUPATION: Literary Agent

BORN: Lafayette, LA

LIVES: Brooklyn, NY

MENTOR'S ANECDOTE:

Onnah impresses me every time we meet. As a freshman in high school, she is already so self-possessed—in touch with who she is and what she wants in a way that comes across as quiet confidence. She's never afraid to ask questions and is always striving to be her best self, whether it's expanding her vocabulary or perfecting a mac 'n' cheese recipe. She is planning for a career as an athletic trainer, and her sports knowledge combined with her warmth make this an apt career choice for her. Forever cool, calm, and collected, Onnah has been an absolute joy to get to know!

Back from Aruba

ONNAH PLUMMER

"Back from Aruba" is about how I began to encounter parts of being a teenager on this trip I took with my nephews Andrew and Jack.

I've been going to Aruba every summer for the last twelve years. When I was on the island, I never wanted to make friends, and when I did want to, I didn't know how. I sat in the hotel room and watched TV all day, or sat on the beach and stared at the water. There were games like Ping-Pong, chess, beach soccer—so much to do but nobody to do it with. There were some stores and gift shops that I could go to, but I didn't want to go by myself. But last year, we brought my two nephews on vacation with us. Andrew is thirteen and Jack is twelve, and I am very close with them even though we don't get to see each other very often. Our time together usually centers on birthdays and holidays, so I was excited for this trip with them.

When we got to Aruba, Andrew and Jack didn't want to sit in the room with the TV. They wanted to go outside, which forced me to hang out outside instead of in the hotel room. At first, it was awkward because I've never had a lot of social interaction with people at the resort before, but soon I had so many amazing new friends. In a two-week span, I was comfortable going up to people and introducing myself, and doing random things in public like cartwheels in the lobby and diving into the ocean. I was stepping out of my comfort zone because of the people I met who encouraged me to be myself.

At this resort in Aruba, people were divided into three groups: families with their kids, couples young and old, and the teenagers. Before this summer, I felt stuck with the family group. I was always with my family, following them around the resort. I felt like a pretzel with no salt—boring. But now I was part of the teenage group. There were about fifteen of us hanging out at the pool and bar. At the bar, anyone could sit for as long as they wanted to. There were comfy, tall chairs and we would sit there for hours, talking to one another or the bartenders, who made us nonalcoholic strawberry daiquiris and chocolate mudslides (which were basically chocolate milkshakes). It was almost impossible to get a seat at the bar, and when we couldn't get there quickly enough we went to the pool, where we would play games until we had to meet our families for dinner. A lot of the games involved rating each other and ranking people from least attractive to most attractive, the kind of talk teenagers are into these days. We all knew it was just for fun and we weren't serious about anything. A year ago, I wouldn't even be in a situation to joke like this because I would have been too scared to say the wrong thing.

My nephews were a big reason I changed on this trip. When I'm around them, I feel comfortable being me. Sometimes I feel like I have to be a different person, because there's nobody I live with who likes the same things I do. It can feel like I have to be like the rest of my family in order to "fit in." But my nephews like the things I like. They play and understand sports like me, and they have the same sense of humor as me. When I'm with them, I come out of my shell. And when I'm being my authentic self is when I make some of my best memories.

In Aruba, I felt so free, more like the teenager I imagined I would become when I was younger. Even though I'm in New York and can't have as much freedom here, because it's a city where the pools are locked away and the bars are for adults only, I still feel a kind of freedom. It feels like the beginning of something new. Like I am transitioning from childhood to adulthood.

People in Aruba have a saying: "Nobody knows you, nobody cares!" Those words make me feel like I can do anything.

RIZOUANA PROME

YEARS AS MENTEE: 1

GRADE: Junior

BORN: Sylhet, Bangladesh

LIVES: Queens, NY

MENTEE'S ANECDOTE:

Hanna is an expert at giving things a purpose. Most of the time when I share my poems or paintings with her, they do not hold any deep meanings. Usually, they are just things I did because of boredom. But when I show it to her, she gets so excited to interpret the different meanings of my work. They are usually ideas that I would not usually think about or come across. This is so special to me because as she tries to figure out the meaning of my work, it sparks so much inspiration.

HANNA KOZLOWSKA

YEARS AS MENTOR: 1

OCCUPATION: Reporter

BORN: Brooklyn, NY

LIVES: Brooklyn, NY

PUBLICATIONS & RECOGNITIONS: *Quartz, The Guardian, The Texas Tribune, One Zero, Politico Europe, The New York Times, Foreign Policy*

MENTOR'S ANECDOTE:

"Unknown Identity" was my favorite poem of Rizzy's—and her least favorite! I think looking at it through my eyes made her see it in a different light. We complement each other in that way. Another example is when Rizzy noticed something about my narrative style that I never caught myself, despite writing professionally for nearly a decade. We jibe so well together (although I don't think we'll agree on who's the best Rory Gilmore boyfriend!).

Unknown Identity

RIZOUANA PROME

Teenagers oftentimes don't know themselves and are not well aware of their identity. This is a poem where I am exploring the different sides of my identity.

"What kind of person are you?"
A question I encounter as if it is
Rain during the rainy season
Too often to be avoided

Sometimes
I am a bear
Destined to be a loner
Avoiding crowds
Addicted to my own company
Sometimes
I am an ant
Surrounded by creatures
With the same goal
Motivated to move forward

Sometimes
I am an angry lion
Quick to make a move
Out hunting for opportunities
Sometimes

I am a sloth
Unbothered and careless
Known for my slow speed

Sometimes
I am a cat
Calm and friendly
Known for comforting people
Sometimes
I am a T. rex
Heartless and selfish
Hurting other organisms to fulfill my needs
Unconcerned about their feelings

Who am I?
Avoiding this question
I am rather invested in
Which side of me is more acceptable?

Wanting to be liked by others
Always wondering
Which side makes me more approachable?
More desirable?

ASHLEY QUIAH

YEARS AS MENTEE: 1

GRADE: Senior

BORN: Queens, NY

LIVES: Queens, NY

MENTEE'S ANECDOTE:

Katie is an inspiration to me every day. She motivates me and always pushes me to do my best. In times when I'm not sure where to go, not only with my writing, but with life in general, she always guides me to the next step. I admire her kindness and patience, her dedication to me and my writing. I'm so glad to have someone so caring and supportive as my mentor.

KATIE ZABORSKY

YEARS AS MENTOR: 1

OCCUPATION: Program and Communications Administrator

BORN: Kiev, Ukraine

LIVES: Brooklyn, NY

MENTOR'S ANECDOTE:

I'm not exaggerating when I say that working with Ashley has been one of the things I look forward to most as we all contend with the isolation and fatigue of the pandemic. Her commitment to personal and creative growth is inspiring—with each session, I see her transforming into a more confident writer, someone who is willing to be vulnerable and take risks. Ashley is not only a talented writer, but a brave one, and I'm so happy to be part of her journey.

What I Wish You Knew

ASHLEY QUIAH

In this personal essay, I reveal the difficulty I undergo when opening up to someone, but also emphasize the hopeful outlook I have in my journey of growth.

I wish you knew about my soft, pillowy core. I wish you knew that my RBF is a shell that protects the delicate parts of my soul. That my shut mouth and tendency to end a conversation as quickly as possible are all illusions presented by the outermost layer of me. That when you take the time to peel away the layers, I promise to reveal myself as a confident, loving, and caring human. That the mother in me makes sure you don't get hurt or completely trip over the things you're stumbling on. That when I'm nervous, vomit crawls up my throat to be the alarm that tells me I am incapable of behaving normally. That I get tangled in my words like they're vines in the quicksand below me. I wish you knew how carefully I observe and how badly I want to communicate, but fear gets in the way. I wish you knew that I was pushing past its brick wall, attempting to climb over or crawl through a hole, just to join in. I wish you knew the weight I lug on my back as I creep out of my man-made cave just to talk to you. That I can run back in quicker than I came out. It hurts to know that instead of sharing how proud I am of who I've become, I remain enclosed in a glass box that presents distortions of what's on the other side. I stare at people with their judgmental faces, their laughs at how pathetic the words coming out of my mouth are. When really, on the other side of the fogged-up glass are just hallucinations. Figments of my imagination that I have conjured up because I worry about the irrationality of the world. But I wish they knew that they have no power over me. That I can blow away the smoke from behind the glass and step out as my truest self. The only things that matter are the people who support me. And I wish you knew how much I appreciate those who support me. I wish you knew more about the things that spark my soul. The things that make my pillowy core cushiony soft. Even though they're buried deep within me, the small moments, the tiny things that make my wings flutter, are what I wish you knew more about. Getting my makeup just right, finding a song that synchronizes with the daydream I'm concocting in my head, the smell of a new book. The strum of my guitar, the scream-inducing jumpscare in a horror movie, the tears that come from laughing too hard. Holding a stone-cold front is meant to preserve my soft soul for those who deserve to see it. My inner happiness, reserved like a seat at a blissful bistro. I wish you knew about the efforts I make to not fall apart, because I know I am capable of growing, even if it seems like I don't believe that about myself. I wish you knew that I am more than just the words you're reading on this paper. But, most important, I wish you knew that while I'm running a million-mile marathon in my head to have one conversation with you, I am also building resilience. That while I am fighting battles in my mind with everything that scares me, I am also getting stronger every second. And I wish you knew that one day, you'll get to see who I really am.

LAMIA RAHMAN

YEARS AS MENTEE: 1

GRADE: Senior

BORN: Queens, NY

LIVES: Queens, NY

MENTEE'S ANECDOTE:

Working alongside Lipi has been an absolute delight. Whenever there's trouble or a burden, she's always so supportive and kind. Conversations with her are always so insightful and relatable, and I find that we can talk about anything. Her drive and authenticity make her an astounding writer and mentor. Learning and writing with her is always such an enriching experience, and I'm so glad to have met her.

LIPI RAGHUNATHAN

YEARS AS MENTOR: 1

OCCUPATION: Marketing Associate

BORN: New York, NY

LIVES: New York NY

MENTOR'S ANECDOTE:

Having Lamia as my mentee has been such a fun experience! We have worked on college admission and creative work, such as podcasts and her poetry anthology. She always comes to our meetings prepared and with very impressive work and research having been done beforehand. It is so fun to talk about topics that interest both of us during our podcast and to hear such a fascinating perspective while learning new things!

things i couldn't tell you: pieces from an incomplete love story

LAMIA RAHMAN

A series of poems offers a small window into a passionate and debilitating relationship, of which our narrator discloses the intricacies and afflictions of the love she endured.

i. when i loved you

i do and say all of the wrong things
i am a klutz, an idiot
i am fumbly with my words
but so were you
the only difference is
i like the things *you* say

-

oh, how i fantasize about our meeting
when we do. where we do.
i hope it's somewhere nice
and i was only a bit older, and you *were* younger
and there wasn't miles and years and things out of our control
separating us
i can only tell my love through these *hidden* words
and i know you despise poems
but would you give mine a chance?

it doesn't matter, these words are too *sacred* and real to say
and my mouth might get me in *trouble*
so i'll keep it here, *unread*
but what's the point when it's as *clear* as day

one day
i'll be able to know the warmth of your skin
the curves of your smile
the *blue* in your eyes
and taste of your mouth

it's *wildly inappropriate*
but you're mine in my head

and that's all *i* choose to handle right now
these words are *brave* enough.

one day
i'll be there
and you'll be here
and we will be everywhere, but not together

maybe my words will resurface
by then, i'll be *drunk* enough on my loopiness to do so

ii. when you were mine

can it be 3am forever? right here and now
can we stay frozen in time, just *you* and i
when the world is half asleep
and our eyes, half *closed*
our lips, swollen and *puckered*
our bodies, flushed

can we stay like this forever?
with our fingers intertwined *and* our souls *locked* in
where i can feel the beating of *your* nervous *heart*
and i can only answer with the trepid rhythm of my own
where our breaths contain unspoken truths
that we love each other
here and now
can it be 3am for all of our lives together?

iii. when we broke apart

i saw a person today
i wanted to collapse, as if gravity was rebelling against me
but i stood there, sat there, did whatever i could to stay still
as i saw your cheshire smile
delightful and goofy, as if laughter lived within your muscles.
when they left, i was scared i'll never see *you again*
but i see you everywhere now
and my brain is no longer doing me any favors

iv. when i was yours

you *have* left me
gasping for air
when i drowned with your silence
and *you* teased me like i was a foolish cat
red light bouncing *every*where, like your words at every nerve in
my brain
and then i'd hear them ringing in my ears, see them tattooed
underneath my eyelids
and soon, bleeding through my wounds
and then i feel your breath and my eyes flutter and my hair stands
and then i remember the red light, and i *wondered* where it was
until i realize you shone it right at me, scoring a hole right through me

instead *of* ripping into my chest and taking my heart out,
leaving it defenseless and me lifeless
you kept your hand in, and squeezed until it burst
your hand bloody and me left with *the damage*
there is no longer a heart to be seen
you made sure of it

-

i once *thought* bitterness was the absence of taste
to never experience the sweetness of honey and saltiness of cheese
an absolute tragedy
but really, it's just an unwelcome and nasty sharpness
that erases the beauty of mint and vanilla on your tongue

i once believed bitterness was the absence of goodwill and kindness
but it is not just that. it's the spite and rage that lived in your bone and
blood
humanity never lived there, you've never known of it
i *apologize* for being so crass
but *i'm afraid* i don't know how else to talk to you
i think i was meant to meet *you*
so i *wouldn't* ever dare *be curious* of what i'm without

v. when i began to heal

i will tell you a story
of when *i found* myself the most beautiful
i was at my lowest, having been strung out of tears
my voice strained and gone, *my body* weak and fatigued
my hair drenched with tears or sweat or drool
my clothes rumpled

when i finally composed *myself,*
i looked at the mirror and the person i see
felt almost uninvited but not unwelcome
she was a maniacal joke
she didn't look vulnerable or fragile
even with her soft lips
and although she had frazzled hair and bruised cheeks
with her glossed over reddened eyes
she was resilient
this isn't a travesty and i refuse to lie to you.
with sincerity,
it felt like the universe gave me a present
"here, you went through the worst of it
you survived.
see how luminous you are, having fought all of that
you got this."
i wish i could *see* this particular *beauty* less, but my comfort lies in the
most arbitrary entities

CHELSEA RJ

YEARS AS MENTEE: 1

GRADE: Junior

BORN: New York, NY

LIVES: Bronx, NY

MENTEE'S ANECDOTE:

When I first met Olivia, I thought she was really great. I remember how nervous I was to meet her, but she really helped soothe my nerves. I definitely learned a lot from her, especially about my grammar and my organizing skills. This is our first time being in Girls Write Now, but she has been doing an amazing job. Hands down, she has to be one of the best mentors I have had. I learned so much from her, and I'm excited to see what is in store for us.

OLIVIA ROCKEMAN

YEARS AS MENTOR: 1

OCCUPATION: Journalist

BORN: San Diego, CA

LIVES: New York, NY

MENTOR'S ANECDOTE:

When I first met Chelsea in October, she said one of her goals at Girls Write Now was to become a better writer this year. But she already is a fantastic writer! What she's really accomplished so far has been a greater confidence in her skills—I'm so excited for her to share her work with the world and I know she has a bright future.

The lies he lives

CHELSEA RJ

*In a world where showing sadness is seen as a weakness, we are often
forced to conceal it. We hide the pain behind the smiles, but what
happens when somebody watches us do so?*

I know this guy,
Who makes Angels sing.

He shines so brightly,
That he almost looks like a king.

His laugh, which lights up the sky,
Makes you deny what's really inside.

While I can't help but admire,
This guy is nothing but a liar.

He wears a mask to hide what's inside,
For he is lost within his foolish pride.

He smiles when he is sad.
He laughs when he lies,
And he sings when he is slowly dying inside.

I know this guy
Who makes Angels cry.

His sadness is at its all-time high.

He sits on his throne, all alone
with subjects and treasures,
but a hollowness in his bones

He needs help but does not want it.
For his pride, doesn't let him admit
That he doesn't have to conceal what he truly feels.

I know this guy
Who makes Angels sing,

His shine is slowly fading.

While I love him, this guy is a fraud.
Oh, I wish he knew it was okay to let his crown fall.

JAYA RAO-HEREL

YEARS AS MENTEE: 2

GRADE: Junior

BORN: Brooklyn, NY

LIVES: Brooklyn, NY

PUBLICATIONS & RECOGNITIONS:
Scholastic Art & Writing Awards:
Honorable Mention

MENTEE'S ANECDOTE:

Tuesday afternoons at three are for laughter, brainstorming, music-making, and drafts. Each week, during our pair meetings, Amanda's encouraging and helpful nature never fails to motivate me to tour new writing styles and topics. Our collective enthusiasm for music and writing brings us on a wonderful journey each week, and the past two years working with Amanda have led me to a collection of growth, gratification, and the utmost gratitude from myself to Amanda.

AMANDA EKERY

YEARS AS MENTOR: 2

OCCUPATION: Musician

BORN: El Paso, TX

LIVES: Brooklyn, NY

PUBLICATIONS & RECOGNITIONS:
Jerome Hill Foundation Artist
Fellow; Women in Music
Leadership Routledge Companion

MENTOR'S ANECDOTE:

What a year it has been, and I'm thankful that Jaya was a part of it! Each time we met was an experiment, trying new ideas, approaching a story in an offbeat way, and learning together. She created intricate, thoughtful pieces that were true to her personal style and exciting to see materialize digitally. This was our second year as mentee/mentor, and I'm continually inspired by Jaya's curiosity and willingness to dive into uncharted waters.

Vacant Heavy

JAYA RAO-HEREL

A trip into a mind, swirling with the chaos of regret and distraction of calm.

Regret is a steady tap on my mind
A solid block of all things entwined

Blinded as sun seeps beneath beds of flowers
Blotting visions, staining walks; my shadow over every hour

Regret is the steam that sticks to bathroom mirrors
Diffuses off my tongue in a rapid sea of vapors

Small swirls of dragonflies skim over the air
Reflections dance in warm hushed lakes as foxes trot with care

Regret is falling though pools of elation
Jumping to passion that later falls to contemplation

Outside a window; the soft patter of snow
Steam drifts into air lit by the sun's soft glow

But I'm still brought back to regret:
The constant thought of our secret journal
Long since blacked out but forever eternal

Sleepy stars hang in the glow of night
A cool soft breeze wiping out light

Heavy eyes shut under the warmth of thick quilts
As the moon rises and the sun wilts

Regret is what blooms into a field of release
When its weight leaves your mind; met transient ease

A hammock rocks with gentle sways
A pendulum swings and carries the weight away

But the vacant heavy still remains
It's the ray of regret that will never decay

ANNE RHEE

YEARS AS MENTEE: 2

GRADE: Senior

BORN: Seattle, WA

LIVES: Queens, NY

MENTEE'S ANECDOTE:

Although we've had to sacrifice trips to museums and parks for weekly Google Meets, I always look forward to talking to Sunny: whether it be about politics of the body, Asian American identity, Netflix show recommendations, Russian literature, or just catching up on life. She's been more than a mentor: She's also been a friend, someone whose advice on writing is something I always seek and someone who's been incredibly willing to help me with anything, ever. I cannot wait to see her back in person, so we can continue to always discuss, collaborate, and think about what it means to write.

SUNNY LEE

YEARS AS MENTOR: 2

OCCUPATION: Freelance Copy Editor

BORN: Ulsan, South Korea

LIVES: Brooklyn, NY

MENTOR'S ANECDOTE:

Anne has grown into a tremendous writer and thinker in the two years that I have known her. The shy junior I first met is now a confident senior who accepts writing prompts and challenges with confidence. She has not only branched out of poetry into short prose and autofiction, but also ventured toward hybrid forms with great gusto. Her experimental side has inspired me to take more formal risks in my own writing, while her dexterous command of language has me reeling to write better.

She and the Remnants of Plants

ANNE RHEE

Exploring themes of mental illness specifically within the Asian American immigrant community and isolation, "She and the Remnants of Plants" centers on a teenage girl's relationship to plants and death.

The bulb of the green onion sprouted, slowly pushing its pale apple-green leaves out of the soil into the seven-year-old's small fleshy hands.

Hands. She was taught to work with them from a young age. Plants had always surrounded her existence and permeated her memories. The Korean community had always been strangely obsessed with community gardens, pressed flowers in the Sunday Bibles. Memories swirling of her mother buying ten-dollar orchids wrapped in pink cellophane that would die weeks later, her grandparents' terrace in Korea encircled with huge swamps of plants that would caress the laundry with their far-reaching leaves. The latter never seemed to die—they always stayed the same, healthy and swollen with life.

To grow plants successfully, one must water them three times a week. She watched as the pale brown soil would turn dark with the moisture that her father told her was necessary for the plants to live; yet the labor that required her hands was not hard labor, but required extreme delicacy. She named her plants, slowly becoming engrossed with the slow pace at which they grew, until one day, as she had marked on her calendar as one of the watering days, she came upon her plants beginning to shrivel, their once healthy veins crinkled like paper origami.

"Why do plants die, Dad?"

"Because they grow, and as they grow, they also age. Aging is what causes them to eventually die—the plants will soon become too withered to support their own bodies."

After this one conversation with her father, Anne had become worried about what she, too, would have to go through by aging. She had read through books and texts about Alzheimer's and ALS, different diseases that withered away people's bodies until their brains no longer retained their perfect shape and function. It was out of this childhood fear that grew an obsession that would eventually consume her life.

After the orchid died, she began to plot out decisions systematically. After school she'd sit in her bedroom, surrounded by notepads, all of the same size and color because she needed uniformity. Using one of her pens, each with a thickness of 0.38 inches and sharp needle-point tip as the box declared it to have, she would think and scribble down each part of her decision.

Mental-mapping, her brother would laughingly tease her, stressing the first word because in his eyes, she was *mental*—who else would go to such lengths to simply make a decision? Her parents would also laugh— they surely believed that the compulsive obsession with organization was just a phase. Mental health was never taken seriously in the Asian community, after all.

On the day of the annual yard sale, Anne had reached her breaking point—her passion for growing plants had been subsumed by her greater, obsessive tendencies.

One of her friends, Ruby, noticed the box of books first. The last time she had visited Anne, they lay on her desk, a thin veil of dust coating the covers; now they were laying in a cardboard box, mostly dust-free. She saw Anne walking up the stairs to her porch.

"Anne, are you sure about selling these?"

Anne turned around. There wasn't a flicker of doubt, but Ruby noticed something else. She seemed dazed, almost as if she hadn't been outside in a few months.

"I don't really have a use for them anymore. Five dollars per book."

Ruby, alarmed, and also a little worried, decided to ask Anne's parents what was happening. But upon being asked, Anne's mother just shrugged. "It's just a phase—no need to worry. I'm sure she's developing new interests that are replacing plants and botany."

Her family had already gotten used to her lost passion for plants and its replacement: her obsessive planning. Soon after, her friends also became numb to Anne's inaction. Little by little, they began to move on with their own lives, leaving Anne to her own devices. Her parents, who had considered bringing her to countless therapists in fear and hope that they would be able to diagnose some sort of curable problem that had a solution, ended up choosing to prioritize themselves with other matters and tasks.

No one bothered to ask Anne why she truly had become so obsessed with staying in this bubble of her own thoughts, interacting with people less and less, and refusing to be influenced by anyone. And the truth was, Anne would sometimes ask herself that question too. The answers continued to remain unclear, confusing, shrouded in mystery. But what she did remember was what her father told her after that fateful day of her plant's death:

"But don't forget—even if plants die, their remains become the soil upon which a new garden will bloom."

ALICE ROSENBERG

YEARS AS MENTEE: 1

GRADE: Freshman

BORN: New York, NY

LIVES: New York, NY

MENTEE'S ANECDOTE:

Kendyl is a wonderful mentor and we have agreed on pretty much every-thing so far. We found out very soon into our sessions that we have read the same book, at the same time, multiple times. So, if that doesn't convince you, I don't know what will. I can't wait to see all the things we will write together in the future.

KENDYL KEARLY

YEARS AS MENTOR: 1

OCCUPATION: Editor at StarChefs

BORN: Jacksonville, FL

LIVES: Brooklyn, NY

PUBLICATIONS & RECOGNITIONS:
San Francisco, Capitol File,
Manhattan

MENTOR'S ANECDOTE:

In our weeks spending time together, Alice impressed me so many times with her creativity, skill, and outgoingness. Her very first poem was lovely, and she knows so much about books, art, animation, and anything she de-cides to jump into. I wish that at her age (or my current age!) I had more of her willingness to put her hand up to ask a question, volunteer for some-thing new, or show off her talent among strangers.

Ophelia

ALICE ROSENBERG

A poem about Ophelia and the thoughts running through her mind.

my brain is
so loud
it is an earth-shattering mind-encompassing cacophony of heartbreak
where the screams and sobs and voices never stop
and I just want this orchestra of insanity to be over

so I choose the pond by the tree that makes shadows on the ground in
    the shape of leaves
when I lie in the water the branches from cracks in the sky that block
    out the sun
the moss on the rocks are pillows where I can rest my head
and the forget-me-nots that litter the shore grow towards the light
they remind me of our childhood

our bare feet on the cold stone floor
the keyhole windows that used to be so far out of reach
our love a masterpiece sealed by acrylics and paintbrushes
I could even see the pond from your bed at night
when the moon was high and the fireflies shone brighter than the stars
sometimes
if I listened hard enough
I could hear the water ripple when a leaf fell

and then there were ghosts
and your promises and love poems were as fleeting as the dead you
    chased
I can't believe I ever trusted you
'til death do us part
the water fills my lungs
my breath is stolen
my clothes billow around my outstretched arms
they weigh me down

I open my eyes while the shadows obscure the branches and the cold
    streams through my veins and I just want to see you again and it's
    taking so long but then I realize—
it's so very quiet when you're dead.

MAHJAZEE RUIZ

YEARS AS MENTEE: 1

GRADE: Senior

BORN: New York, NY

LIVES: Staten Island, NY

MENTEE'S ANECDOTE:

Jaanelle is an exceptional mentor. She always finds ways to make our time together lively and interactive and we never have a dull moment. Jaanelle has been guiding me through my writing, including my first poetry book. She has provided me with the resources to make sure I can do it, like letting me borrow her paid Canva account to access everything. We have bonded and come up with so many ideas. She is hard working, funny, bubbly, and overall an amazing person to be around. I feel inspired by her and I'm continuing to work on my art and to perfect it—as well as letting it flow as my work becomes the most authentic version of myself. I believe we have grown so much since we first met on Zoom. In this digital age, many things are fleeting and it is hard to make long-lasting connections with people, but I have made a strong one with Jaanelle and I am looking forward to keeping it for a long time.

JAANELLE YEE

YEARS AS MENTOR: 1

OCCUPATION: Film Writer-Director

BORN: Miami, FL

LIVES: New York, NY

MENTOR'S ANECDOTE:

We've had a great time at our weekly creative brainstorms. Sometimes MJ just plays songs in progress or reads her poetry for me while I sit back and clap after each song. Sometimes we write stories together with both of us contributing lines. Other times, we design together in Canva. It's great to have someone to consistently share our creative thoughts with and instantly jump off into new ideas.

The King of Hearts

MAHJAZEE RUIZ

"The King of Hearts" is random from a deck of cards where truly the title is meaningless but the poem somehow makes it seem relevant.

The depth
Of my breath
The throbbing
Of my head
To think of a problem
One once said
Heat through my body
A tightly closed mind
Calmness and peace
Too difficult to find
A shaking leg
A pounding heart
Racing fingers
Can't stop
Just start
From white
To purple
From purple
To blue
Current situations

I cannot undo
Pressure, a boulder
Thoughts, a drum
A challenge, a climb
A war I've won.

MARIA ISABELA RUIZ

YEARS AS MENTEE: 1

GRADE: Sophomore

BORN: Bogotá, Colombia

LIVES: Queens, NY

MENTEE'S ANECDOTE:

Aside from being a mentor, Amy is a friend and a wonderful author, writer, and artist. Despite being able to see her only on a screen, she made me feel comfortable. She listened and understood. I genuinely enjoyed signing on to Zoom every Friday, knowing we always had something to talk about. She pointed out strengths in my writing that I would never have noticed before. Amy has also been a great help in my academic writing and has made me love and appreciate writing more, even if it is just a hobby.

AMY ZHANG

YEARS AS MENTOR: 1

OCCUPATION: Author

BORN: Jinan, China

LIVES: Brooklyn, NY

MENTOR'S ANECDOTE:

I've really loved watching Maria grow more comfortable expressing herself in writing this past semester. Given how tumultuous the news cycle was in the first few months we were working together, we both found comfort in a more informal and honest approach to writing. Maria mentioned to me that she liked jotting down stream-of-conscious notes in her phone—when she showed them to me, I was really impressed by the tenderness and openness with which she was able to express herself. Maria has this incredibly generous optimism for people, and I find myself continually inspired by her.

It Wasn't Your Fault

MARIA ISABELA RUIZ

To contemplation and betrayal.

"It wasn't your fault."

I lay still. Staring off into space because I can't even collect my thoughts. I don't know what to say, think, or feel. I'm not sure if I should feel guilty. Can I be sad? I have a reason to feel this way. Should I not get mad? I can't help but feel responsible. Why couldn't you just be a little less threatening? Maybe things would've been different.

"No. It isn't your fault."

I go back and forth, as if one side of my brain was a different person, someone speaking to me over my shoulder.

"This is just my consciousness, my inner voice."

My body sinks into my bed while my mind sinks deeper and deeper into a pool of knotted thoughts, and slowly loses awareness. It feels like I'm falling down a never-ending dark tunnel.

Falling, falling, falling.

My mind is a mess. It's nothing but a scribble of pen marks on paper. Just never-ending circles, one on top of another, until it fills up and everything turns black.

LILLY SABELLA

YEARS AS MENTEE: 2

GRADE: Senior

BORN: Queens, NY

LIVES: Queens, NY

PUBLICATIONS & RECOGNITIONS:
Scholastic Art & Writing Awards:
Gold Keys; American Voices
Nominee

MENTEE'S ANECDOTE:

Toni is my confidante, in more ways than one. In addition to trusting her with my writing, something that makes me feel vulnerable, I trust in being able to tell her about my life. As an editor at her workplace, Toni has taught me how to approach and accept criticism, and because of her, my writing has improved drastically. Toni helps me process my struggles as a writer, from comparing my work to others' to feelings of inadequacy. I'm a better person and writer because of her.

TONI BRANNAGAN

YEARS AS MENTOR: 2

OCCUPATION: Content Manager

BORN: New York, NY

LIVES: Queens, NY

PUBLICATIONS & RECOGNITIONS:
The Vagina Book: An Owner's Manual for Taking Care of Your Down There

MENTOR'S ANECDOTE:

This is my second year being paired with Lilly, and while I'm so proud that she's graduating and moving on to college, I'm going to miss reading her poetry every week so much. We didn't get to meet in coffee shops this year, but I'm so proud of how Lilly persevered through such a stressful time, juggling school, work, college applications, and life in general. 2020 wasn't easy for anyone, but talking to Lilly every week about writing (. . . and TikTok and Harry Styles) was a highlight of mine.

Forever Queens / The End of the N

LILLY SABELLA AND TONI BRANNAGAN

We wrote two poems about our relationship to our residing borough, Queens. (Lilly is a lifelong native and Toni moved to Astoria five years ago.)

Forever Queens

LILLY SABELLA

I saw glimmers of God in the
  streetlight
lamps that shined through the cracks
of my fingers
as I covered my eyes from the New
  York City night
exhausted in yet another $8 Uber ride
  from Roosevelt to home
the fast lights dragged my heart to
  exit 33
as I bloomed beneath my forever,
my Queens.

I couldn't write fast enough to fill the
  train rides
my legs numbed on the E
where I memorized poems to recite in
  French class
my eyes closed on the 7

The End of the N

TONI BRANNAGAN

the first apartment is what they mean
  when they say "shoebox"
a Craigslist listing with no photos
ceiling-high windows frame the
  lofted tracks.
I learn to let the subway lull me to
  sleep at night
I race it to the station most mornings
and lose most mornings
taking too long to climb up to the
  platform
where the wind blows fierce through
  the tunnel
the city sounds from below echo
  above.

Living at the end of the N means
you always get the seat you want in
  the morning

always on the way to work and back
Hunters Point and sweeping sunsets
printed on the inside of my eyelids
as I soared above food trucks and
    groups of teenagers
I memorized boots and heels and the
    toes of strangers
our sides pressed together
each passenger connected through a
    chain of thighs touching and arms
    rubbing
swaying to the beat of the closing
    doors
and endless delays.

There were buses and buses
because my friends live deep
Buses because I do too
because this place is so big and
    broad
you can sink in it
the subway can't reach it all
Buses I begged for free rides on
and waited in the rain for
some passengers obeying the
    unspoken rule of law
in the land of blue chairs and
yellow wires,
some not.
and as I looked in my seat
(farthest in the back, last one on the
    right)
around at the mothers wearing
Paw Patrol backpacks

tucked in the corner of the car
where no one asks you what you're
    reading
if you keep your head down.

On Saturdays I write on barstools
where they know how I take my
    coffee
and what time I switch to wine.
When the lights dim low
I nod along while other locals
    grumble,
Train was stuck at Queensboro for
    half an hour today.
Did you hear about that Target
    moving in?
Maybe in five more years
I'll weigh in, too.

I'm constantly lost in Queens
23rd Ave or 23rd Road or 23rd
    Drive
the best I can do
is estimate
above or below Ditmars
towards the park
down by Steinway
by this friend or that friend's
    apartment.

One day I walk the wrong way out
    of a bar
a sun and trio of stars on a yellow
    awning catch my eye

and their children, so small, their feet
    not yet touching the ground
all I could think was that everyone
    seemed so tired
as we rode together, without the
    luxury of cars to take us on
    our own.
all the days spent here,
together,
blurring into something that
    mattered.

I've run all throughout Queens
    searching for my name
from Jamaica to Jackson Heights
Astoria to Corona
until the borough became a part of me,
where I spent hours walking under
    the El
feeling everyone was so alive
eating outside of food trucks and
    blasting music in languages I
    couldn't understand
buying iced teas from the bodega
    men and petting deli cats
my whole life spent here
a part of me, with pride

and I step into a modest storefront
    filled with *titas*
who have my mother's tongue.
I've never seen a Filipino grocery
    store before
and there was one right here
this whole time
and when I Google it later
because I was worried I'd forget the
    cross streets
there are more.

On my way to the park I visit our
    elderly neighbor, Maya
petting her nose through the garden
    gate
(Maya is a Siberian husky.)
Then I stand on our side of the East
    River
down the hill where the concrete
    slopes into green
until the sun ducks behind the Hell
    Gate
replaced by Manhattan's glow
I turn and walk in a straight line
    home.

KASSIDY SAMUEL-ANCRUM

YEARS AS MENTEE: 1

GRADE: Sophomore

BORN: Brooklyn, NY

LIVES: New York, NY

MENTEE'S ANECDOTE:

The writing relationship between Shanille and I is one that works well. Adding to each other's thoughts, and being able to share ideas about formatting and topics is something hard to find between mentees and mentors, but in this duo nothing is impossible. As we have spent more time working together, I feel like the both of us have grown to adapt to each other's writing style. Even though our favorite genres are different, it is awesome having a mentor that I feel connected to and someone who is helping me improve as a writer.

SHANILLE MARTIN

YEARS AS MENTOR: 1

OCCUPATION: Editor, Technician

BORN: Kingston, Jamaica

LIVES: Brooklyn, NY

PUBLICATIONS & RECOGNITIONS:
"The Beast," *Nymphs Magazine*;
"Love Poems," *Stuck in Notes*;
"Birmingham's Little Angels,"
Gandy Dancer

MENTOR'S ANECDOTE:

I am so honored to have Kassidy as my mentee for my first year serving as a mentor. I remember being a mentee myself and can recall how large an impact my mentor Amanda had on me; I can only hope to help Kassidy in the same way. Kassidy is a brilliant writer, who grows more and more each week that we meet. When we first began, Kassidy was interested only in journaling and nonfiction, but now she has a portfolio of poems and short stories that she is truly proud of. I can't wait to witness the rest of her journey.

To the only girl that understands

KASSIDY SAMUEL-ANCRUM

This poem is a love letter to myself.

Dear Kass,

This letter is to the girl I love. The person I love a lot but never have to say out loud. Kass, I love it when you smile. A smile that gleams when I look back in the mirror. Do you remember the time when you were tight-roping? You were so nervous. I felt that tension release into joy on your face in the form of a playful grin. My heart lights up every time I look at that truly joyful girl.

I appreciate it when you are *you*. When Kass doesn't let anyone alter her vibe. Like that time at the school dance where you looked so beautiful. Dressed up in a cyan ballgown with midriff. Feeling so powerful with makeup and braided bantu buns. Stepping onto the dance floor blossoming like a flower in a field as the bottom of your dress flowed to the music. People I knew were all around me, yet you were the only one I could fully focus on. Your presence is the only one I felt from heel to the last braid on your head.

The pain you're going through now is only temporary, but the essence of joy you hold is eternal. I don't think I tell you this as much as I should, but you are enough. You matter. You will be remembered for all your great accomplishments, present and future. No, you are not a burden. A person with all your qualities can never be. You are better. You are improving. You should be proud of the charming Black woman you are turning out to be. Have pride in that. Don't let anyone try to take away what you have earned for yourself.

DIANA SANCHEZ

YEARS AS MENTEE: 1

GRADE: Sophomore

BORN: New York, NY

LIVES: Queens, NY

MENTEE'S ANECDOTE:

For the longest time, I never had anyone to give me second opinions or different choices. Katy showed me that it's all right to be indecisive and to question yourself, that while you may think you're the only one who has these thoughts, it doesn't mean you're alone. While I have never met Katy face-to-face, she seems like the person who would give great hugs and be the shoulder to cry on, especially over difficult things and simple fears.

KATHRYN CARDIN

YEARS AS MENTOR: 2

OCCUPATION: Freelance Writer and Editor

BORN: Springfield, MO

LIVES: Brooklyn, NY

PUBLICATIONS & RECOGNITIONS: *Tart Magazine*, editor; *Katy's Kitchen*, author

MENTOR'S ANECDOTE:

I was so scared to do a year of Girls Write Now virtually because I tend to connect best with people in person, but even over the computer I could tell immediately that Diana and I were going to be a great match. Diana is a resilient, thoughtful, and sweet human being. I'm so looking forward to continuing both our writing and our personal relationship and know one day soon we will be able to support each other, complain about whatever, and laugh together in person.

Martha "Marty" Farias

DIANA SANCHEZ

2020 f*cked with us all, and no words can describe the pain and trauma people all over the world went through. This is a tribute to the people we lost, to the pain.

How do we explain our trauma to those who will never understand?

My children will never understand the crippling pressure of having to stay inside for months on end, never know the feeling of fear when you hear the ambulance outside of your apartment building. I will never be able to explain the helplessness I felt when my mother lost her aunt. My great-aunt passed away in a hospital far away from her family, far from the girls and boys she raised as siblings, far from the comfort of her cats, who she adored. She died 2,989 miles away from her home. She was never buried but burned into a million pieces, just like snowflakes. She was given the chance to float away again on the seas of her people.

And I know that I'm not the only one still hurting, still haunted by the ghosts and memories of a better time that will never happen again. There are wasted opportunities and altered fates for everyone. Everyone paid the price for a futile virus. Yeah, I sound bitter and angry, but at this point I deserve the right to scream and cry for everything that was taken—not just from me but from my family. For the first time I wondered if I would be parentless and homeless.

Was life cruel enough to leave me empty and cold, to leave my cousins
    and aunts and uncles without their loved ones?
I know life did not f*ck with just me, but when communication is
    obsolete it feels so lonely. Life has a way of dragging us down farther
    when everything already feels so empty. Life in general has felt so
    crushing and devoid of anything since quarantine struck. I even
    miss waking up and traveling long hours to school. We've all been
    derailed from normalcy.
Nothing feels normal after what we have learned about the world,
    about the people closest to us, about ourselves.

I can't and I won't speak for everyone looking for understanding or a
    voice of reason. I don't know what the hell I'm supposed to do.
Some of us hold on to whatever we can, whether it's a petty argument
    or simple words that changed our day. We hold on and attach
    ourselves to our memories because we fear what comes next, we fear
    what we can't see or hear or control. I hate so many things I can't
    control, including myself.
But that is what makes me human. That's what makes all of us human.
"I had all and then most of you, some and now none of you."

April 26, 2020.
Hopefully someday I will be able to visit her, even if just to feel her still
    around me. I've never been religious, but part of me believes that my
    aunt is still and will always be around me. Things would be simpler
    if none of this ever happened. I could place my blame on COVID-19
    or Trump or anyone in the world, but nothing changes what
    happened; it was a horrible chance that hit us.

She was my aunt,
she was a mother to so many people, not just her own children.
She was caretaker,
an inspiration,
a light, a ghost.

For now, until I feel that I have done her memory justice, she will be remembered as a mother, a hero, and as a human being in a crowd of so many.

In loving memory of Martha Farias
October 12, 1955–April 26, 2020

ISABELLE SANDERSON

YEARS AS MENTEE: 3

GRADE: Senior

BORN: New York, NY

LIVES: New York, NY

MENTEE'S ANECDOTE:

In a café around twilight, sitting across from two cups of tea, Anna pulled out a book about Medieval medicine. I was immediately intrigued. I am a lover of the strange books you find in the recesses of antiques stores: from a nineteenth-century children's book about farming to a guide on wildflowers filled with poems and watercolors. After Anna showed me her book, I knew she was the same. Bonding over our love of the unique and peculiar, Anna and I have explored uncommon genres, and I have been inspired to create art out of the abnormal.

ANNA J WITIUK

YEARS AS MENTOR: 4

OCCUPATION: Musician, Grant Writer, Barista

BORN: New York, NY

LIVES: Stanfordville, NY

MENTOR'S ANECDOTE:

In my second year of getting to know and work with Isabelle, I have thoroughly enjoyed experiencing the creative expansion, the new depths of descriptiveness, and the blossoming playfulness of Isabelle's writing. We have had so much fun this year building strange characters and exploring new styles and genres of writing together, like magical realism and cut-and-shuffle poems.

Taraxacum: Case Study

ISABELLE SANDERSON

A controlled experiment on the nature of memory, romance, and dandelions.

Control:

In summer, I picked two dandelions,
handing you one, tucking
the hair behind my ear,
listening when you told me
about the girl you liked.
You blew on yours,
seeds scattering and
the stem lies limp
in your hands
till it dropped
unceremoniously
into a puddle.

x = Expectation

"Most specifically, the expression of Hera, the Greek goddess of marriage and womanhood, gives numerous insights into the expectations of an ideal wife and woman in this culture. We see that she should gain power from her beauty, be obedient to her husband, and not expect that in return from him."*

Most specifically,
in summer, I picked two dandelions,
handing you one, tucking the hair
behind my ear, *the Greek goddess of marriage and womanhood*
listens when you tell me *numerous insights into the expectations of*
the girl
you liked: *an ideal wife and woman in this culture.* You blew on yours and
we see that she should gain power from
seeds scattering
her beauty;
be obedient
to the stem that lies limp in your hands
till it drops
unceremoniously.

x = Envy†

In summer, I picked two dandelions
which smoked with bloody execution and
handing you one, *O valiant cousin,*
worthy gentleman tucks the hair behind
my ear—*too full o' th' milk of human*
kindness—listening when you told me all
about the girl you liked. *He unseam'd*
me *from the nave to the chaps.* You always
blew on yours. *My thought, whose murder yet is*
but fantastical, seeds scattering to

---

* *The Ideal Wife*, Isabelle Sanderson.
† *Macbeth*, William Shakespeare.

prick the sides of my intent, but only
the stem lie limp in your hands: *a walking*
shadow, a poor player till it dropp'd
unceremoniously, *and then is*
heard no more.

x = Fulfillment

"All / Proceed from the heart / And, in consequence / Enter between skin and skin / Do not meet / each other; and / Become contracted / This they say nature has done / Finding the ways / between membrane and membrane / To penetrate into the interior / To spread out / And turn back / The remainder: superfluous"*

In summer, I picked two dandelions
handing you one,
And, in consequence
Enter between skin and skin
tucking the hair behind my ear
and listening when you told me
about the girl you liked.
Do not meet each other; and
Become contracted
You blew on yours
seeds scattering
This they say nature has done
and the stem lies limp in your hands
Finding the ways between membrane and membrane
till it dropped
To penetrate into the interior
unceremoniously

---

* *Anatomy 125*, Isabelle Sanderson.

into a puddle.
The remainder:

A puddle in summer:
unceremonious.
Two dandelions, the girl, the stem, you
scattering.
I dropped into
a puddle in summer,
the hair behind my ear lying limp in your hands.

MELANIE SANTIAGO

YEARS AS MENTEE: 1

GRADE: Senior

BORN: New York, NY

LIVES: New York, NY

MENTEE'S ANECDOTE:

I feel so excited about my first well-written screenplay and I owe so much of my success in writing this to my mentor, Arianna, who believed in my vision and helped me create something I'm very proud of. Receiving feedback on my work has made me that much more passionate about writing screenplays. During our Saturday sessions, Arianna and I often talked through film inspirations and writer's-block challenges. She pushed me to reflect on what skills I want to develop, what experiences I'm after, who I want to learn from, and what I want to make.

ARIANNA FRIEDMAN

YEARS AS MENTOR: 1

OCCUPATION: Urban Planning

BORN: Changsha, China

LIVES: Brooklyn, NY

MENTOR'S ANECDOTE:

As a first-year mentor, I didn't know what to expect from the Girls Write Now program—during a pandemic, no less. I'm so glad Melanie and I were paired together to figure it all out. I thoroughly enjoyed watching her idea grow from a school assignment to the final anthology piece. Her ability to reflect on her experiences creatively and honestly is a wonderful strength. I was so happy to hear that she's proud of the piece, because I am too! I'm looking forward to reading the full screenplay and seeing it on-screen one day!

If You'd Only Let Me In

MELANIE SANTIAGO

Everyone tells Lucia she needs help, so she goes to an esteemed counseling center. Despite wanting to open up, the scars from her past make it difficult, but are they warning her of something sinister?

1 INT. EQUII COUNSELOR'S OFFICE—DAY

    Lucia, seventeen, sits across from the
    EQUII counselor at a long boardroom
    table in a rather warm room. Lucia has
    dark, thick hair that sits on her
    shoulders, big brown eyes that scream
    "help me," and a scar running down from
    her left cheekbone to her lower lip that
    she tries to hide with her hair.

    For several weeks, Lucia has been
    distant and stressed and eventually
    stopped going to school. After
    disclosing that recent family issues
    resulted in arguments and even physical
    altercations, she was referred to EQUII,
    a renowned facility that specializes in
    emotional equilibrium.

The EQUII counselor, a particularly
feminine and petite woman with
light skin and platinum blond hair,
stares directly at Lucia with piercing
blue eyes.

                    COUNSELOR

Can you tell me more about how that made you feel?

                    LUCIA

Uh, can I pass on answering that question?

                    COUNSELOR

Sure. How about another question? Can you tell me
more about your family?

                    LUCIA

Well, I live with my mom, my fifteen-year-old sister,
Valeria, and my seven-year-old sister, Isabella . . .

                    COUNSELOR

Oh, so you're the oldest? How would you describe
your relationship with your family?

                    LUCIA

I love them so much, but I . . . I don't really want
to get into that.

COUNSELOR

Lucia, I understand, but know that I just want to
help you, and if you would only let me in, I could
do that.

LUCIA

I appreciate it, I really do, but I don't think that
I'm ready to go into detail about my family and my
personal life.

COUNSELOR

Okay, so how about instead of voicing your feelings
out loud to me, you write them down and I won't be
able to see it. Does that sound like something
you'll be able to do?

> The counselor passes Lucia a piece of
> paper and a pen. Lucia starts writing
> and floods the page with her
> frustration, sadness, and anger.

COUNSELOR

It seems you're writing a lot. Does writing help?

LUCIA

Uh-huh. It's really the only way I'll be able to
talk about this stuff.

COUNSELOR

I'm glad to hear that.

>   The counselor focuses on Lucia with a
>   creepy grin on her face. Lucia looks up
>   and the grin disappears.

COUNSELOR

Is something wrong, Lucia?

LUCIA

No, I just wasn't sure if it was okay to write
instead of talking to you . . .

COUNSELOR

It's perfectly fine. Just go ahead and write as much
as you can, okay?

>   A mysterious banging sound disrupts
>   Lucia's concentration.

LUCIA

What was that?

COUNSELOR

I'm sure it's nothing. It's probably just the pipes.

>   The counselor continues to stare at Lucia
>   and smiles with artificial sincerity.

                         COUNSELOR

Why don't you go back to writing?

          Lucia returns to the paper and continues
          to write.

                         COUNSELOR

Lucia, if you don't mind me asking, how did you get
your scar?

          Lucia looks up from the paper and
          touches her scar. She has a flashback of
          the night she got it.

FLASHBACK

          Red and green flashes blur Lucia's
          vision as she begins to breathe hard and
          sob uncontrollably. The sound of a high-
          pitched scream snaps her out of her
          trance.

                         COUNSELOR

What happened? I lost you for a second.

                           LUCIA

I just um . . . um . . . I heard a scream. What's
going on out there?

                         COUNSELOR

I'm sure it's nothing.

                         GIRL (offscreen)

No!!! Please!!!! I don't wanna die!!!!

                              LUCIA

That doesn't sound like nothing. I need to help her.

                           COUNSELOR

I guess I can't stop you.

          Lucia enters the hallway.

INT. HALLWAY—DAY

          Lucia sees a girl lying against a wall.
          Her eyes are the color of pure darkness.

          A man comes out from an office room and
          throws the girl over his shoulder. He
          pulls out a phone and dials a number.

                              MAN

Hey, boss, I got another one. Bringing her down now.

          Lucia runs in the opposite direction
          away from the mysterious man. She
          continues down a hallway and comes
          across other individuals who have
          encountered the same fate as the girl
          she left behind.

          The counselor sees Lucia run and takes
          out her phone.

                            COUNSELOR

She's heading to the west wing, retrieve her for me,
please. Unharmed, of course.

        Lucia runs into a dark corner where she
        encounters the counselor.

                              LUCIA

What the hell is going on here? Who are you people?

        A dark and tall figure appears behind
        Lucia and knocks her out.

MYSTERIOUS ROOM

        Lucia wakes up to shrieking cries and a
        pulsing blue light. She tries to pick
        herself up from the ground, but realizes
        that her hands are chained to the floor
        and she's trapped in a clear box.

        Across from her, Lucia sees another girl
        in a box with her back to Lucia. She
        wears a white jumpsuit with the numbers
        #0912. Lucia tries to get the attention
        of the girl.

                              LUCIA

Hey, do you know where we are? Do you know how we
can get out of here?

The girl turns around revealing pitch-
black eyes. The skin on the right side
of her face is peeling off, exposing her
teeth.

#0912

It's the eyes.

BLACK SCREEN

PRINCESA SANTOS

YEARS AS MENTEE: 3

GRADE: Junior

BORN: Cartagena, Colombia

LIVES: New York, NY

MENTEE'S ANECDOTE:

During this past year, although difficult, Camille and I were able to become closer as a pair and develop an understanding for each other. Camille is bright, organized, and encouraging. I love being able to talk about anything. Whether it be a conversation about our lives, troubling issues in society, new writing techniques/styles, or geek out over our favorite movies and shows, we always seem to have a great time! She truly is a force to be reckoned with. I couldn't imagine experiencing a global pandemic with any other mentor!

CAMILLE BOND

YEARS AS MENTOR: 2

OCCUPATION: Graduate Student

BORN: Washington D.C.

LIVES: New York, NY

MENTOR'S ANECDOTE:

Last program year, I got to know Princesa as a poet who creates striking images and writes movingly on weighty, important themes. Since September, I've seen her shapeshift into a brilliant podcaster, short-story writer, and essayist—challenging herself with new media and genres. Although the transition from in-person to online meetings has taken some getting used to, her positivity and sense of humor make our Zoom sessions a highlight of my week! Princesa is more than a writer, she's also a leader, and I know that her words will make the world a fairer, kinder place.

All Lives Matter

PRINCESA SANTOS

"All Lives Matter" is a collaborative protest poem that takes both formal poetic writing techniques and a sample of an informative article to express the detriment of using the phrase "all lives matter."

I

People always ask,
"What's wrong with saying, 'All Lives Matter'?"

II

"All Lives Matter,"
but "the gays can burn."
"All Lives Matter,"
but "go back to where you came from."
"All Lives Matter,"
but "he fit the profile."

III

"It is true that all lives matter, but it is equally true that not all lives are understood to matter."*
"If we jump too quickly to the universal formulation, 'all lives matter,' then we miss the fact that [diversified] people have not yet been included in the idea of 'all lives.'"*

---

* George Yancy and Judith Butler. "What's Wrong With 'All Lives Matter'?" *The New York Times*, January 12, 2015.

IV

As I turn on the TV,
I wake up to see
another dead black body,
mocking me.
When I walk through the streets,
old men watch me.
Anxiety overtakes me.
I pray to God
I'll get home
safely.
Whenever I walk into a store
employees follow me,
always staying behind me.
They fear that
I
may take something.

RACHEL SEKYERE

YEARS AS MENTEE: 1

GRADE: Junior

BORN: Bronx, NY

LIVES: Bronx, NY

MENTEE'S ANECDOTE:

When starting Girls Write Now, one of the things I was most excited for was meeting my mentor and creating new pieces of writing with her. Even though I haven't gotten the opportunity to meet Sherrill in person, she has been inspiring and encouraging. She always strives for me to do my best, whether it's a writing piece or with school and my future education. She's always there and always reaches out if I need help with anything. For example, when working on one of my writing pieces I showed her some of my artwork and she encouraged me to continue my art, even buying me art supplies. Sherrill is a supportive woman who pushes people to do their best in everything they do.

SHERRILL COLLINS-RICHARDSON

YEARS AS MENTOR: 2

OCCUPATION: New York University Administrator

BORN: New York, NY

LIVES: New York, NY

MENTOR'S ANECDOTE:

"Remember" was written for my mentee, Rachel, who has been forced to forge through a time of unsafe and uncomfortable spaces. Since our first Zoom meeting she has given her best and never given up. Her writing and art work together to tell beautiful stories that will be told one day and her name will be—*remembered.*

The Diaspora

RACHEL SEKYERE

This poem is about the African diaspora and the struggles and experiences of being a Black woman.

These wild curls,
That go in different swirls
The naps of my ancestors
Who gave birth to protesters
With deep dark flesh like the night and the earth
Hair that looks like trees, the world gave birth
Like brown sugar and everything sweet
It's our rhythm we swing to our own beat
Like the African diaspora
That spans from Jamaica to Madagascar
Like Yaa Asantewaa
The freedom my ancestors never saw
Did they know we would hate ourselves so?
Even though we secretly glow
I know they envy my grace
And try to make us hate the world's true birthplace
We came from kings and queens, tribes and more
And the bodies who refused to be enslaved, spirits still live in those
  shores
And they laugh at our names, names that survived, could have been
  forever lost
Do they know the cost?

Telling me I should achieve straight blond hair, blue eyes, and pale skin
Where should I begin?
Like Breonna, Breonna Taylor
'Cause even though she died she didn't go a failure.
Yes my nose is wide, so are my lips
My culture falls on me like the beads on my hips
I'm black as black as the night as black as tar
But for a while, I wasn't my number-one star
Saying I'm whitewashed, but this blackness could never be tainted
I'm sorry if you can't see the picture that's been painted
Surprised when I make my way down these Bronx streets with my
    vernacular

   But once this little girl found her voice everything that came out of it
been spectacular.

Remember

SHERRILL COLLINS-RICHARDSON

Remember
Losing lives is hard to trace
The Pandemic
But the world will know your face
Breonna Taylor
As we March to save our race
Black Lives Matter
Let Humanity be our grace
Attack on the Capital
And set the temperature of this place
Girls Write Now
To give mentees their writing space
Rachel Sekyere

JASMINE SELLARS

YEARS AS MENTEE: 1

GRADE: Senior

BORN: Brooklyn, NY

LIVES: Brooklyn, NY

MENTEE'S ANECDOTE:

Completing this project with Anna has given me a safe space to creatively express myself through writing. Though I haven't done any creative writing activities in a while, writing this story allowed me to freely come up with a story from my imagination. This project gave me the time to focus on doing something that I enjoyed without having to follow the rules of a rubric. I hope to do more activities like this one during the year.

ANNA PERLING

YEARS AS MENTOR: 2

OCCUPATION: Writer

BORN: Atlanta, GA

LIVES: Atlanta, GA

MENTOR'S ANECDOTE:

Jasmine and I worked together to write this story, imagining a different world and creating characters that were like us, but still unique. I so admire Jasmine's patience, dedication, and creativity, even under the strain of applying to college. Our writing sessions are a time to reflect and dream, and I look forward to them every week. Jasmine, you're an amazing writer and person!

Jaz's Adventure in Time: A Poem

JASMINE SELLARS

This is the story of Jaz, a young time traveler who found herself lost in the future. She's on a quest to find the last missing pieces of the puzzle so she can find her parents.

Jaz's Quest was long overdue
Her parents went missing
So she was confused

They left her alone
To fend for herself
So she turned to their notes
For some much-needed help

She built a machine
To travel through time
In hopes of her parents
She wanted to find

Jaz was unsafe
And her parents told her
That she needed the Book
Of Maps and Ciphers

The shadows approached
And Jaz was so scared

So she jumped in the portal
And she disappeared

She woke up in danger
And searched the new city
Jaz found a library
In the year 2050

She met Anna and her mentees
In their secret headquarters
And she learned about the government
And their new world order

They found all the books
And burned what they had taken
Except for the copies
In the GWN basement

Though the book was coded
And no one could understand
Jaz had been studying
And practicing beforehand

The puzzle was complete
Jaz had what she needed
But she couldn't help
But feel defeated

She thought to herself
And told not a soul
A world with books
Is a world without control

How can we live
In solidarity and peace
Without our stories
That bring us escape and release

MICHELLE SEUCAN

YEARS AS MENTEE: 1

GRADE: Junior

BORN: New York, NY

LIVES: Staten Island, NY

PUBLICATIONS & RECOGNITIONS:
Songs of Peace, Finxerunt: Across the Spectrum of Socioeconomics, Climate Speaks Spoken Word Finalist

MENTEE'S ANECDOTE:

Stevie is one of the wisest people I've ever known. Not only does she offer refreshing perspectives on my work that I otherwise never would've thought of, but she's also been such a great friend to me. From talks about traveling the globe to laughing about the uncertain future, our discussions have taught me so much about being a writer and a person. Her guidance has transformed the way I approach life, school, and other matters of the world. I admire her ability to create these safe spaces where we can talk about anything and for that I am grateful!

STEVIE BORRELLO

YEARS AS MENTOR: 1

OCCUPATION: Freelance Producer/Writer

BORN: Danbury, CT

LIVES: Brooklyn, NY

PUBLICATIONS & RECOGNITIONS:
Vice, Quartz at Work

MENTOR'S ANECDOTE:

It has been such a pleasure to meet and work with Michelle this past year. Not only am I amazed at how motivated and diligent she is with meeting deadlines for all her creative endeavors, but her vulnerability and skill in writing on themes of love, nostalgia, and childhood produce an intimacy that feels so raw and gives me goose bumps. I always look forward to meeting with her and reveling in our shared love of writing. It has helped me rediscover my passion for the craft, and I cannot wait to see the work Michelle continues to create.

October is a strange feeling

MICHELLE SEUCAN

A love letter to my October experiences. Through it, I reflect on what I've learned, who I met, and how I've grown. It's an ode to those who have also fallen victim to false realities.

October is a strange feeling

so many things happening
all at once, how quaint

my life feels like a silent film
where the main character is stuck on an imaginary island
situated on a faraway planet
in a solar system
in some galaxy
that doesn't actually exist

kind of like when
you wake up in the morning
after a slumber party at your friend's house
wondering what time it is,
why you feel so disheveled,
and how you ended up
on the trashy pull-out sofa
instead of the warm, cozy bed
that you fell asleep in the night before—
where her mother put you two to sleep

Maybe detaching from reality isn't the worst thing in the world

it tends to hit you
during the most unexpected of times
like when you hold in your hands
a colorful mosaic of fragile rocks
that you randomly found
on a random beach
somewhere far from home

how can you have become so irrationally maternal
towards inanimate objects
as such?
not just with rocks,
but with people too—
friends, lovers, family,
or souls that just pop up in your life,
then leave unexpectedly

i guess lana del rey was right
when she said that black
was her favorite color
and favorite tone of song,
for when is it ever not colored into my life
by broken people

more specifically,
by a broken boy?

even months later,
my heart aches still for him
but his heart aches for someone else
do you know how many times

i used to lie awake at night
wondering what her name was

It always hurts knowing there was another before you

but despite his
sweet words
soft hands
tender eyes
and how he trusted me
with secrets not even his friends knew,
this boy was nothing more
than Negativity personified

he would leave in his wake
a trail of defeat and doubt,
viewing the world
with a little bit of poison,
for he gave up on love long ago
when She left him.
foolish of me to think
that i might be the One
to change who he was
and what he stood for

All girls are the same, he would say

oh, how pathetic you must think i am
once i tell you that the ghost of him
haunts the corridors of my mind,
where the songs we both loved
still echo
everywhere

i can no longer listen to those songs consciously
without thinking of that one night
back in october
before he left me
like She did him

It's strange when they become strangers

thinking of october
makes me sad,
happy,
confused,
but mainly sad
because i had so much time
and spent it in the weirdest ways,
making me rethink
and dwell
on things i can't control
and refuse to let go of

why do i insist
on continuously swimming in oceans
that keep fighting to drown me

why do my dreams
keep predicting the future
of things that i don't want to happen
but happen anyway
showing me that intuition
is both a blessing
and a curse

God, I hate being so intuitive!

we are blinded
by the false reality
of that one person

to us,
they are the universe
in human form
they are as miraculous
as a purple sunset
and as powerful
as the moon
when it pulls tides out of oceans
they are
a fever dream,
that seems too good to be true

Because it is

they are a mirage,
a fraud,
an illusion!
anything
but the universe itself
you are your universe,
not them

Sweet child, you must never forget this

october has taught me
that people don't belong to people

we are simply floating throughout life
experiencing one another,

experiencing ourselves,
experiencing the world
nothing was ever promised to us
so why grip the thorns of a rose
if it will wilt anyway?

enjoy its beauty, but don't for even a second
think that it was ever yours to claim
the rose's regal red
will eventually fade,
and the thorns will sting you
so do yourself a favor child

and let it go

LULU SHA

YEARS AS MENTEE: 2

GRADE: Senior

BORN: Beijing, China

LIVES: Queens, NY

PUBLICATIONS & RECOGNITIONS: Scholastic Art & Writing Awards: Gold Key

MENTEE'S ANECDOTE:

When I first met Jenni, I was an awkward and sweaty girl who didn't quite understand herself. Through our meetings, Jenni has really helped me come out of my shell and discover my values and self-worth as a person. She's been with me in my darkest moments, from college applications to a strained relationship with my parents. We've discovered our shared passions for activism, racial justice, and helping young women find their strength and independence. Jenni has helped me find the courage to share a part of my soul with the world.

JENNI MILTON

YEARS AS MENTOR: 2

OCCUPATION: Writer

BORN: Rochester, NY

LIVES: Brooklyn, NY

PUBLICATIONS & RECOGNITIONS: *A Distant Memory Zine, Juked*

MENTOR'S ANECDOTE:

The year 2020 was full of challenges, but working with Lulu was truly one of the highlights. When we first met, I was so impressed with her intelligence, grace, and humor. We found ourselves having a wonderfully meandering discussion about race, class, gender, and sexuality. I love how Lulu embraces complexity in her life and in her work. She's endlessly curious and unafraid to explore painful themes in her writing, whether she's working on a love poem or researching the Asian American identity. I'm so grateful to be her mentor!

Scary Things / Midsummer

LULU SHA

These pieces explore my ideas on love, loss, and emotional valida-
tion. They're the products of a girl who got lost inside her own head
for too long.

Scary Things

INSPIRED BY SEI SHŌNAGON'S *THE PILLOW BOOK*

-Talking to strangers

-Talking to a crush and seeing that their feet are pointed away from you

-Dying alone

-Watching your partner grow old and weak. They can no longer run
     towards you, or run away from you

-The feeling of bug legs crawling on your skin

-Having to kill the spiders yourself

-Losing your virginity

-Being a virgin after college

-The expensive gifts from your partner after a fight. This time it's a
     watch with a painted white rabbit in the background

-Knowing they will mention the watch in the next fight to make you
     feel guilty

-Grabbing a hammer to smash the watch, but not being able to because
     you don't want to hurt the rabbit

-Feeling ashamed for still needing your partner

-Accepting the shame

-Eating your favorite childhood dish and not feeling any nostalgia

-The scale in shopping mall bathrooms
-The weight of everything you haven't done yet
-Not being afraid to die

Midsummer

WE MET THE LAST DAY OF JUNE.

You were singing
and playing
the six-string in my heart.
You were undoing
the strings of my heart.
And all the boys bring you roses
but do you remember
when I kissed the daisies
we planted in the Garden of Eden
before God made the night?
And if you still wear
flowers in your hair
do you still remember
when you bloomed
at my touch
and I discovered the firmness of Eve
lying between the breasts of a woman
who's never been born?
So I did not come to the hospital that day
because Man begets Man
but what does Woman
keep for herself?
It's been many years
and I wonder
how he touched you
and you danced

in the palm of his hand.
Because I heard
when you dance before God
there is no music
but his heart beating fast.
I wonder if there's
flowers in heaven.
I wonder if your room has a window
because through the window you can see I still kiss
the flowers that shower your grave.

LILA SHARP

YEARS AS MENTEE: 1

GRADE: Sophomore

BORN: New York, NY

LIVES: New York NY

MENTEE'S ANECDOTE:

Although there were definitely some challenges that came with working together virtually, Deenie and I found a good balance and were able to create something that we can both be proud of. Producing this with Deenie was fun and inspirational, and helped me learn a lot about revising and expanding on my work.

———— ～ ————

NADINE MATTHEWS

YEARS AS MENTOR: 2

OCCUPATION: Freelance Writer

BORN: Jamaica, WI

LIVES: New York, NY

PUBLICATIONS & RECOGNITIONS: Coveteur.com, StyleCaster.com, AmsterdamNews.com

MENTOR'S ANECDOTE:

It was tough bringing something together during a pandemic, with our perfectionist tendencies and differing approaches to creating, but I'm happy we've come up with something interesting and thought-provoking that will hopefully be expanded on later!

The Hunt

LILA SHARP

This flash-fiction piece brings us sixteen-year-old Carrie, who is bright, brilliant, and ambitious. Carrie is also sweet, kind, and loving. Why, then, is Carrie sitting in jail, accused of mass homicide?

On August 24, 2020, Dr. Basek interviewed mass murderer Carrie Solend regarding the brutal slaying of her classmates.

Why did you do it? How did they make you so angry?

Well, for starters, they were all jerks. Started out small enough: rude remarks in the hallways, tripping me, throwing out my lunch. Soon it progressed to them ruining my grades. They jumped me multiple times. One of them found out my address and trashed my house, leaving roadkill and garbage on my front step. I didn't even feel safe in my own fucking home.

I don't know the real reason why. They said different things: I was a freak, I was ugly, I was too poor, gross, dumb, and weird. I existed too much, enough to be offensive to them.

You know one of them tried to kill me once? This guy, Johnny, I'm pretty sure he's the one I disemboweled, thought it'd be funny to try and push me in front of a train. Hilarious, right? You know the type too: comes from money, handed everything he ever wanted. Of course he'd be the one to try to do it.

There's . . . a certain entitlement needed to kill someone. The act of taking another human's life: to erase them from this world, from its beauty and coarseness and hardship, to take away their joy and sorrow, love and hate and *divinity, **forever.*** You gotta feel like you deserve to do it. Somehow, he did.

But you think you're different from him? That you're not entitled?

I'm not saying that, but we *are* different. He acted that way out of cruelty; I did it for revenge. To be free.

Carrie, teenage girls don't generally commit mass murder on their own. I'll ask you again, did you do this by yourself?

Yeah. I'm almost fucking proud of it, y'know? There were, what, six of them there? And it wasn't even hard. So blinded by their fucking arrogance and power, they didn't even notice themselves getting lured to their *untimely* deaths.

Your father is currently in prison himself. Did growing up with such an unstable parental figure influence you?

Maybe, but not for whatever Freudian bullshit reason you think. He's a man's man. Y'know, those guys who fish and hunt and stuff for fun. One of the first things he taught me was how to field-dress and skin a deer, and we spent almost every weekend hunting. Whenever he was around, I mean.

Because of him, I learned I could go up against an animal twice my size and *win.* I realized I could fight back with everything I had. Because of him, I could bring down the fucking beasts.

What were you feeling right after, Carrie? What did you feel in the immediate aftermath, when you saw the result of what you'd done?

I wished I hadn't gotten blood everywhere. It would've been easier to clean up otherwise.

I remember looking at them; I could see that same dread, that intoxicating fear. Their eyes still pleaded with me to let them live. Well, those of them who still had eyes.

Those first few minutes, god, they were insane. It took a while to come down from the adrenaline high.

Okay, so am I right in hearing that you felt a sort of exhilaration? Because of the fear you saw them experiencing?

It wasn't so much because of the fear. It was . . . just finally letting everything out.

People think they can push you around and if you don't do anything at first, they can keep doing it. Especially with girls. People do whatever the fuck they want and they expect us to just sit there quietly and take it and then apologize for being there in the first place. They don't think it adds up. It does. This anger, this gut-wrenching, soul-crushing rage slowly, just, *builds* and spreads until it's all you can feel.

There's catharsis in acting on that rage. There's the storm after the calm, and then the calm again after that.

Sure, I knew it wasn't technically the most moral thing to do, and I did have to think about that a bit. But in those moments when it happened, and I held their lives in my hands like they were the tiny, fragile eggs my dad and I would find hunting, it didn't matter. When *I* was finally in control, and they knew it, it didn't matter. They had it coming . . . They had it coming.

So, no empathy for their suffering?

You wanna talk about empathy? I'm the *enforcer* of empathy. When I was there, in that room with them, I made sure that they could feel *everything* they did to me.

Sure, there were parts of me saying not to do it. You know, there's that big argument: Revenge doesn't make anything better. It only keeps the pain going, 'round and 'round. Forever, probably, but I'm okay with that. They deserved that, for every time *they* hurt *me*.

Still, I can see their eyes, their expressions. The fear and despair lingers. It's still going, 'round and 'round.

ISABELLA SODDU

YEARS AS MENTEE: 1

GRADE: Junior

BORN: New York, NY

LIVES: New York NY

PUBLICATIONS & RECOGNITIONS:
Scholastic Art & Writing Awards:
Honorable Mention

MENTEE'S ANECDOTE:

The first time I met Brooke this online year, we were both navigating the murky waters of bad "middle of nowhere" Wi-Fi. Ironically, I was immediately connected to her both as a writer and as an individual. That first day, we were both smiling ear to ear as we uncovered how much we shared in common, from eyeglasses and blue sweaters to a shared love of environmentalism. This year, Brooke has continued to keep that smile on my face as she has helped me unveil my voice and confidence as a writer and has continuously cheered me on.

BROOKE MAZUREK

YEARS AS MENTOR: 1

OCCUPATION: Journalist and
Editor

BORN: Baltimore, MD

LIVES: New York, NY

PUBLICATIONS & RECOGNITIONS:
The New York Times,
Billboard, NPR

MENTOR'S ANECDOTE:

When Isabella and I met for the first time on Zoom, I couldn't help but laugh: dark hair, glasses, pullover sweaters. We have birthdays a few days apart and a shared passion for environmentalism. It all felt kismet. Most weeks we start our session with a free write. I'll open a book, pick out a word, and we'll both put pen to paper. "Let's see what happens," I'll say. Without fail, I find myself in awe of what emerges from Isabella's pen—her imagination, the way she is able to marry imagery and sound. Unedited, it's all just there.

Marmalade, Bread & Butter, Honey

ISABELLA SODDU

This trio of poems explores big feelings through the lens of a small and nonsensical subject matter: breakfast condiments.

Marmalade

morning

It's half-past nine and you're ready to dine
on twenty minutes of misery

Painted marmalade toast I watch you engrossed
in the sunny weather advisory

Your knife a pendulum I sing a soft hum
but your eye gives me a quiver

Day after day I'm wasting away,
And your silence is spreading me thinner

night

dirty window panes made lipstick stains
you delight in seedy affairs

They think you sweeter than most, marmalade toast
you never bothered to care

My worth served on a platter; it didn't matter
Am I dressed in the costumes of sinners?

How am I to cope I'm clean out of hope
when I am spread so much thinner

Bread & Butter

Bread and butter you smiled at me
As our hands were broken by the maple tree
Your face was dappled with blemished light
And so we laughed together in warm delight

My words were betrayed by lust that day,
Maybe something inside told me not to say,
"Bread and butter back to you my love"
If requited, is bread and butter even enough?

Honey

I walked with my kitty-cat umbrella
In my world of sugar and honey
Twirling in the beeswax pavement
humming echoes into my world

Honey in my tea
Honey on his face
Honey on my brain

I'm stuck on honey,
I can't twirl on sugarcoated pavement
So I hide behind my kitty-cat umbrella
An echo becomes my world

SYLVI STEIN

YEARS AS MENTEE: 4

GRADE: Senior

BORN: New York, NY

LIVES: New York, NY

PUBLICATIONS & RECOGNITIONS:
"You Will Be Found" College Essay Writing Challenge: Finalist; *Hypernova Lit*; Scholastic Art & Writing Awards: Gold Keys, Silver Keys, Honorable Mentions

MENTEE'S ANECDOTE:

Nan has helped me face a year of what once seemed to me to be impossible hurdles—the pandemic, college applications, growing up, and growing as a writer. I miss our after-school meetings in Le Pain Quotidien, but we've kept the spark up through Zoom and through swapping *New York Times* articles. Thanks to her support and encouragement during my time as her mentee, I've been able to learn more about myself and about writing than I ever thought I would.

NAN BAUER-MAGLIN

YEARS AS MENTOR: 7

OCCUPATION: Writer, Editor, Professor Emerita

BORN: New York, NY

LIVES: New York, NY

PUBLICATIONS & RECOGNITIONS:
Widows' Words: Women Write on the Experience of Grief; The First Year, The Long Haul, and Everything in Between

MENTOR'S ANECDOTE:

While Sylvi and I have not seen each other in person this year, we have worked together regularly over the summer as she wrote and rewrote her college essays. We exchanged audio diaries about our days inside our apartments because of the COVID-19 lockdown. Teaming up with another Girls Write Now mentor-mentee pair, we wrote and analyzed poetry—a plus in these confined times. In her spare time, Sylvi wrote stories and plays and was the editor-in-chief of Hunter High School's literary magazine. Her energy, her range of topic and genre, and her original images take my breath away.

Life's a Circus

SYLVI STEIN

The personal narrative of how my journey to learn to juggle taught me about life.

The summer when I was fifteen years old, I learned to juggle. There was no particular "why." I had never been to the circus before, and I had no ambitions to become a clown, or one of those performers in Central Park. I wanted to learn to juggle as a skill, the same way some other kids can read sheet music or wiggle their ears. Why not? I could picture myself at a fancy restaurant, dressed to the nines, juggling the complimentary rolls to the amazement of whatever esteemed guest I was dining with. I would defy expectations.

So, I sacrificed my free time to the juggling gods. No after-dinner card games or canoeing races for me; I spent my summer camp activities periods engaged in the thrilling pursuit of chucking beanbags up in the air and trying (and, more often, failing) to catch them. None of my friends questioned my motives; they just shrugged and sighed when I told them that sorry, I couldn't come with them to arts and crafts, I had to get in another hour with the juggling balls if I wanted to be ready by the end of the summer.

Juggling is mostly muscle memory, but it requires practice. Fortunately, one thing I've learned from high school study sessions is that repetition is your friend. My palms memorized the weight of the beanbags, the circular catch and throw, the exhilaration of the toss, and the wrenching moment of the drop. Barefoot on the rubber mats in the gymnastics pavilion, I practiced until I could juggle balls without my tongue between my teeth, without holding my breath. Then I picked up the rings and the clubs.

From this period of practice, a time of sweat, blood, and tears (those clubs can really hurt when they hit you in the face), I certainly was learning to juggle, but with every dropped ball, and every black-and-blue bruise, I began to realize I was also learning something else, something much more poignant—the reason for my determination. Learning anything from scratch is a struggle, but this was the first commitment to a skill that I had undertaken completely of my own volition. But why? In the way tossing a pinch of salt over your shoulder is supposed to ward off evil spirits, I was learning to juggle to forestall a bleak future of cubicles, nine-to-five office hours, and the soul-crushing inevitability of "a realistic career." Stock market advisers on Wall Street don't know how to juggle; waiting-room secretaries can't flip juggling clubs through the air with just the right flick of the wrist; corporate CEOs surely don't know the difference between a diabolo and a rolla bolla. No amount of money could entice me away from the promise of a life of chaos and adventure, a life filled to the brim with excitement. I don't have to conform to our society's model of the ideal, rational adult; I can be an eccentric artist, a reclusive writer, a circus clown for hire. If I could juggle, I could preserve my fiery, determined enthusiasm for the bizarre and the unexpected.

On the last day of summer we had the circus and gymnastics show. As twelve little girls did cartwheels and somersaults next to me, I juggled for the audience. During the performance, in front of all the eager parents, bored younger siblings, and proud counselors, I dropped the clubs no less than seven times. Barnum & Bailey would not exactly be knocking down my door to offer me a job—but that didn't matter. After hours of practice, I can miraculously make the balls dance through the air, teach them to defy gravity. I might one day be a newspaper columnist, or a divorce lawyer, or an accountant, but I will never be just that; there will always be a part of me that remembers how to embrace the extraordinary.

KILHAH ST FORT

YEARS AS MENTEE: 2

GRADE: Senior

BORN: Brooklyn, NY

LIVES: Queens, NY

MENTEE'S ANECDOTE:

If you look up two peas in a pod, you'll find a picture of Amber and me! We always seem to be on the same wavelength. From loving musical theater to understanding the pains of Zoom call intruders, we get each other. We can talk about nothing and everything all at once. She's the only person I never feel nervous about showing my work to. She's always ready to give me a pep talk when I need it and has unwavering confidence in me and my abilities. Even when I don't. This is more than a mentorship; it's a friendship.

AMBER LOVELESS

YEARS AS MENTOR: 2

OCCUPATION: Librarian

BORN: Illinois, USA

LIVES: Queens, NY

MENTOR'S ANECDOTE:

I love writing with Kilhah. We spent the summer plotting a story together after a Girls Write Now world-building workshop inspired us. Working in a new genre with Kilhah has pushed us both beyond our normal boundaries and being able to support each other in creating something new has been one of the best parts of this year.

Concepts

KILHAH ST FORT

This piece is a series of vignettes that are able to be read either as one or as stand-alones. Each one carries an emotion that is specific to its content.

Above Highway 89, a boy dances barefoot across a metal tightrope. His arms held out wide, one foot in front of the other. Wind bites his face, his fingertips, his left knee peeking out of Goodwill jeans. The boy kisses back. In the clash of teeth and spit and air, he sees their wedding. Wind holds him tight, arms compressed against his hollow ribs, and when gravity takes hold, they exchange vows. In the church pews, there are birds. Blue jays, robins, warblers, even the white pigeons are allowed. Instead of rice, they throw rain. The newlyweds drive away in a carriage of clouds.
"Until death do us part."
Until—

* * * * * *

it rained for a month.
no one thought to tarp the merry-go-round or the slide or the swings. when the sun returned & dried the water, rust clung to metal. we couldn't spin as fast. swing as high. slide as quick. after the chains snapped during a swing off & mary was sent flying, we stuck to hopscotch. a week later, we went through five boxes of chalk. mom said no more chalk. so, we jumped rope but no one wanted to sing the same rhyme. jump rope ended quick. bored, we went inside & said, "next

summer. we'll play next summer." a year passed & june rolled around. the grass had grown tall, itchy, & dry. the rust had babies. we'll play next summer.

* * * * * *

Chamomile flowers sprout from concrete.
Bursting out of cracks destined to break
a mother's back; a bundle of gentle petals and

                          apple breeze.

A butterfly lands on an iron bench. Wings unfurl &
ochre and black and white are on display.
Overhead,
              the center of the universe
                         smiles down.

ALBA SUAREZ

YEARS AS MENTEE: 1

GRADE: Junior

BORN: New York, NY

LIVES: Queens, NY

MENTEE'S ANECDOTE:

While working with Zoë, I've been able to spend time working on creative projects and writing prompts that helped me stay creative during the pandemic. Being able to spend time on nonacademic writing with my mentor has allowed me to find happiness and entertainment in writing again instead of only getting to experience it as something I need to do for school. Zoë is incredibly supportive and outgoing, and she has so much passion for writing that I have been lucky enough to get to learn from.

ZOË WEINER

YEARS AS MENTOR: 1

OCCUPATION: Beauty and Fitness Editor at *Well+Good*

BORN: Providence, RI

LIVES: New York, NY

PUBLICATIONS & RECOGNITIONS: *Glamour, Teen Vogue, Allure*

MENTOR'S ANECDOTE:

Alba is one of the funniest, most original writers I have ever known. No matter what the two of us are working on together, she never ceases to surprise me with her ability to think outside the box. Her creative brain challenges me to think differently, and I am so proud of the pieces she's put together this year. Hearing her responses to the prompts I give her has become the highlight of my week, because I truly *never* know what to expect, and am always blown away by the words she puts together. Her writing is sharp, thoughtful, and engaging, and I am so excited for her to share it with the world.

Zoom to the Moon

ALBA SUAREZ

While writing this essay, my goal was to keep things lighthearted and tell an entertaining story that also shared a bit of my personality and interests.

I hop from the scalding-hot concrete sidewalk into my family car, with my parents and best friend Sama, sheltering ourselves from the sticky, humid summer air with the glorious freshness of the AC. We are on our way to the beach. Unfortunately, when you live in New York City, beaches tend to be an hour-and-a-half car ride away minimum, but that's no problem for me. I came prepared.

As soon as we're set on our way down the Long Island Expressway, I whip out my favorite game, very descriptively titled Things They Don't Teach You in School: A Crazy Mix of Fun Facts, Random Trivia, and Totally Useless Knowledge. In theory, the structure of the game *should* involve reading questions aloud and your fellow players shouting answers to accumulate the maximum number of points possible, but my company seems to be less than enthused. I suppose I can't really blame them for not being particularly excited to hear that the average human produces two pints of mucus every day, but by this point, their brains are likely saturated with my incessant blabbering of fun facts.

You see, random trivia has been quite the passion of mine ever since I got my hands on the Do You Have What It Takes to Be a Millionaire board game circa 2012. Ever since, the latest episode of *Jeopardy!* (airing every Friday at seven p.m. Eastern Time) or any other evening TV trivia game show has never failed to bring out an inordinate amount of competitive adrenaline in me. Where else would I learn that humans shed an average of twenty-two kilograms of skin in their lifetime, and that one out of every two thousand babies is born with teeth, or that the calcium carbonate found in fish poop reduces the amount of CO_2 in seawater and is being investigated as a potential key to success in the battle to lower greenhouse gas levels in the atmosphere?

Realistically, the majority of people in my life don't need to be reminded of these random ordinances of their existence. My mother could live without being told that nail polish was originally used by Babylonian soldiers as a method to intimidate their enemies every time she comes home with a pedicure. My father is understandably aggravated when I remind him that "fatbergs," rock-hard balls of human waste, are an increasing problem in New York City waste-processing plants due to the rise of disposable wet wipes flushed down the pipes every time he has to unclog our bathroom toilet.

However, I can say with confidence that knowing these things gives me more than just the satisfaction of being able to impart a bit of knowledge at the most inconvenient times. Take this fact, for example: Neil Armstrong's footsteps will remain on the moon for more than 100 million years. Although the moon's lack of an erosive atmosphere is fascinating in its own right, there is more to it than that. Knowing this reminds me every day that human life may be painfully temporary, but the footprints of the achievements we make have the potential to last for generations. Understanding how short-lived and fragile the human experience is makes wanting to absorb every little tidbit there is to know about the world we call home seem much less bizarre.

PAROMITA TALUKDER

YEARS AS MENTEE: 1

GRADE: Junior

BORN: Sylhet, Bangladesh

LIVES: Bronx, NY

PUBLICATIONS & RECOGNITIONS:
Scholastic Art & Writing Awards:
Silver Key, Honorable Mention;
staff writer for *The Science
Survey*, newspaper of The Bronx
High School of Science

MENTEE'S ANECDOTE:

While writing this poem, my mentor and I learned a lot about each other and discussed our commonalities. We brainstormed together in a shared Google Doc, watching each other's icon pop in and out, type, delete, etc. In order to let both of our voices shine, we had to communicate our entire thought processes, which was intimidating in the beginning, but proved to be essential for teamwork. I think we both developed more perspectives on writing and editing in general through our shared ideas. Although there were various obstacles, we managed to create an incredible piece of poetry.

PRISCILLA GUO

YEARS AS MENTOR: 1

OCCUPATION: Policy Adviser at
Day One Project

BORN: New York, NY

LIVES: Queens, NY

PUBLICATIONS & RECOGNITIONS:
The New York Times

MENTOR'S ANECDOTE:

I love the way Paromita sees the world and finds new ways to share her perspective. In her world, eyes become "piercing orbs" and people move with "levelled staccato footfalls." At the beginning of the year, she expressed interest to me in exploring a new genre—poetry—which happens to be one of my passions. We explored inspirations in feminist art, from the Guerilla Girls to Jenny Holzer, and poetry about identity, from Ocean Vuong to Ofelia Zepeda. This poem is a testament to our journey and growth together as mentor and mentee and as two women poets.

We Are Girls from the East

PAROMITA TALUKDER AND PRISCILLA GUO

The poem speaks to our shared history as Asian American women, emphasizing a colonial past in China and India, our liberation, and the formation of new rituals between generations all through the lens of tea.

I. we are girls from the East

the Buddha's eyelids drop to the floor
or a leaf blows into the Emperor's cup*
so goes, the beginning of a 5,000-year sojourn
down the Yangtze, across the Ganges.
drink in all the yin†
clear the humours
a daily ritual spent in tonnes.

from the fields to the drawing rooms‡
to sate that peckish feeling
in the afternoon.

---

* The origin stories of how we came to have tea speak of a tea plant springing up from the fallen eyelids of the Buddha, which he had torn off upon breaking a vow of meditation, and the happenchance of Emperor Shen Nung.
† Bodies are made of a balance between yin and yang elements. When there is too much yang, traditional Chinese medicine advises drinking more yin, like tea.
‡ A drawing room was a parlor used by English court ladies for entertaining. It was a term widely used in India and Pakistan, dating from colonial days.

our exotic medicine transformed
for consumption in fancy China far away from the China man.

a history that is darker than the brew
steeping until the water takes our color,

We are girls from the East.

II. our Oppression ≠ their Oppression

they took tomahawks to the ships*
our oppression was their oppression,
so they said.
our oppression was a distraction†
like a spill from the same cup,
quickly, they slap
using the flimsiest chiffon—treaties and diplomas and deeds and
    Deeds,
the white papers browned and yellowed
yet the spill seeped through.
blindly the Men of Commonwealth try to give shape
to the elephant carrying Ashoka's wheel
here lies Pakistan and here India
a Partition, blind.
yet, even the elephants with stars and stripes have lost their eyes
and clumsily, they charge in stampedes into the house they call home,

---

* Tomahawks are a type of axlike tool used by Native Americans. They were used
by the American Revolutionaries in the Boston Tea Party to feign their identities
as Indigenous peoples.
† During the War of 1812 between Great Britain and European colonists, the English were predominantly occupied with their colonies in South and East Asia. The
American Revolution was merely one battle within a larger worldwide conflict with
France, Spain, and India. Thus, Britain was forced to use military resources elsewhere instead of America.

drinking the tea, made from tobacco leaves and petrol
a slow poison,

too late to finally *see the elephant**

III. a drink for the Leopards

a 3000 B.C. Ayurvedic remedy trails
trading hands
hands
and hands
wherever we go

fissure on the shell, carved with black gold
stolen from the gardens of Assam
crackle, sizzle, pop
followed by the emancipation of an aroma
that exhilarates the wind and invites guests:
an excuse for a discussion
an excuse that cannot be refused.

sip
stay alert during long court hours, the Emperor Ashoka said,
it came
down the Yangtze, across the Ganges
bitter as it left its home
cursed China in cursed China.

the Angrezi, the gwailou,[†]
invite us to drink

---

* *Seeing the elephant* is an Americanism of the Wild West that alludes to journeys
and experiences that came at a significant cost.
[†] Angrezi and gwailou were names for the British in India and China.

to accept brings a different death
than to refuse and frown.
blood from the kettle tainted the soil
as the Red Coats trampled a path through the brown man's garden,
and men from the Middle Kingdom swam in poppy tears.

Leopards keep breaking into the temple for a drink,*
once in the morning
a soft pearly brown to open the sky
once in the evening
when it's absorbed the day's light,

the asperities of our porcelain cup dissolve
in stygian waters.

We are girls from the East.
we write to
remember the temples before the leopards came
before blind men were led by blind elephants
for the plants without roots to hear
to hear,
wails of long-gone shadows
chanted in the waves of the Indian Sea†
held in the march of the Children of Troubled Times,‡

carried on the back of tomorrow's wind is
the story of
how we regained our independence on foreign soil.

---

* "Leopards break into the temple and drink all the sacrificial vessels dry; it keeps happening; in the end, it can be calculated in advance and is incorporated into the ritual." (Franz Kafka, "Leopards in the Temple")
† This phrase is taken from the Indian national anthem titled "Jana Gana Mana," written by polymath Rabindranath Tagore.
‡ The "March of the Volunteers," the national anthem of the People's Republic of China written by Tian Han in 1934 during the Japanese invasion of China, was first featured in the Chinese film *Children of Troubled Times.*

SANDY TAN

YEARS AS MENTEE: 2

GRADE: Senior

BORN: New York, NY

LIVES: New York, NY

PUBLICATIONS & RECOGNITIONS:
2020 Teen Writing Contest and Ned Vizzini Teen Writing Prize Poetry Finalist; 2020 New York City Youth Poet Laureate Finalist

MENTEE'S ANECDOTE:

Over the past two years, Claudia has taught me so many things about what it truly means to be a writer. From exploring poetry to flash fiction, I have learned that the possibilities are endless in creative writing. Claudia has helped me find my voice as a writer, and she has shown me that I should never be afraid to use it.

CLAUDIA MARINA

YEARS AS MENTOR: 2

OCCUPATION: Lecturer at Parsons School of Design

BORN: Miami, FL

LIVES: Brooklyn, NY

PUBLICATIONS & RECOGNITIONS:
Preface to the 2020 Edition of *Wild Things: The Material Culture of Everyday Life* by Judy Attfield; "Making and Unmaking the Ephemeral Object: Design, Consumption, and the Importance of Everyday Life in Understanding Design Beyond the Studio"

MENTOR'S ANECDOTE:

Sandy has inspired me over the last two years to explore creative aspects of my writing long forgotten and replaced by "work." I cherish our weekly meetings and the poems we write, the genres we explore, and the conversations we have about how writing is what we make of it and also so much more.

The Believer Who Didn't Believe

SANDY TAN

*Macy is far from being the math whiz her parents want her to be.
Will God be the one to change this?*

Macy was remarkably average. Her hair was black and straight. She had almond eyes with deep brown irises that would give you the impression that you had something on your face. Standing at five feet one and a half, Macy was the definition of the average little Asian girl. Not a piano prodigy, a math whiz, or anything else Americans would peg as Asian, for that matter. In fact, she despised math and would spend hours doing it for homework. Macy's parents weren't the type to tutor her, and they couldn't even if they wanted to. They would ramble on and on about how they were busy picking firewood at Macy's age back in China, and finding X in an equation wouldn't feed any mouths. Once report card day arrived, however, their attitude changed. Since they couldn't help Macy, they did what every good parent would do when they couldn't help their child: send them to after-school care.

It was one of those "after-school camps" that virtually everyone signed up to attend. It's always the same "limited-time-only, 10 percent–off sale" that gets each and every one of them. Of course, Macy's math skills didn't improve at all. She was too busy playing Sudoku and Connect Four to care about such trivial matters.

When she returned home, her parents would tell her their decade-old tales of farming back home and how it had all been replaced by skyscrapers and new shiny developments that Macy's cousins inhabited now.

"You see those pictures they send? The road repaved, houses rebuilt, nothing feels like home anymore. Your cousins keep talking about their houses, but what do we get?"

Macy's mom was not much of a tiger parent, but she still loved spewing comparisons to anyone who would listen. It was the same things she would tell the tiny Buddha statue that adorned the red altar she prayed to during those special holidays marked on the lunar calendar. Macy didn't dare question her mom's faith, but she didn't particularly believe that lighting up incense that triggered the smoke alarm and pouring tea to the gods would grant any of her wishes. If the gods were listening, she would've been five feet five already.

Macy continued to attend after-school camp, and the community leaders would sometimes bring in guests to talk to the students. After many failed attempts to gain anyone's interest, the camp staff invited Mary, a skinny, tall Asian lady in her mid-forties. Her voice was soft, but it commanded your attention. She had small spectacles perched on the top of her nose and a tiny Bible in her hands. Every afternoon, Macy would sit in during Mary's lessons, where she would turn to a new section in the Bible. Mary talked about morals and the messages of God. She spoke about forgiveness and sin. Good and evil. When Macy told her mom what she had learned, her face turned sour.

"They brainwash you. Do not listen," she demanded.

In the following week, Macy found out that her mother had disenrolled her in the after-school camp. Her mother gave her a $30 AMSCO textbook to study off of instead. This time, Macy's math scores were finally showing some improvement. Before long, Macy had forgotten about the whole incident.

Math would still be a difficult subject for Macy in the subsequent years, but her trusty AMSCO textbook had it all. For good measure, however, Macy would close her eyes and make a wish before every test. You can never be too sure if someone is listening.

THE UNOFFICIAL HAFSAH

YEARS AS MENTEE: 1

GRADE: Junior

BORN: Bronx, NY

LIVES: Bronx, NY

MENTEE'S ANECDOTE:

Through the entire crafting process, Amanda has supported me and encouraged me to continue to write despite my fears. With her motherly and loving demeanor, she pushed me to write about topics that were important to me. As a first-time mentee, I feel Amanda has made this experience extremely fruitful and I can never thank her enough.

AMANDA SMITH

YEARS AS MENTOR: 1

OCCUPATION: Visual Artist

BORN: Auckland (Tamaki Makaurau), Aotearoa/New Zealand

LIVES: Poneke/Wellington, Aotearoa

MENTOR'S ANECDOTE:

As a first-time mentor, I am proud and awed to work with Asta. We are, in many ways, from differing universes, and I suspect that scared both of us in the beginning. I love our quick writing prompt sessions, which highlight the ways we see the world. Asta's drive and perseverance are so impressive to me. She finds the same joy in creating that I do, using it to contain the swirling world. It is joyous to read. Nga mihi, Asta.

Stop

THE UNOFFICIAL HAFSAH

A soul's response when the world is too noisy and a heart is silenced for too long.

Can you please lower your volume,
Hush down,

Can you be quiet,
Quiet now,
Silent.

Let the tears fall silently coating the pages

With the rubble of the storm within
Let the pain roar
And be HEARD and SEEN
UNAFRAID, and UNTAMED

And let the world stop needing you to perform
To conform
To do amazing things!
Let it all stop,

And be SILENT.

May Allah grant us the ability to appreciate and claim back our silence.

ANNA VAVAGIAKIS

YEARS AS MENTEE: 1

GRADE: Freshman

BORN: New York, NY

LIVES: Brooklyn, NY

MENTEE'S ANECDOTE:

I had never had a mentor before Rachel and always loved the idea of having one. Rachel is so much better than I ever pictured. She is amazing to talk to and hang out with. She is so supportive and helpful. Every time we meet she always makes sure that I'm not stressed with work. I know that if I ever need any help that Rachel would be there for me. I wouldn't have been able to write this short story without her. I can't wait to do more projects with her and couldn't be more proud to be her mentee.

RACHEL CANTRELL

YEARS AS MENTOR: 1

OCCUPATION: Senior Verbal
Designer

BORN: Los Angeles, CA

LIVES: Brooklyn, NY

MENTOR'S ANECDOTE:

As a first-year mentor at Girls Write Now, I was nervous about how I'd be able to foster an exciting and welcoming environment for writing through Zoom. But that all went away when I had my first conversation with Anna. I was immediately inspired by her room at home—her walls are covered with amazing artwork, much of which she's created herself. She's brought that same creativity to her writing, from speculative fiction to fun horror stories, and she surprises me every week with her brilliant ideas and sharp prose. I can't wait to read what she writes next.

Again

ANNA VAVAGIAKIS

I wrote this piece on 2020: the events that occurred then, and how it might affect people in the future. I encourage everyone to look forward—be strong, be brave, and stay safe.

"Okay, class, are we clear on our assignments?" the teacher says. "Remember, if you can't find someone who lived through 2020, then you can just write a two-paragraph essay."

"Yes, we get it," Young Girl responds, irritation clear in her voice.

"Have a great day, students, and don't forget to go outside today—"

Before her teacher can finish, Young Girl clicks the red button.

* * * * * *

Buzz buzz. A woman picks up her phone, seeing a text—and above it, the date. She can't believe it's actually December. She sits at a large table across from her daughter.

"What are you learning about in school nowadays?" the mother asks, stabbing a piece of chicken.

"We just finished learning about the Obama era. Our new unit is on 2020."

The mother laughs. Ignoring it, Young Girl continues.

"We are supposed to write an essay on 2020. I was thinking I could interview you. You went through it, didn't you?"

"Sure did!" the mother remarks.

"Well, can I interview you after dinner?" Young Girl asks through a mouthful of chicken.

Her mother sighs. "Manners. But sounds good."

✳✳✳✳✳✳

"So, what happened?" Young Girl brings her notebook to her lap.

"2020. Wow, okay. There were so many big moments, and I don't remember all of them. Granted, it was over a decade ago.

"I was in eighth grade and I was, at first, separated from the news. I did not pay attention, I did not have social media, and that did not help either. That was until the pandemic started. Then, I couldn't help but read the news and know what was going on. It began, I believe, with me and my classmates thinking World War Three was going to happen. We were kids, so we did not know what was really going on. We were dumb too, so that didn't really help. We ate Tide Pods, for God's sake."

"What?" her daughter interrupts.

Her mother gives her a soft smile. "Never mind." She continues.

"My whole world was flipped upside down, and I was scared. We started online school, which was supposed to be temporary." The mother raises her eyebrows.

"We had to wear masks outside. We could not touch the people we loved. And as if that was not enough, we lost some of the greatest people that ever lived. Kobe Bryant, Chadwick Boseman, Ruth Bader Ginsburg"—the mother glanced at a "Males Only" sign on the house next door—"and so many more. We had to deal with injustice and unfairness left and right. We had to deal with losing loved ones and losing ourselves. And when we thought we hit rock bottom, we just hit it again. It was absolutely . . . horrific."

The woman has her head in her hands. She is crying. Her daughter sits beside her, unaware of what to do.

"People went crazy, and I couldn't blame them. No one could. I remember when the election happened. I had so many news tabs open on my computer and kept checking them. I was so stressed. But there were still good things that happened too."

The mother wipes her tears away and looks up at her daughter, smiling.

"Timothée Chalamet hosted SNL with Pete Davidson. Man, I was what they used to call a fangirl! Donald Trump got COVID-19, and, of course, Joe Biden and Kamala Harris won the presidency. That must have been one of the greatest and happiest days of my life. Everyone went into the streets and started to holler, blasting music and celebrating more than I have ever seen. It was amazing. Seeing that celebration gave me hope to last me a lifetime." The mother shakes her head, sniffling.

She continues for hours. Young Girl is barely able to write everything down.

"That . . . was a lot," Young Girl says softly.

"Yes, yes, it was. And I am sure I still missed things," she says, laughing at her daughter's shocked face. "Sorry, that got a little intense."

"No, it's no problem. I'm definitely going to have the best essay."

Her mother smiles at her and puts her hand up to Young Girl's cheek. "It is way past your bedtime, honey. Why don't you head to bed?"

"Okay, love you, Mom."

"Love you too, sweetie." The mother kisses her forehead. Young Girl leaves with her papers, full of notes. The mother, alone, stares at the clock, light tears coming down her face. She does not sob. After a few minutes, she turns off the lights and walks upstairs.

* * * * * *

"Mom, I am going to play outside!" Young Girl, in a short-sleeved shirt and shorts, puts on her shoes and ties them while sitting on the stairs.

"Okay, sweetie, be careful," the mother shouts from the dining room.

Young Girl gets her mask, hanging next to the keys by the door, and puts it on. She hops on her bike and glides ahead—right past the Madison family's "Whites Only" sign, gliding past the café's "Females Not Allowed" sign—all the way down the street, wondering what life was like before 2020.

GRACE WANG

YEARS AS MENTEE: 1

GRADE: Junior

BORN: Queens, NY

LIVES: Queens, NY

PUBLICATIONS & RECOGNITIONS:
Certificate of Excellence, Essay
Contest "What Makes a Hero"

MENTEE'S ANECDOTE:

Abby has been more than a mentor to me; through the pandemic and through weekly Zoom calls, she is also my friend. I can count on her and talk to her about anything that's on my mind. Although I am not the best writer, Abby has helped me improve and see writing in a different light. My favorite memory with her was when we were working on our pair project. We worked together to make our ideas come to life, and with all the effort we put into our work, two months later, it came out beautifully. Thank you, Abby!

ABBY S

YEARS AS MENTOR: 1

OCCUPATION: Writer,
Communications

BORN: Berkeley, CA

LIVES: Brooklyn, NY

MENTOR'S ANECDOTE:

Grace has a great sense of humor and is excited and passionate about the world around her. Since we met last fall, she's talked often about her interest in STEM—especially chemistry and computer-programming languages—and it's great to hear her describe these areas and what's going on in her life week to week. Her writing is wonderful, and I'm really excited about the work she's been doing this year and getting to know her.

COVID Rewind: Thoughts & Reflections

GRACE WANG AND ABBY S

A look into 2020 through the diverse eyes of interviewees from New York City. These interviewees describe their thoughts and experiences living through the pandemic.

2020 was a year like no other. With coronavirus, millions of people have died worldwide, and millions have lost jobs, income, family, and security. And the pandemic is still raging.

2020 started with celebration, laughter, gathering, partying, sleepovers, playdates, concerts, movie theaters—one kind of normalcy. But in New York, since last spring we've found ourselves in isolation, separation, and lockdown.

What has it been like? Words and phrases that didn't mean anything—Zoom, breakout rooms, social distancing, toilet paper, alcohol, gloves, masks, soap—suddenly have taken on new meaning. It can seem that we are drowning in a new reality.

Samantha Rodriguez, a high school senior in Brooklyn, describes her year as a "whirlwind. Definitely nothing anyone could have predicted." She reflects on last year, "I just feel extinguished."

In the midst of the chaos and uncertainty, Rodriguez had to go through the college application process. "Deadlines were up in the air, constantly moving and shifting. Schools were not even sure what was happening," she says.

Luckily, Rodriguez had been preparing for the application process prior to COVID. She applied for a Posse Foundation scholarship, which is awarded by a nonprofit organization to individuals with leadership potential. Rodriguez won the full-tuition Posse scholarship to attend DePauw University in Indiana. "I am blessed enough where my father has a job, and I have a full-tuition scholarship for college," she adds.

Thinking about the future, Rodriguez says she wants to live in the present. "To not get stuck in the whirlwind of technology and social media."

Still, Rodriguez notes that even as time can seem to be at a standstill, things have happened. "Everyone is waiting for 2020 to be over, but life still goes on. People are still being born, birthdays are happening, anniversaries are happening."

Other residents face different challenges.

Amanda, a Girls Write Now mentor, has struggled making finances work to continue living in the city. At the end of February 2021, she plans on returning home to New Zealand because she is unable to stay here when there is no work. "I am really struggling with living off New Zealand money. Every time I bring over a dollar from New Zealand, I lose $0.40. And it's just not making sense anymore," she explains. It deeply disappoints her, because she loves being in New York.

Even so, as a visual artist, Amanda has been able to continue doing the thing she loves—creating art through the pandemic. Amanda admits, "I'm pretty impressed with myself that I've managed to maintain what I'm doing, even though at points, it felt pretty hard."

She's taken great value in the little moments she's had with people in person and has learned the importance of social interactions and communication with neighbors.

Olivia, another Girls Write Now mentor, took a job a couple years ago as a journalist in New York, and felt panic as lockdown began and she realized she would have to work from home all the time. "I definitely felt trapped," she says. "I mean, my bedroom and the living room in my apartment both don't have windows!"

Like many others, over time, Olivia finally accepted that the pandemic wasn't going to be something short-lived. She has learned many lessons through her experience, such as finding that even in such a bustling city, "it's okay to take breaks—whether that's going for a walk, listening to a podcast, calling a friend or family member, or doing ten minutes of posture stretches." Sometimes we are trying to set healthier routines and a path meant for healing and mindfulness in the life we currently live.

Grace and Abby, the mentee-mentor pair writing this piece, have both experienced ebbs and flows throughout the past year. Grace, who lives in Queens, says that the pandemic took a toll on her mental health: "I eventually got better. I got used to this new routine." She has also gone through some pretty big changes. "I got my first job working at an ice cream shop," Grace says. This year has also helped Grace find new communication tools and styles. "I've subconsciously gotten better at what I need," Grace says.

Abby, who lives in Brooklyn, says, "I need more sleep than I used to," describing this year as tiring. "It's strange to me that soon it will be one year from March 2020," she adds. "There's a tree outside my window and it's a beautiful big tree. It's nice to see the seasons change," she says of the things that make her happy.

Although we all struggled collectively in different ways, some have found new methods to cope and adapt to this new lifestyle. The pandemic is not over yet, but the world still moves on, and the other side is still waiting for us. Hang in there, as better times are ahead.

TRACY WANG

YEARS AS MENTEE: 1

GRADE: Freshman

BORN: Brooklyn, NY

LIVES: Brooklyn, NY

MENTEE'S ANECDOTE:

My mentor and I together have voiced our own burning concerns and worries for the events that are happening in the world right now. It is disheartening, but as we brought together our individual fears into writing, we established a place of comfort and safety that only being open-minded and vulnerable to one another can achieve. Through intimate confessions, we found writing to be a great way to free ourselves from a terrible reality while still being consciously aware. We present to you a glimpse of what we both have experienced, questioned, and learned from during a pandemic lifestyle.

CAROLINE COOPER

YEARS AS MENTOR: 1

OCCUPATION: English Teacher at City College of New York

BORN: New York, NY

LIVES: Brooklyn, NY

MENTOR'S ANECDOTE:

Tracy and I have explored a number of themes and topics together in our sessions, with a focus on poetry, personal narrative, and reflective writing. After much discussion and exploration of topics that interest us both deeply, we found ourselves writing about and reflecting on the current pandemic and its many facets. We are excited to share these segments that provide a bit of a glimpse into our own experiences and observations at this time.

A Winter in Quarantine; My One Year Story

TRACY WANG AND CAROLINE COOPER

And then I feel anxiety for a good thirty minutes, hating how I was the only one concerned at that moment.

Tracy Wang

Why does it glaringly seem as if our history is obviously repeating?
The history I have not seen but seen vividly in my head through
historical accounts.
Passive words that described our history, the American history.
Was it leptospirosis?
Or was it smallpox, measles, or the lethal influenza?
Then if not the three, was it polio or the swine flu?
And was it the great depression when unemployment statistics rang
throughout the entire nation at petrifying rates?
Since segregation ended, discrimination was riding its reins and finally
found sprinkled all over our government officials today.
Why were they still up there?
Why was there another injustice on the news today?
Why can't I do anything to stop these sickening crimes in the legal
system?
Why was there even a debate on whether the death penalty was
unconstitutional,
When a presidential pardon on any acts of crime was constitutional?

When we say to write down history so we can learn from it, did we
    truly learn the events that happened a century ago?

When we call the pandemic an unprecedented time, was that true?
Haven't pandemics happened before?
Haven't we just relapsed and against our better judgment, against our
    controls, we had turned back time and were again reliving a truly
    terrible reality?
Imagining death around corners and the elderly especially,
Who anticipate an outstretched hand towards them that's coated with
    a sickly virus.
Or first responders who put up a smile for their dying patients,
But faced internal clashes as they themselves tried to cling onto their
    own lives.
For whoever is in danger of losing their homes after their jobs, they
    aren't on the streets, right?
And for those who were stuck in their houses, are they fine too?
Could they leave as they wanted—whenever, wherever?
In a year that drew a dark streak across the lives of many, that cast a
    dark shadow in history books, we found ourselves asking the
    question *why* more than ever.
When I flip through the articles that educate me in the place of school I
    can't help but feel anxiety.
And then I feel it for a good thirty minutes,
Fretting the dire need for change and hating how
I was the only one concerned in that moment.
Where do we find the balance between ignorance
and knowing too much to the point that it hurts?

Why is the future so unstable?
Why was there such an urgency to earn money at the age of fourteen?
Why did I have to learn to talk to myself kindly from someone other
    than my parents?

Whatever do I do as I bear witness to a police officer abusing their
    power, perhaps on a black stranger, perhaps on a black friend?
Whatever do I do when I see a woman being assaulted on the streets?
Whatever do I do when these scenarios, ugly as they are enough, are
    suddenly directed at me?

Does this sort out to make me sound like a victim?
Was it like that?
Nonetheless, things from here on have taken an unprecedented
    new face.
People would want a voice, people would want to be heard, people
    would fight for change, this time unmuted.

Caroline Cooper

Every day, we're bombarded by choices, messages, opportunities, warnings. As the one-year anniversary of the COVID-19 pandemic approaches, it's impossible not to see all the many ways our lives have
forever changed, some all at once. I have struggled with this strange new
world. Even as we are confined and isolated, we consume more media
than ever before. This social disconnect and the level of cognitive disso-
nance it engenders have left me feeling strange, sometimes physically
sick.

I've always been a loner, never really looking for big groups of friends
or joining crowds. So when the pandemic first hit, I thought the ensuing
isolation would be tough, but manageable. I thought I could lean in to
being an independent person and just get by as best I could.

As the crisis worsened, however, and American leadership failed to
meet the moment, my earlier confidence in my little dingy of independence started to get whipped and tossed on this vast ocean of chaos.

I am a forty-four-year-old woman, without children or strong ties to
my family. When the pandemic started, I was living with my husband
in a small town in faraway Holland. We don't speak Dutch. When the
government decided to shut down all nonessential businesses and restau-

rants, Dutch people came running through the streets of their village and formed lines to make desperate, last-minute purchases for who knows how long. When we reached the front of the grocery store line, a man suddenly shut and bolted the doors. We couldn't understand. The man on the other side of the door couldn't explain.

But then after a few minutes, the man simply turned around. He opened the door. We wandered around for a few seconds, blinded by the infinity of the place. We were inside a grocery store again! See? It happened very fast. We did not expect it.

All the major events of a life unfold in the instant, in mere seconds. Everything of importance, of any real consequence, takes exactly one second. The look exchanged between two new lovers. The moment the baby is placed on the mother's chest. The statements "You're hired," "Stage four," "Marry me," "I don't love you anymore." One second. Our lives tick by as we wait for these seconds. They pass thunderously, leaving a trail of the buckled and battered who both cannot believe and yet want to believe.

To experience an unrelenting series of these moments, to watch them pile up like produce in the sometimes-open, now-closed-again grocery store, is to potentially contract "Ta-ko-tsu-bo syndrome. This ailment starts with a weakening of the left ventricle, the heart's main pumping chamber, usually as the result of severe emotional or physical stress, such as sudden illness, loss, profound heartbreak, or natural disaster. The condition is also known as stress-induced cardio-my-op-athy, or broken-heart syndrome. The heart comes to resemble the shape of the ta-ko-tsu-bo, a Japanese octopus trap in which the animal can climb in but never escape."

While this is a real and serious medical condition, I believe you can conduct your own tests at home. The pandemic has provided ample room and time. Lie in your bed. Put your hand on your heart. Feel its valves and pulses. Wonder at its industry. And consider—what is keeping me alive? Is it the meat of this flesh-muscle in the center of my chest? Or is it a Japanese octopus trap, one into which I seem to have climbed but may never escape?

ZUZANNA WASILUK

YEARS AS MENTEE: 1

GRADE: Junior

BORN: Brooklyn, NY

LIVES: Brooklyn, NY

MENTEE'S ANECDOTE:

My mentor takes what I write and dissects it to give me a better understanding of my writing and my intentions with the piece. This provides more clarity when I'm editing. When we begin a new piece, we follow an outline that follows a structure Aphrodite taught me. I shared a piece of writing about tea that moved her, but she still asked for me to distill each paragraph to the bare bones as an exercise. The exercise made me realize how much of my writing is ambiguous and how easily I get lost in details.

APHRODITE BRINSMEAD

YEARS AS MENTOR: 1

OCCUPATION: Product Marketing

BORN: Hampshire, England

LIVES: Brooklyn, NY

MENTOR'S ANECDOTE:

I feel incredibly lucky to be mentoring Zuzanna. She's impressively productive and always seeks out feedback, taking suggestions into consideration. Although our writing styles couldn't be more different, I think we make a great team. She loves descriptive, unique language and metaphors, whereas I prefer simple, punchy sentences. This helps me to be more creative in my own writing and Zuzanna has added more action and active voice into her work. The taxidermist story really shows how Zuzanna has developed as a writer to create a curious tale of loneliness and strange behavior.

The Taxidermist and His Dog

ZUZANNA WASILUK

Ted was a taxidermist who lived in Albany. He adopted a dog when he broke off his only friendship with an intelligent university student when the friend's family died in a house fire.

Ted was an isolated character who outstretched the hand of friendship to only one talented university student. The pair of friends had undeniable gifts that separated them, yet the fear and guilt that plagued them were sisters. The day before the student's birthday, the friend grieved for every single member of his family that passed in a house fire. Ted remarked how the term *house fire* didn't do any justice toward the enormity of their family mansion.

Ted's friend murmured, "Are you an arsonist now? It was only seventy-five hundred feet, hardly a mansion. We even had to build a house near it for our maids."

"Did that burn down too?"

"I'll check for you." But instead his friend walked to his bed and the tension between them increased.

Abandoning his friend to deal with the sweet shame of his life without companionship entitled Ted to a dog. On the same day he brought the dog home, he bought toy soldiers for the dog's entertainment and blockaded the door to his studio with belts he'd outgrown. As soon as he'd fed the dog, Ted returned to his studio. He spoke out metaphors that disqualified him from being both a taxidermist and a pet owner until the dog's purpose occurred to him . . . He was growing terrified that his habits and preferences perpetuated a mechanical way of living. He knew that if his mind was limited it would be reflected in his craft.

His plan for the dog worked like a disembodied clock. It had all the right elements to work: the dog, toys for the dog, food, and a place solely dedicated to the dog's rest. But it didn't because Ted was too proud to accept creative help. He was agonizingly aware of the dog's potential contribution to the project he'd been stuck on but refused this help.

One Sunday, during a time where there were two different kinds of light peering through the window, the dog turned a corner too fast. Its legs became hooked on the carpet, which shifted the vase into colliding with the floor. This Sunday, Ted was particularly exhausted because he'd been up all night monitoring his dog's strange intestinal affliction that caused him to retch and gag.

Without brushing his teeth, he took the dog to the vet, who briefed him on the contents of his dog's stomach: "He appears to have eaten three cherry tarts in the last twenty-four hours, which caused the upset stomach. It didn't help to flush it all down with mint tea and pistachio macaroons." The Bastard.

The vet held up her clipboard and jotted down a series of instructions for Ted to follow over the next week. She turned to him but kept her eyes to the paper. "What do you do for a living?"

Ted anticipated her reaction if she had bothered to look up from her clipboard. He answered, "I'm a taxidermist."

Suddenly, the vet appeared to forget the lengthy list of instructions she required Ted to complete to prevent the dog from dry-heaving for seven additional days. She moved closer to him, too close, and whispered, "Is this . . . a project . . . of yours?"

Ted weighed the idea of using his talent in taxidermy on his dog by imagining two golden scales. "Maybe, if there were ways to preserve the digested cherry tarts or the odor of the mint tea in his stomach."

He asked her to hand over the instructions, noticing the vet scribble a message in the corner of the page, a ten-digit phone number and her name. Was he supposed to call her if he taxidermied his dog, or was this an extension of her impeccable bedside manner? Were vets actually morbid, rescuing and healing animals after lunch and before dinner, while by night they watched the deconstruction of their anatomy? He reached for the dog with his left hand while the dog stared at Ted's hand, trying to understand what the gesture could mean. He walked toward the vet, who held out a treat for the dog's good behavior, and threw it in the carrier. Ted took the carrier in his right hand.

Driving back home, Ted stopped at the grocery store for a few ingredients. He needed onions and garlic for himself, and the organic dog breakfast mix recommended by the vet. Who pays $20 for dog food? He held up the dog food next to a bag of children's breakfast cereal to show the dog his options. Gesturing to the two bags, he said, "One of these is supposed to cure cancer and the other childhood obesity! You're getting this one!"

When the cashier scanned the breakfast cereal, Ted lied by telling her he had two beautiful kids named Theodora and Junior. The head vet's name was Theodora and she expected Ted to call her . . . but he still wasn't sure why. He thanked the cashier and started to plan his dinner with such intensity that he forgot to signal one hundred feet before turning. Decidedly, it was going to be a dinner without any cherry tarts for dessert.

LAUREN WEISBERG

YEARS AS MENTEE: 1

GRADE: Senior

BORN: Staten Island, NY

LIVES: Staten Island, NY

PUBLICATIONS & RECOGNITIONS:
Chalkbeat, The 74 Million

MENTEE'S ANECDOTE:

Our relationship is one centered on horror and suspense, whether it be talking about real-world issues or fictional works. I appreciate Lucy's constant encouragement throughout the writing and college processes, insisting I apply to programs that I really like even when I'm doubtful and to continue unearthing story ideas when I'm not sure of them myself.

LUCY CARSON

YEARS AS MENTOR: 1

OCCUPATION: Literary Agent

BORN: New York, NY

LIVES: New York, NY

MENTOR'S ANECDOTE:

Reading and writing with Lauren is always the highlight of my week. She is full of wildly creative ideas and she's an expert at executing plot twists. It's an honor to watch her grow and challenge herself as a storyteller.

The Man

LAUREN WEISBERG

As college draws nearer, Nora's recurring nightmares begin to catch up with her real-life anxieties.

As Nora sat down at the dinner table, she grabbed for her butter knife and clutched it in her hand, knowing her fate well and hoping to prevent it.

"How was your day?" her mother asked lovingly, yet obliviously, placing a plate of chicken parmigiana in front of her. The smell made her mouth water, though she knew she wouldn't have time to eat. He would be coming soon.

It began to rain; a harsh tapping noise against the window told her so. It always rained in this dream.

"What a nasty day!" her father said, as though it all hadn't just started a moment before.

"Honey, I asked about your . . ." Nora's mother was cut off by the sound of the front door whipping open. There stood a man in the doorway tall enough to fill out the frame. Even though it had happened a few times before, Nora's heart dropped so low that she could feel its beat in her toes. Though he was all the way across the room, his face was clear to see: oblong and gaunt, with charcoal-colored hair and eyes.

"Honey, we didn't let him in," Nora's mother and father said in unison, staring at her so hard it nearly pierced her skin.

Rain poured into the house from the open doorway as the man advanced into the living room. With the butter knife still in her hand, Nora ran toward the stairs. She knew what the man wanted to do.

The stairs were so close to the door that she was within arm's reach of the man, but she knew that he wouldn't grab her yet. She stopped half-way up the stairs to observe him. Every time she had this nightmare, she tried to notice something new, though after she'd had it so many times it was hard to find anything. He wore his usual dark blazer that hung in torn shreds over his arms. His unusually long legs were dressed in corduroy pants that exposed his bony, hairless ankles. This concoction of fashion was pulled together by round silver glasses.

The man stared intently at Nora. His cheeks blushed pure red and he reached for his glasses. Taking them off, he said, *"You better run."* His voice sounded like crunching leaves.

She pounded up the stairs and ran into her parents' bedroom, closing the door and pressing her back up against it, splaying her hands out over the painted wood like a snow angel in the winter. A sick feeling settled into her stomach. She *knew* she was going to die.

"Nora!" said a familiar voice. She opened her eyes to see her younger sister, Hailey, lying in bed next to her.

"I can't nap with you anymore if you're going to keep waking up screaming like that," she said, unleashing her golden hair from its bun.

The two had a habit of taking naps together, especially during the lazier summer months. The sun came in through their open window, pouring light over their bare tummies. They had reduced themselves to bras to deal with the heat.

"It was a bad dream," Nora said, hoping the nervousness in her voice would let Hailey know she meant it.

"The one about the man?" Hailey asked.

"I keep having it," Nora responded, tired despite the rest she'd gotten.

"You know what'll take your mind off it? Video games," Hailey said with a sweet smile, but Nora wasn't paying attention.

"What time is it?" Nora asked.

"It's ten minutes to four," Hailey said, pulling on her pink unicorn shirt. At fifteen, she still hadn't outgrown her childish obsessions.

"Ten minutes." Nora groaned, holding her head in her hands for a prolonged moment.

"Oh," Hailey said, finally connecting the dots. Nora had an interview with a college admissions officer at four. She was a finalist for a full ride scholarship at a school a thousand miles away in Missouri.

"You better run," Hailey said, and the words sent chills down Nora's spine, though she guessed her sister was right.

She ripped open her closet door and pulled out the gray dress she'd specially bought for this occasion. This was her last interview, the bridge between her and that scholarship.

Nora pulled it on and looked at herself in the mirror. It hung loosely on her petite frame.

"You look great," Hailey said, and Nora nodded in gratitude, then shooed her sister from the room. She pried open her laptop, logged on to Zoom, and tried to mentally prepare herself for the interview.

She typed in the Zoom meeting code and then stared anxiously into the virtual waiting room. She watched the circle spin on and on, waiting for it to finish loading. She held her breath. The room opened. A man with soft, dark eyes stared back at her.

"Hello there," he said, with a surprisingly warm smile.

She swallowed the lump in her throat. The man wore a black poncho that almost resembled a cape, draped over his arms. A minute passed.

"Are you all right?" the man said, pulling off his round silver glasses and resting them on his desk.

"Yes," Nora replied, trying to keep herself calm.

"Are you ready to start the interview?"

TATYANNA WILLS

YEARS AS MENTEE: 1

GRADE: Sophomore

BORN: Botswana

LIVES: Queens, NY

MENTEE'S ANECDOTE:

I enjoyed working with Kate because she always helped me put my ideas on paper.

KATE MARIENTHAL

YEARS AS MENTOR: 1

OCCUPATION: Solutions Engineer

BORN: Chicago, IL

LIVES: Brooklyn, NY

MENTOR'S ANECDOTE:

I enjoy writing with Tatyanna because she is extremely creative and thoughtful. It's been so much fun getting to know each other through writing and poetry.

Garden of Change

TATYANNA WILLS and KATE MARIENTHAL

In heaven, two virtues think about what the future holds for them both.

In an empty garden Diligence sits and thinks
The flowers bloom the birds sing, but to her that doesn't change a thing
It's lonely but hopeful, beautiful but quiet
And if someone else in heaven cared to join her
She definitely would not have minded it

Things have changed since she was brought here
And she wonders how things will change when she leaves
Her heart may still desire to carry on, but she knows this is a role she
    cannot keep
The sun starts to rise, and as the rays warm her face
She quickly realizes that one day it won't be her sitting in this place

But who will it be?
Could it be Chastity?
No she's far too young
Could it be Humility?
No she wouldn't last in a world where everyone is so high-strung
Or could it be another Diligence?
A younger bright-eyed version of her
She must stop thinking about this, her head was starting to hurt

New to this place Chastity sits and thinks
She wonders how she will live up to the expectations
It is clear that Diligence has an icy hold on this world
She sees it as her kingdom
And while she wasn't expecting a warm embrace
She wonders if she'll be willing to share her wisdom

She feels the bed beneath her, it's soft to the touch
Slowly she stands and moves through the room
As she explores she tries not to assume too much
She feels the smooth surface of glossed wood
And when she lifts her fingers they are coated with dust
This space has been long uninhabited
So she moves slowly as she knows she must

As she wanders she wonders if she is the chosen one
She digs deep into herself, and decides what must be done
She will go and meet Diligence
To prove her worth
She will make it known
That she could have a hand over earth

Still Diligence marvels at this place
And how dramatically it has improved
She thinks back longingly on all of the lives she has moved
And wonders what it will mean to begin to say goodbye
To loosen her grip means allowing her companions to grasp on tighter
Acknowledging the power she holds while letting it slip away from her
Knowing that she will no longer be the only history writer

She worries she will not be able to pardon her companions' absence so far
And doubts their ability to maintain what she has built
But alas she tries focusing on what their strengths are
And realizes that without her, heaven will not wilt

As she ponders this decision, it is Chastity who comes to mind
While she is young, she does seem to be kind
And she is so concerned with minding her virtue
She would need certainly to be nurtured

Chastity moves into the hallway, which is warm as always
Heaven was a paradise after all
She hears the conversations of the others
Even so she avoids their call
For what is Chastity if not lonely
What is the use of being a virtue
If she doesn't follow her role perfectly
And what is she worth if she isn't holy

The garden is close now
She senses it all completely
As she approaches the door
She starts to wonder, was the leader thing really meant to be?
Out of all the virtues, would the one who ends up leading really
     be me?
She moves her hand to knock, but hesitates
No, she brushes her thoughts aside, this was most definitely the right
     time and place
She reaches out, takes a deep breath and enters the room
With a smile on her face

Diligence looks up
Chastity is finally here, a smile slowly spreads across her face
Of course she was here
This was the perfect time and place
Her eyes gaze upon the blind girl
She looks nervous, even afraid
Therefore she invites the girl to sit with her
And teaches her how to influence the world

While Diligence should've been the one to make the first move
She is happy that it is not something she needed to prove
It is clear Chastity is brave, eager to learn and ready to pave her way
After all Diligence no longer has the option of doing this alone
And for the first time she feels ready to dive into the unknown

ADELLE XIAO

YEARS AS MENTEE: 1

GRADE: Sophomore

BORN: Queens, NY

LIVES: Queens, NY

PUBLICATIONS & RECOGNITIONS:
Scholastic Art & Writing Awards:
Silver Key

MENTEE'S ANECDOTE:

While I was scared I wouldn't feel comfortable or connected with my mentor, Sarah and I have definitely bonded throughout these past few months. Sarah is authentic, understanding, and supportive, and I genuinely find the time we spend together to be meaningful and valuable. She's really inspired me to become more outspoken and push myself to improve, and I can't wait to see what we can do together in the future!

SARAH A. CUSTEN

YEARS AS MENTOR: 4

OCCUPATION: Educator

BORN: Ogden, UT

LIVES: Brooklyn, NY

MENTOR'S ANECDOTE:

Adelle is my youngest mentee, more reserved, and the first one I haven't met in person. All this made me worry that we weren't really connecting. In our Zoom meetings, she was visible only from the eyes up; I assumed she just wasn't feeling it. One day I asked if she could adjust her screen so I could see her face, and she explained that she meant no disrespect—she's just short. "Wait, how tall are you?" I asked. "Five-two," she said, "How tall are YOU?" "I'm five-nine!" We had a good laugh, and the joy and connection continue to grow.

City Girl

ADELLE XIAO

This piece talks about my relationships with nature and my parents in order to explore my feelings around living in New York City.

I am a city girl. My home is in New York City. In my neighborhood: the blasting of Spanish music and the food trucks I always pass by when I walk to the subway station. Home is the subway during rush hour, repetitive dings of swiping MetroCards and robotic train announcements, and the crowds of people in a train car who make it hard for me to breathe. I imagine home as twinkling luminous streetlights and bustling streets, familiar sights of towering buildings that reach up to hide and cover the sky.

I am a city girl. When I think of nature, I think of hurriedly taken snapshots of cotton-candy clouds and breathtaking sunrises that I save for when I'm stuck at home, longing to venture outside in the world. I am reminded of the unnoticeable plumes and dirty air that I have become accustomed to in my fifteen years here. I clearly picture the sidewalks I walk on every day: strewn with trash bags and things that no one cares about anymore. I mark my footsteps, and I wonder how much of the filth on the concrete sidewalk has come from me over the past four years that I've been walking these same paths.

I am a city girl. I was raised in the city of dreams itself, raised to chase passion and pursue my goals. I grew up reading and fantasizing over unrealistic fairy tales—wishing stars, miracles, and perfection. On cold, lonely nights I remember to dream, to look up and wish on a shooting star. Time freezes in the moment when I lose myself staring at pitch-black, never-ending skies, with the occasional light flickering up above. Are the lights from airplanes passing by, or are they real stars? When I do remember to look up, I pretend that these are stars, pretend that somewhere a wishing star is listening. But I think it's strange that in the city of dreams, I sometimes dream of leaving.

I am a city girl. I've been limited to my life here in New York for so long, but I know my parents cannot say the same. I found myself looking at pictures of the village, imagining that nature was everywhere, in the open, vast skies that seem to reach out and touch every corner of the earth. I imagined living by a still, serene river, waters rippling soothingly and bringing solace. Mountains and hills reaching up and merging with the sky. I grew up hearing occasional snippets of stories about living in a Chinese village from my dad at the dinner table. Stories of having dogs and cats, walking to school, enduring hardships as they came. I never listened.

I am a city girl. I realize I barely know anything about my parents and their upbringing. I don't know firsthand what life in a village is like, what it was like for my parents. I don't know what provinces they came from, what year they came to the US; I don't know anything about my aunts and uncles and cousins, not even what they look like. Although I want to know these things now, I feel ashamed, guilty for not really caring before, for letting their stories die.

I am a city girl. But sometimes, when I think about it, I don't want to be a city girl. The unknown calls for me and I search for a place where I can break free, and no longer feel so small and limited under towering buildings in suffocating crowds and shadows. So now, I remember the stories, and I wonder. What must it have been like to wake up to fresh air and mountains and rivers, to feel so close to the sky? To go from that to life in America, to pitch-black darkness and smoke and starless skies? To leave everything you know behind for a city of dreams: false promises and no guarantees? To have not seen your family for years, miles of deep ocean stretching between you and your motherland?

I am a city girl. I remain ignorant of struggle, living in stability but still selfishly searching for something more. I live in a city of dreams, and I take it for granted. I don't have to understand what it's like to live a life in a village, what it's like to walk miles to school every day, to struggle, to be truly hungry. I am able to look down on everything I have, to want to run away to a place where city noises and this life can never find me. For so long, I've been able to overlook the fact that the foundation of my life and dreams is built upon my parents' sacrifices.

So here I stand. Accepting my identity as a city girl, and dreaming to truly do something to give back. To make something of the life I have been given.

MEGAN XING

YEARS AS MENTEE: 1

GRADE: Junior

BORN: Queens, NY

LIVES: Queens, NY

MENTEE'S ANECDOTE:

Jihii is a wonderful mentor who puts up with my perpetual procrastination and short attention span. She is unimaginably considerate, and finds the fact that I have the memory of a concussed Dory funny rather than irritating. I have never been a consistent person, but Jihii has helped me discover new ways to keep writing, and to polish the flaws in my work instead of giving up and hating it all. Her constant encouragement and infinite patience have helped me become a better writer, and she is slowly helping me learn to love what I create.

JIHII JOLLY

YEARS AS MENTOR: 1

OCCUPATION: Journalist and Writer

BORN: New Delhi, India

LIVES: New York, NY

MENTOR'S ANECDOTE:

Megan is one of the smartest writers I've met! Working together has been so much fun and it feels like we have just barely scratched the surface of what she is capable of. She writes quickly, thoughtfully, and confidently, and I'm learning so much from her as well as remembering why I fell in love with writing in high school in the first place. She feels like a kindred spirit. I can't wait to follow her growth and read her work over the many decades to come.

# of remembrance and regret

MEGAN XING

This essay is a tribute to my grandmother and an immortalization of my biggest regret.

My grandmother was a kind person. She grew forgetful in her later years, and often fretted about things of little importance, but I remember running in from a snowy day and being greeted by her warm smile and gentle words. We used to be closer, back when I was still young enough to require looking after; she would stay in our house all winter and spring and go back to her small Queens apartment when the rain clouds gave way to blue skies.

I regret that now—regret letting our connection break, letting school and work and the harried blur of everyday life take over my world and jumble my priorities. Somewhere along the line, I began making decisions—subtle enough to evade my conscience, but impactful enough to strain our relationship. I thought of my grandmother every now and then, but dismissed it quickly—after all, I could go visit her anytime, but my middle school friend was free only this weekend. And maybe I hadn't seen my grandma in a while now, but I had procrastinated a biology project that couldn't wait any longer.

Over time, this became our relationship—a fleeting, easily dismissed afterthought that flitted by every now and then. Now all I have left are snippets; flashes of memory so intangible I can't tell if they were reality or merely dreams manufactured by my subconscious to ease my guilt. Small, delicate hands working to prepare dinner, blue veins pulsing beneath translucent, paper-thin skin; black-lined eyes creasing in an endearing smile; and then those same eyes, closed forever within a shiny mahogany casket. I have that purple glass necklace on the red silk string—the one she gave me for one of my birthdays, God knows which—the one encasing a snippet of beach, filled with purple sand and shells and a small starfish. I can hear my grandmother's voice, saying "Mui Mui, sik fan le," but I have nothing left of her beyond dim fragments and a paltry collection of objects.

Sometimes, when it's so late at night that the only sound left in the world is the rumbling of a passing car or the fierce howling of the wind stirring the branches of the old oaks, I wonder how it all slipped away so fast. How do people grow apart so quickly? How did I go from seeing my grandmother every day to kneeling at her funeral, my head bowed and my senses clouded by the cloying smell of incense? How is someone who used to be an integral part of my daily life now nothing but a passing memory?

And what do I know about her, really? I know she loved to dance, even when she was a young girl. That didn't change, even after she had wandered out somewhere and fallen on the concrete or taken another tumble down the stairs. But what else do I know? How many siblings did she have? What was her favorite food? What did she think when she first came to America? What did she think when she first met me, saw the small, red-faced, crying baby, her first (and only) granddaughter?

Near the end, she was in and out of the hospital frequently. I visited her only once, that final time. I walked in, and by then her memory was so bad that when my mom asked her who I was, she studied my face and then called me by the name of her younger sister. There was a distant look in her eyes, like she was looking at me but not really, like she was seeing not the hospital room but her village and her childhood, surrounded by her family and friends. When she called me by that unfamiliar name, I stared at my hands and pinched the fleshy part between my thumb and my index finger, physically suppressing the threatening tears. When it was time to go my mother repeated the question, and she looked at me then, looked at me like she saw me, and smiled. "Mui Mui," she said, as if it were obvious. I almost cried again then, out of shame and regret—because what kind of person was I, to not see that it had gotten so bad? To go out with my friends and read my books and think nothing of my grandmother's deteriorating memory and increasingly lengthy hospital visits?

Occasionally, during those overly introspective periods of night, a shard of guilt buries itself in my heart, spurred by the knowledge that it was so easy to move on, almost as if she'd never even existed in the first place.

I think about that a lot too. Because what is death, really? In the end, all that matters is the life you lived, and the things people remember you for. Perhaps that's why my greatest fear is not death, or pain, but being forgotten. Erased, bit by bit, from the minds of everyone I cared about. Remembered once every so often, but only briefly—accompanied perhaps by a flicker of pain, a flash of guilt, like an indent in the sand before a wave washes it away.

CHELSEA YAN

YEARS AS MENTEE: 2

GRADE: Senior

BORN: Xiamen, China

LIVES: Staten Island, NY

MENTEE'S ANECDOTE:

My second year with KK has been a special journey. With her kindness and support, I've navigated the college application process and adapted to on-line school. More than ever, our conversations have become both a refuge and an outlet, especially when things get tough at home. Every week I look forward to Thursday afternoon when we meet virtually, catching up with each other and unraveling our thoughts about recent events. KK's patience, humor, and open-mindedness taught me how to be confident with my writing and I'm incredibly grateful to have worked with her for the past two years.

KK APPLE

YEARS AS MENTOR: 7

OCCUPATION: Writer and Comedian

BORN: Indianapolis, IN

LIVES: Brooklyn, NY

MENTOR'S ANECDOTE:

I'm so proud of Chelsea's tireless work ethic and openness to new kinds of writing—especially as a senior juggling college prep, school, and more amid a pandemic. I've had the joy of watching her tackle every challenge thrown at her, all with a big sense of humor. Our weekly pair meetings have been a bright spot in my year, sharing new music, creating together, or just finding a time to connect. I can't wait to see what she does next!

Both Sides of the Moon

CHELSEA YAN AND KK APPLE

This pair of cento poems was crafted out of song lyrics, news articles, and poetry, reflecting the moods of dark and light. Which one is sinister and which one is hopeful? Or maybe both are . . .

Villain

With a swirl of harps
dipping and rising,
he says please
I'm not myself.

What happens in between is a mystery,
chunky and noisy
He was a musician of grief,
that should have been the end of it.

Lee, however, hasn't recovered.
Over and over again
he felt nauseated
but Lee accepted the challenge.

Please send all your
dangerous and noble things.
I am thinking now
who's putting needles in my baby?

In Starlight

The cosmic lost-and-found,
gone silent,
in starlight should have been
a dance of titanic forces.

It was a surprise,
it's an intriguing mystery
of anything to eat,
one gigantic mouthful of nothing.

The stars in the knots were jiggling around,
a kind of sparkling cloak
was of the utmost importance.
What happens when
billions of suns
meet
a kink of extra light?

Sources: Sasha Sloan, Prince, Mary Oliver, Joshua Davis in *Stanford Magazine*,
Dennis Overbye in *The New York Times*.

CHRISTINE YAN

YEARS AS MENTEE: 2

GRADE: Senior

BORN: Queens, NY

LIVES: Queens, NY

PUBLICATIONS & RECOGNITIONS:
Redefy Stuyvesant

MENTEE'S ANECDOTE:

Working with Avery for another year in Girls Write Now has been very special to me. As the high school chapter of my life comes to an end, Avery has showered me endlessly with her guidance and support in surviving my senior year and the college process. From recommending TV shows to laughing about the latest online trends, our weekly calls have been a saving grace for me during this time of isolation. Avery's humor, boldness, and creativity continue to inspire me to be a better writer and person. I have made so many wonderful memories at Girls Write Now.

AVERY CARPENTER FORREY

YEARS AS MENTOR: 2

OCCUPATION: Writer

BORN: Greenwich, CT

LIVES: Riverside, CT

PUBLICATIONS & RECOGNITIONS:
How to Skimm Your Life, NYU
MFA Graduate

MENTOR'S ANECDOTE:

While this past year has been both unpredictable and monotonous, my conversations with Christine have been a steady bright spot. I love our weekly calls about writing, reading, and our daily lives. As she's dealt with the stress of applications, I've been amazed by her creative and generous spirit. Christine sees the world with kindness and clarity, whether through a camera lens or beautiful prose. I can't wait to watch her grow even more next year at college and cheer her on from the sidelines!

Bruised Pork

CHRISTINE YAN

Emilee finally returns home to Chinatown after a long semester, welcomed by her family members who have been preparing for their restaurant's opening. But before she even sets foot in their door, an unexpected trip happens.

When Emilee turned the corner, a familiar scene greeted her. Fruits were laid out on storefronts and teens lined up to buy rice cakes from small food carts. Making her way through the locals and tourists in Chinatown, she heard someone call to her.

"Emilee, you're back!"

A large truck was parked in front of their building, and she could see the outline of someone moving in the cargo bed. "Box number four with chair covers."

Emilee immediately broke out into a smile and ran over. "Mama! I missed you," Emilee said. "Let me do the rest."

Emilee scanned the list on the clipboard, took a deep breath, and hoisted herself into the cargo bed. She let out an involuntary cough while waving her arms to clear the dusty air. Using her feet, she cleared the scraps scattered on the floor to form a narrow pathway.

Boxes of supplies and pieces of furniture were haphazardly stacked on top of one another. She smiled when she spotted the LED signs she'd designed. Emilee thought back to how she stayed up several nights in her dorm, sketching over and over her drawings of lanterns and their signature ramen. She even traveled back and forth from her school in Boston to New York on weekends to practice Chinese calligraphy with her father. The traditional aspects of their restaurant had to be perfect.

Placing the clipboard to the side, Emilee picked up the top box from the pile and passed it back to her brother.

She updated the list and began to lift the next box filled with customized glasses and plates. She faltered from the weight and started to stumble. Barely able to see past the large cardboard, Emilee was dangerously close to tripping over her own feet.

Emilee's muscles started to cramp. The box she was holding flew out of her hands, landing a few feet ahead with a loud thud. She let out a small scream as her knee and fingers on one hand smashed right into the hard floor of the truck.

Emilee looked at her hands and grimaced. There were roughly two weeks left until the restaurant's soft opening. With the injury, it would take twice as long to make the launch invitations alone.

"Emilee!" a voice called. It was her mother.

"I'm sorry, Ma," Emilee said, trying hard not to cry.

As she was being treated, Emilee studied Ma. For the past twenty years, her mother had been working from home as an accountant, balancing raising kids and carrying out job responsibilities. Emilee could feel the calluses on her mother's hands: evidence of all that she had labored through.

"Done," her mother said. She carefully wrapped the finger. "Let's get you inside. Baba will be back home soon."

* * * * * *

Emilee sat in the kitchen and watched Ken speed in and out. She couldn't remember the last time she and her brother actually had the time to bond. They grew up playing basketball together in Columbus Park with Baba and the other kids from the neighborhood. They all made memories there. Ken once got stuck in a baby swing and Emilee had to run home to call for Ma's help. They held water-balloon fights and played tag through the sprinklers during the hot summer days. They cheered on Baba during his Ping-Pong matches and competed in endless rounds of amateur chess with strangers.

But after Emilee started high school, the time she spent with her family was replaced with volunteering at Red Cross events, painting wooden sets for school plays, and completing her art internship at the Metropolitan Museum of Art. Before she knew it, the only time Ken and Emilee had together was taking the uptown 6 train in the morning to school.

$$* * * * * *$$

Feeling that her knee was becoming numb from the ice, Emilee limped over to the smell of red braised pork belly that filled the kitchen area.

She placed a piece in her mouth and savored the sweet and tangy soy glaze. The meat was just the right amount of tender and had the "melt-in-the-mouth" texture. She quickly took another one, layered a piece of bok choy on top, and popped it into her mouth. Her mother looked at Emilee with fond eyes.

"Grandma's secret recipe," her mother said, taking a piece from the bowl for herself.

Just then, a jingling sound came from the bell hanging near the front door.

Everyone's home—just in time for dinner.

$$* * * * * *$$

Colorful side and main dishes soon filled the table. The sounds of spoons and chopsticks clinking against the bowls filled the room.

"Have you guys been eating these dishes every night while I was away at college?" Emilee playfully glared over her bowl at her parents and brother.

Her father shook his head. "Of course not, this is our first meal together again as a whole family and as soon-to-be restaurant owners!"

Excitement filled the atmosphere as they clinked their cups to a toast for the busy coming weeks. Emilee smiled as she listened to her father and brother's meaningless banter. Although her finger was hurting, her heart was full.

KAITLYN YANG

YEARS AS MENTEE: 4

GRADE: Senior

BORN: New York, NY

LIVES: New York, NY

PUBLICATIONS & RECOGNITIONS:
Scholastic Art & Writing Awards:
Gold Key, Silver Key, Honorable
Mention

MENTEE'S ANECDOTE:

One of our favorite parts of our pair sessions is taking pieces we've worked on, reading them aloud, and then brainstorming ways to make them even more emotionally compelling. We have a great time going back and forth together and something even more interesting always seems to emerge through our discussions. That is what happened with this story and why I thought it was a meaningful piece to include as our final anthology submission.

MEGHANN FOYE

YEARS AS MENTOR: 4

OCCUPATION: Digital Media
Director, Parade.com

BORN: Lynn, MA

LIVES: Jersey City, NJ

PUBLICATIONS & RECOGNITIONS:
Parade.com, Brit+Co, and
Refinery29

MENTOR'S ANECDOTE:

Always at the beginning of our pair sessions together, Kaitlyn and I will set the timer for eight minutes and see what comes out. Sometimes it's a piece of poetry about the stresses of the day. Sometimes it's a beautiful little gem of an idea that Kaitlyn will save for later. This piece came from one of those free-writes, and it shows how the subconscious can turn our everyday emotions into beautiful, remarkable metaphors.

Sweetness

KAITLYN YANG

I wanted to explore the little dialogues we have with ourselves when the parts of us wanting to grow up conflict with those that feel lost, scared, and alone.

A blast of artificial cold air hits me as I step through the automatic sliding doors. I march straight toward the freezers in the back. *Ice cream on sale!* The sign catches my eye on my way to load up on this week's worth of frozen pizzas. Exhausted from a week of freshman college finals, I will myself to stay awake and raise a hesitant hand to the freezer handle before feeling a tug on my coat sleeve. I look down. A teary face looks up at me. We stare at each other until she tries to wipe her nose on my sleeve. I yank my arm away.

"What's the matter?" I ask reluctantly, looking up and down the aisle for a frantic mother or babysitter, but it's empty.

"I'm lost," she says and sniffles.

"Clearly." I regret my bluntness as soon as I see her eyes fill again. "I'm sorry, I'm sorry! Don't cry." The little girl pouts. "Good. Hold it in. Wait here." I run to the end of the aisle, but the next aisles over are empty as well. I trudge back.

"I'm sorry." I shrug. "Maybe wait here until someone—" Her lower lip begins to tremble. *How weak,* I think for a second, but quickly push my mom's voice out of my head. Desperately, I throw the freezer door open and grab a carton of Neapolitan ice cream.

"Here. Ice cream." As expected, she calms instantly.

"Ice cream?"

"Yup." I plop down and lean back against the freezer, remembering how I was always told to stay put whenever I was left alone for a few hours. I pry open the lid.

"I saw spoons over there," she announces, and runs over to an unmanned sample stand that holds a foam cup of plastic utensils. She grabs the cup and sprints back. "Here!"

"There are only forks."

"Oh." Sniffle.

"Forks! Forks are great."

"No, they're not." Another sniffle.

"They're great!" I insist, forcing a grin. I grab a fork and overenthusiastically stab at the chocolate stripe. "Look!" I shovel the ice cream crumbs into my mouth. The girl wipes her eyes with the sleeve of her bright yellow YMCA summer camp T-shirt and plops down next to me, scooping into the strawberry. I watch as she shovels crumbles of ice cream into her mouth, my chocolate bite slowly melting on my tongue. I wait until she's taken another bite before speaking again.

"Are you looking for your mom?"

"Yes."

"Do you remember where you were separated?"

"Over there." She points to the end of the aisle. I don't tell her that no one's there anymore. I take another bite of chocolate ice cream and pass the carton over. She holds it between her legs and struggles to break off another piece.

"Here." I hold the carton down for her.

"I can do it myself." She tugs the carton away and manages to scoop out another pink bite. She shoves it into her mouth and glances at me.

"You're not mad?"

"Why would I be mad?"

"Because I sassed you."

"You did?"

"Yes. You're supposed to get mad."

"I'm not." Just mildly annoyed that my grocery run was taking longer than the fifteen minutes I'd expected, maybe. She eyes me doubtfully.

"You promise?" She sticks her pinkie out in my direction. I hook my pinkie around hers.

"Promise." After, she slides the carton back to me.

"You really like strawberry, huh?" I ask, glancing at the canal she carved into the ice cream.

"It's Mommy's favorite."

"You don't have to," I say quietly.

"Don't have to what?"

"Like strawberry just because your mom does. You don't have to."

"Strawberry's the sweetest. Mommy likes it when I'm sweet. She gives me kisses." *What does she do when you aren't sweet?* I want to ask, but shake the thought out of my head. I shouldn't assume that this little girl's mom was like mine—and I shouldn't care. I pass the carton back over and watch as she scoops into the strawberry ice cream until all that remains is a faint pink stain inside a third of the carton.

"Let's go." I stand and brush off the seat of my jeans. She gets to her feet, hands me the carton, and follows me to the cash register, where I hold the carton up to be scanned by a slightly disgruntled cashier.

"Please pay for your items before eating them next time."

"Sure," I say. "By the way, this girl has gotten separated from her mother. Do you mind if she waits with you?"

"All right," the cashier says and sighs, handing me my receipt. "Have a nice day."

"Thanks." I turn to the little girl. "Wait here, okay?" She nods. I walk away, tossing the sticky carton into the trash can on my way to the exit.

"Mommy!" I hear the little girl yell behind me, and expect to hear a relieved cry in response. But nothing. I step out through the sliding doors, only to notice one remaining sticky swipe of strawberry ice cream on my own cheek, along with a single falling tear.

RACHEL YOUNG

YEARS AS MENTEE: 1

GRADE: Senior

BORN: Queens, NY

LIVES: Queens, NY

MENTEE'S ANECDOTE:

Elizabeth is authentic, honest, and supportive. Sometimes I believe when I speak I'm just a whirl of different thoughts that represent my confusion, but Elizabeth is always there to spin me in the right direction. Life with such digital barriers made me think that connection would be difficult, but I'm happy to say that I have found a new lifelong friend and mentor in Elizabeth, who I know I can always be open and honest with. I've learned how to write with Elizabeth, but I'm also really happy that I've also learned how to be myself in my writing.

ELIZABETH KOSTER

YEARS AS MENTOR: 5

OCCUPATION: Teacher

BORN: New York, NY

LIVES: New York, NY

MENTOR'S ANECDOTE:

Rachel and I clicked on the first day we met. She is open and thoughtful and recently asked me: "How does someone gain confidence?" At first, I wasn't sure how to answer: Trusting myself is something I have struggled with for almost my entire life. I tried to articulate that confidence doesn't just materialize—it's an ongoing process. The older we get, the more it becomes clear that our decisions will not lead to catastrophe, and that it all works out in the end. Rachel reminds me so much of myself. We are both working together on writing and on becoming.

Finding Home

RACHEL YOUNG

*I wrote this after going to a doctor's appointment during the COVID-19
pandemic and it made me think about what leaving for college would
mean to both me and my family.*

Sitting in a stroller, I see my mother struggle to open the doctor's office
door. My brother is running up and down the hallways pretending to be
a race-car driver. I know my brother likes toy cars and watching *Ben 10*,
and that we like to play pretend at my grandmother's while we wait for
Mom to come home. I wonder how come no one makes things easier for
Mom when she is trying so hard.

Sitting alone in the dentist's office at fifteen, I'm waiting for my turn
with music playing through my earbuds. I'm trying to be more responsible for myself so that Mom does not have to come running to save me.
My brother is at home staring at his computer, smashing away at the
keyboard with the friends he meets on the Internet now. I no longer
know what he likes to play and we don't talk much anymore. Hearing the
door open to my right, I see a mother trying to make her way in with a
stroller, her son running about the hallway, and I run to hold the door
open.

With high school coming to an end now, I'm breathing through a
mask in the doctor's office I have been going to since I was born. No
more unlocked door, no more toys, and no more screaming babies. Just
a quiet, empty room with children old enough to walk on their own. My
mom is by my side and no longer needs to push me in a stroller, and next

year I will never see this office again. I wonder if college will make this different, scarier, to not have Mom with me. I used to sit on her lap to get shots, burying my face into her shoulder. With my mom in the waiting room, now I sit alone hugging my hoodie as I look away from the impending needle.

My mom used to look at all the things I could not bear to see so I never had to. She hugs me tenderly when I come out of my room after a bad exam. She makes my favorite foods like she can read my mind when all my thoughts are too jumbled in my head. She's always there for me: When I rode the train with her on the first day of high school, she waited outside for me to get out of class so I wouldn't get lost on the way back home.

I wonder if home will mean something else to me in a few years and if I might end up losing my way back as the years pile up like miles. I wonder if I will be okay alone. In a couple of months I won't have my mom by my side. My brother will no longer be there to shovel snow in my stead. My dad will not be there to ply me with chocolate bars when I'm studying for finals. With college coming, I begin to hold those I love tighter to my chest because I don't want to let them go, and I don't know if the distance will begin to weaken the bonds we have.

When I was younger, growing up was a milestone to be celebrated, but I never realized I would be leaving behind the warmth of my family. Just when I think I've figured out seventeen, eighteen's impending arrival has me scared that everything I've ever known will suddenly get up and leave me without a word.

I suppose that even when I am at college, in my heart I'll know what my parents' love for me means. I'll never lose the parts of myself that have been formed by them. My obnoxiously cheerful greetings come from a time when my dad's health weakened and I wanted to brighten his weak hellos when he came home from work. My untimely habit of laughing at all the wrong moments comes from my mother, who has taught me to laugh at myself when I stumble, but to continue trying harder next time. Even far away from home, I have hope that I will create new friendships and discover that the possibility for warmth is possible so long as I am ready to feed the flames. When I remember all the parts of myself my parents have given me, the dark clouds of thought seem a little bit lighter and the waves of emotions settle to a calm sway because I know I can always find my home within myself.

CLAIRE YU

YEARS AS MENTEE: 3

GRADE: Junior

BORN: New York, NY

LIVES: Queens, NY

PUBLICATIONS & RECOGNITIONS:
Scholastic Art & Writing Awards:
National Silver Medal, Gold Key

MENTEE'S ANECDOTE:

This is my second year having Jesse as a mentor, and she always gives me so much support and advice about everything from writing to college applications. It's been so fun and relaxing to meet with Jesse once a week over Zoom and vent to each other about all the stressful aspects of quarantined life. Being able to have someone to depend on even when we can't see each other in person is so reassuring, and our meetings always put me in a good mood!

JESSE CHEN

YEARS AS MENTOR: 2

OCCUPATION: Public Relations/ Marketing

BORN: Edison, NJ

LIVES: New York, NY

PUBLICATIONS & RECOGNITIONS:
Crain's New York Business "2020 Rising Stars in Banking & Finance"; Gramercy Institute's "20 Rising Stars in Financial Marketing"; Academy of American Poets University and College Poetry Prize

MENTOR'S ANECDOTE:

Working with Claire on her writing for the second year has been a lovely experience. Claire is an excellent writer and student, always dedicating herself to her studies, classmates, and community. In spite of the challenges posed by the pandemic, on top of the usual stresses of being a high school junior, Claire has continually shown up for our weekly meetings and Girls Write Now events, going above and beyond to continue developing her writing. I've greatly enjoyed getting to know her work more this year and helping her continue to evolve her voice as a writer.

we were made to be poets

CLAIRE YU

*"we were made to be poets" is about poets, and the reasons why we
write and connect with this form of art.*

we were made to be poets
to sanctify our tongues as a church of words
to reach into our throats and let the sounds pour out
to glorify everything we see in a flurry of description
sprinkle our fairy dust so the world doesn't forget
the magic everything holds inside

we feel the urge to name our surroundings
the thrill Adam and Eve felt as the syllables flew
out of their mouths at each stroke of inspiration
dewdrop. peacock. pebble. tongue
the only muscle not connected to bone at both ends
always reaching out for something to wrap around
something to swallow
something to call our own

how can we not try, at least, to make sense of the world?
try, at least, to match this feeling with a word.
love? loneliness. try to seem like we're in control
make sure no one knows the desperation with which
we hold on—find a metaphor, find a sound
something to remember this moment by when it's gone

write it down on paper and protect it
the more you write the longer it will take to slip away

we find solace in the promise of poetry.
music is a poem, and so is this sky.
a story mostly blacked out is a poem
a paragraph missing vowels is a poem
a memory mostly blacked out is a poem
a person missing love is a poem

we were made to be poems
we were not meant to last forever, only
long enough for the people who watched us break,
line break, time and time again to write us down on a
piece of paper and protect us, folded
in between dog-eared pages and wallets
repeating our verses under their breath until
we slip away, gone except for a phrase,
a word, hovering off the tips of their tongues,
added as an afterthought to the ends of their own poems.

GRACE YU

YEARS AS MENTEE: 3

GRADE: Junior

BORN: New York, NY

LIVES: Queens, NY

PUBLICATIONS & RECOGNITIONS:
Scholastic Art and Writing
Awards: Honorable Mention;
*Taking Our Place in History: The
Girls Write Now 2020 Anthology*

MENTEE'S ANECDOTE:

This year, I have been so blessed to continue my writing journey with Sarah, my wonderful mentor. She supports me in every aspect of my life, including my piano music, writing, and love of animals (especially her cat, Cricket). Sarah has inspired me to try many new things, from music composition/arrangement to drafting college essays. During my very tough (and entirely remote) junior year of high school, her constant encouragement and loving friendship has given me the confidence to face numerous obstacles in my life.

SARAH McNAUGHTON

YEARS AS MENTOR: 2

OCCUPATION: Executive Editor,
LIVESTRONG.com

BORN: Denver, CO

LIVES: New York, NY

MENTOR'S ANECDOTE:

Few things bring me as much joy as Grace saying the magic words: "I have a new poem for you to read." As much as I never know what's coming (What's her brilliant mind working on now?), I also know what's coming. First, I'll be stunned by her artful use of language and imagery, then I'll be grateful and honored that she's shared it with me. Every reading and every conversation—it doesn't matter if we're talking about big stuff like gender stereotypes or small stuff like capitalization—with Grace is a gift.

Leather in Heaven

GRACE YU

*This piece challenges the gender stereotypes surrounding masculinity
through two father-son relationships. The narrator's father associ-
ates masculinity with anger, but the cowboy father teaches his son
that true strength comes from being kind to others.*

There's leather in heaven I think
on tiny cowboy boots slicked with mud
Rough hands of blackjack oak stroking
your boy's miniature fingers. His sun is
helianthus and warm brown hickory tree and
your sun is his warmth. He rides
Shetland ponies, among
blue cornflowers in tallgrass prairie and you
saddle your warhorse.

Back then,
I thought people starved for spring
Frozen dirt clinging to cracked nails and
gayfeathers kissing purple feet and
back then,
I followed lost deer pricked by
false indigo promises and
back then,
my father thought he could stitch
the wounds cut from his anger

with black-eyed susans. I had no one
to fix my flower boots.

You hammer leather for him with
Gentle oak hands, his ankle bones
curved with adoration and
You sew the cowhide bent into his laughter.
His ankles are never frigid
like mine.

You play cowboys but
don't tell him to kill Indians. The best soldiers hesitate
before killing a man and
that's a fact, anyway,
he doesn't need a warhorse yet. He gallops
smiling high heels raised and pointed toes
with grass stains because
his heart is lifting out of his boots and
his boots are rising in his stirrups and
his stirrups are three and a half feet above ground and
swinging lightly in the warm spring breeze, so
this is how little boys become ballerinas
even after they play with fake guns
and shoot wide-eyed deer. Cowboys
carried their own handkerchiefs and
you told him,
Who says they couldn't cry too?

My heels have not forgotten sharp Indian grass and
my insole is cleaved to my outsole
with loneliness. Your
hand-fastened lemonwood pegs,
delicately stitched cording
trace flowers on his boots.

There's leather in heaven and
my father's black-eyed susans are pressed flat
underfoot.
Your legacy is in the embroidery
you leave on your boy's boots.

KAELIANA YU

YEARS AS MENTEE: 1

GRADE: Senior

BORN: Queens, NY

LIVES: Queens, NY

MENTEE'S ANECDOTE:

Though we don't wish for a pandemic, I used my new free time to sign up for Girls Write Now, and wouldn't have met Ellen without it. I wanted to share a playlist with her, but I was worried about whether the curse words and melancholy vibes might say something about me. However, when Ellen gladly listened to my "Chill Drives" playlist and enjoyed it, she had unknowingly accepted a huge part of myself. My music taste is as personal as my writing, and I'm so glad that she was the one to have heard it all.

ELLEN HORAN

YEARS AS MENTOR: 1

OCCUPATION: Novelist

BORN: Philadelphia, PA

LIVES: Brooklyn, NY

PUBLICATIONS & RECOGNITIONS:
31 Bond Street

MENTOR'S ANECDOTE:

As a novelist, I have been so amazed to see Kaeliana bring to life a fantasy fiction accompanied by her own artwork for her Girls Write Now project. It has been a joy to meet weekly and collaborate and write together. Although I would love to explore museums and culture together, our virtual discussions during COVID have transported me, as Kaeliana has shared her avid interests in music, art, and writing.

The Little Girl and the Fox (Excerpt)

KAELIANA YU

A little girl goes on a journey through a floating kingdom to seek out a magical fox in order to satiate her endless desire for companionship.

A little girl in a white nightgown gazes into the tendrils of an amber fire in the fireplace. She is very small, no larger than a dog if it were to stand on its hind legs. Her limbs are stick-thin, and she seems like she would fly away when faced with a gust of wind. The little girl doesn't flinch when the flames skip too closely. She holds her hand out invitingly, waiting, waiting, then striking—but she can't catch an orange flame. She feels disappointed, but her dismay is extinguished in a heartbeat. The little girl looks down at her hand. The skin is red and singed, but she doesn't feel any pain. She looks back at the fire.

The girl thinks the flames look like dancing fire ribbons, waving their bodies cheerfully. She wishes she could catch a ribbon. If the girl did, she would drag a ribbon out of the fire to see if there is an end to it. Or perhaps, she wonders, is it infinitely long, like the beautiful ribbons at the fair? The Magician would pull endless ribbons out from his sleeve, and the girl liked to imagine there was a tiny man spooling threads together in seconds from inside his arm. She saw the Magician at a small fair that only the sons and daughters of the wealthier families in the kingdom could attend, where the infamous Magician presented his whimsical tricks. Rumors of his feats, from surviving a thousand arrows in the back to breathing life into inanimate things, traveled so far that even the King—the girl's father—had heard of them from up on his three-hundred-foot-tall throne that had an enormous indigo gem embedded at the top. The King had wondered if the Magician's tricks could stir some emotion into his own daughter, so by his order the maids had dragged the girl out of her room and promptly brought her to the fair.

The little girl is lost in her memories while reminiscing of that magical night at the fair. Of the trinkets and toys, the bright lights and the noise. Of a particular red fox that the Magician held tight to a glittering orange ribbon. Nothing compared to it. The girl wishes she had snagged the ribbon with that fox and dragged it home. She wishes the fox were by her side right this instant. The little girl pleads to the fire desperately, asking it to give her the orange fox.

The little girl's parents are keeping an eye on their daughter, but neither are there in person. The King, who refuses to leave his tall throne for fear of someone stealing its indigo jewel, uses his four-hundred-foot telescope to peek into the girl's room. The Queen, too busy touching up her pristine makeup and staring lovingly into her mirror's reflection, has her three maids running back and forth to report what the little girl is up to.

The King and Queen receive word of the girl's interest in the fox. The King sighs because he's already bought so many things for her. The Queen cries in her heart—she cannot afford to have her makeup ruined by real tears—because her daughter is not like other children. The King thinks it's futile to add another useless toy to the little girl's collection. The Queen thinks that other mothers will gossip about her poor parenting.

The King's manservant will go to the fair to grant the little girl's wish. He will recognize the fiery orange fox and grant the Magician an audience with the King. The King will offer the Magician a sum he thinks no man could refuse. However, the Magician will give the King the fox, free of charge, because he is secretly happy to see it go. The King will order his manservant to deliver the gift to the girl so she will have another toy.

The little girl cannot believe her eyes at the fiery fox yipping before her. She grasps the orange ribbon and drags the fox back to her room, where the fire is still ablaze. She slowly sits down and watches the fox with brimming curiosity as it probes its new surroundings. The ribbon is still held tightly in the little girl's grasp. The fox sniffs around cautiously. Its amber eyes glint in the darkness whenever it glances at her. The fox stares curiously, and tiptoes gently toward her. The little girl holds her breath. Soon, she feels its warmth curling around her.

The girl is elated to have this new friend. She smiles, for the first time in years, from ear to ear. The little girl hugs the fox excitedly and laughs out loud, and her laughter, which sounds like the sound of twinkling fairy bells, echoes through the dark mansion.

YASMIN ZAYED

YEARS AS MENTEE: 1

GRADE: Sophomore

BORN: Brooklyn, NY

LIVES: Staten Island, NY

MENTEE'S ANECDOTE:

There was an interesting introduction that occurred between the pair, involving Yasmin's terrible Wi-Fi and a Zoom application that wouldn't stop crashing. Even so, they managed to seize the rest of their first meeting. It would be fair to say that their entire collaboration required perseverance. Yasmin, a teen navigating the world from a laptop, and Aoife, paving the way, found a balance of work and fun, making every new objective their own.

AOIFE SHERIDAN

YEARS AS MENTOR: 1

OCCUPATION: Chief Customer Officer at a Financial Technology Company

BORN: Dublin, Ireland

LIVES: Brooklyn, NY

PUBLICATIONS & RECOGNITIONS: *Cut the Blue*, a self-published novel; blog posts on LinkedIn for professional purposes

MENTOR'S ANECDOTE:

We enter Zoom room six. A forty-eight-year-old and a teen aged fifteen. We're nervous with first-date jitters—or at least it has the excitement of one. Yasmin, mentee, and Aoife, mentor. The screen fills on one side with dark brown, curly hair, glasses showcasing bright, curious eyes and a bashful smile that could warm the coldest of souls. The other half is occupied by cropped, platinum-blond hair, nerdy specs, and a hopeful grin. Our nerves subside, the laughter begins. The chat bubbles and effervesces and we know it will sustain us. This is the start of a beautiful friendship.

The Seasons of Love

YASMIN ZAYED

Love has been written about in thousands of ways across the short 4.5 billion years the Earth has spun around the sun. Read the perspective of this young, hopeful romantic, navigating nature and the seasons of love.

Love, a universal language translated hundreds of ways. There are many forms: romantic, platonic, familial, self. Each with vast and endless possibilities. Romantic love is that of perception, but also of continuities: the love stories that take up our bookshelves contain different, specific details, yet all remain consistent in their core sentiments. These sentiments are what I, a hopeless romantic, have chosen to categorize in four phases, or, more specifically, seasons. Because I, just like those very love stories, am a continuity of possibilities.

Summer, quite frankly, is the most cliché setting for the beginning of romantic love. A season representative of youth and a lack of, well, reality. It becomes the lotus flower of life, entrapping you with a single bite. Summer is a time for adventure and exploration of new possibilities without the restrictions of responsibility, but this can also present a problem in itself. Attraction, lust, aphrodisiacs—all words that describe the hazy allure of the season. *Romeo and Juliet* is the prime example of this heady stage of attraction. The pair barely knew each other long enough to consider themselves in love. However, the air of possibility and freedom is what attracts them toward something hopeful. Now, this isn't to say that attraction is always a negative thing, but it's a tool, a very powerful one, that you must use with caution. Love is extremely tricky; its magnetism can occur at any time within the relationship, but what happens when other feelings get involved . . .

Spring, the material of classic tales. This season is one of pure, vibrant adoration. A feeling that makes the world brighter and the birds sing. It's emergent, graceful, a possibility. It could be the start of something new (get the reference?). It's a hopeless romantic's favorite, because in a picture-perfect world, it is truly innocent. This is the honeymoon phase of feelings and it is beautiful; it is, again, powerful. For those blinded by delusion, this may become the end of what was once a beautiful story. But who knows? Maybe there are some people out there lucky enough to never have to abandon spring and its bright-eyed feelings? Maybe it's about enjoying what has been in front of you the whole time. Maybe it can blossom just as the flowers do.

Fall, a season overlooked just like the feelings pertaining to it. What accompanies the innocence of adoration is the unknown. This is when you have to endure the issues undiscussed and find a balance, both together and alone. It is a time of reflection and exploration of what was evaded for so long. A time of maturing in ways you didn't know were possible before. Just as Robert Frost once said, "Two roads diverged in a wood, and I— / I took the one less traveled by, / And that has made all the difference." You must diverge from one another long enough to find where you end and your partner begins. Balance is difficult; finding it with a new person who has all new feelings, possibilities, and hopes is even more difficult. But in the end, it's important to recognize that even if the brown leaves aren't as bright as the flowers, they're still just as hopeful.

Winter. For those of you reading right now, I understand your confusion in this timeline of seasons. True love doesn't follow any course set for it. Romance occurs just as naturally as grass grows, and with the right nurturing, it can sustain. Winter, the time of sustenance. This season is when the holidays occur, lives are merged, and the gap between intersectionality is bridged. This is a time of finding warmth in the cold through each other. Consider this the yang of all the seasons: light and warm, even though chilled outside. It's also a moment of continuance for the cycle of the seasons. Making new memories with the adventure of summer, the vibrancy of spring, and the maturity of fall.

Attraction, adoration, reflection, settlement, all forces that come together in whatever shape and form to become romantic love.

JENNY ZHENG

YEARS AS MENTEE: 2

GRADE: Senior

BORN: Queens, NY

LIVES: Queens, NY

PUBLICATIONS & RECOGNITIONS:
Scholastic Art and Writing
Awards: Gold Key

MENTEE'S ANECDOTE:

Saira has been sending me a variety of short stories and we discuss them when we meet. This process has worked well during quarantine. We focused on flash fiction during one meeting, which turned out to be great prep for this anthology submission.

SAIRA KHAN

YEARS AS MENTOR: 2

OCCUPATION: Senior Platform Editor

BORN: Karachi, Pakistan

LIVES: Brooklyn, NY

PUBLICATIONS & RECOGNITIONS:
The New Yorker, The New York Times

MENTOR'S ANECDOTE:

Jenny and I once went to see the Tyler Mitchell exhibit at the International Center of Photography, where one of the artworks was a multimedia piece that you experience by lying on the ground on a bean bag to watch a short film being projected on the ceiling. I watched one loop and then got up to leave. Jenny wanted to stay, so we both lay on the floor for five minutes watching the film. The experience of watching that film on loop was beautiful and I'm so glad I stayed. Sometimes you need someone to remind you to slow down, and I'm glad Jenny was that person for me that day.

Two Days

JENNY ZHENG

About a family, and how they drift in and out of things.

"How do you use those earplugs?" Mom asked.

"Why? Did Dad take some?"

"No," she said, so naturally. I later found some while cleaning the house. Three bright pink earplugs, lying front and center on Dad's desk. I pocketed them.

I managed to sneak in some yoga practice before bed. Mom was nearby watching TV, but the volume was kept low. Dad's voice was drawing closer, calling out my name amid "hey"s with increasing urgency. I had a leg up in standing split position, barely balanced. Then I was supposed to bend a knee out. I nearly face-planted onto my mat with a "Hey!" Then I growled a "What?" at him.

"Hey! What? Hey! What? Is that how you speak to me?"

I lie there hearing the pulse in my ear. Later, however, I did think back to whatever he sounded so excited to tell me about. Though I regretted it when I later caught him still in the mood. Right before bed that night, "Li Jing, do you want this apple?" he asked Mom. "No? Guess we'll have to throw it away, then," he said, and chucked the half-apple into the trash.

The next morning, I'd just about finished making myself an egg sandwich when Dad popped into the kitchen to casually tell me to prepare one for him as well. I decided not to. He told me that I was lazy upon returning. I told him that not making a sandwich does not make me lazy. I also half made up that I'd placed just enough oil in the pan for one egg and two pieces of bread, to which he asked what was wrong with just adding some more oil.

"Why couldn't you just make him an egg sandwich?" Mom said after he'd left. I shot a glare at the kitchen table. She was supposed to be on my side, since I was kind of avenging her.

We'd all woken up late that day, so Mom made a pot of thin rice porridge for lunch, which we had just an hour after breakfast. Mom disapproved of me dumping brown sugar atop my bowl of porridge in place of the side dishes she'd prepared. Dad arrived at the table as I was on my way to the living room, which Mom had especially disapproved of.

"Your daughter," Mom said, "is bringing her food into the living room."

"Do not bring your food into the living room," Dad called out with conviction. "You have to stay in the kitchen to eat your food." However, he didn't hunt me down or anything.

I stayed in my room for the entire rest of the afternoon, coming out at five for dinner before retreating back in. A while later, I passed by the kitchen. Dad was on his phone at the table. One of our fancy metal bowls was upside down at my feet. Carrots, goji berries, and pork ribs dotted the tiles. It was the soup we'd had for dinner, which was supposed to stay on the table to cool for a while before being put into the fridge.

"What happened?"

"Mom did that," he said.

"Why?"

"She got angry. Then she went out."

I remembered hearing a brief, loud crash while in my room. It was an unwelcome interruption to the paradise of screeching vocals my headphones teleported me to.

We had dinner early that day. I gave my stomach an egg sandwich around eight. Dad came by the stove to give me tips on making egg sandwiches. He also informed me of the several boxes of water bottles he'd purchased a while back, and that they were stored in the basement, where I'd rarely explored. "But still stick with drinking boiled water whenever possible," he said. "It's just that you always go through the bottled water so quickly." Later, he asked if I needed him to boil some water for me. I said no, but he filled a kettle shortly after.

I wandered into Mom's line of sight when I heard her come back. She wasn't even wearing a jacket.

"Why didn't you call me? You were gone for so long."

"I just don't ever call people. I don't use my phone for calls."

"Stupid," she chuckled out to my relief. "It was raining," she added.

"Oh, I didn't know that it was raining."

"It was drizzling a bit."

Later, I found Dad in my room, on my bed, on his phone.

"Mom's back?"

"Yeah," I said, flopping right next to him, but he didn't budge. "I want to sleep now," I said, though I had a few more hours of homework planned. "I'll stay here for a while," he said. He had my blanket behind his back for full-length spinal support. He had my pillow in his lap, resting his hands and phone upon it. My earplugs, which had been beneath my pillow, were out in the open and very noticeable. My bed would probably be less enticing if I stopped making it every morning. But then I wouldn't want to sleep in it either.

IVY ZHU

YEARS AS MENTEE: 1

GRADE: Senior

BORN: Brooklyn, NY

LIVES: Brooklyn, NY

MENTEE'S ANECDOTE:

Kathleen has helped me out so much this year with college applications and essays, as well as more fun writing. I'm so grateful I was paired up with her.

KATHLEEN SCHEINER

YEARS AS MENTOR: 10

OCCUPATION: Senior Medical Editor

BORN: Biloxi, MS

LIVES: Brooklyn, NY

MENTOR'S ANECDOTE:

Ivy is bubbling over with enthusiasm and questions. She's super creative and our Friday-evening sessions start my weekends off right.

Where Are the Children?

IVY ZHU

We wrote stories based on old nursery rhymes, giving them a new twist. Ivy's story "Where Are the Children?" is a reimagining of "The Pied Piper of Hamelin," which Kathleen Scheiner has illustrated.

Sam's hometown of Hamelin had been overrun by rats. Rats in the shower, rats in the kitchen, and rats in the playground. It did not matter what anyone did. The rats would not go away.

All the adults did was moan and groan. "Someone get rid of these rats!" they cried.

Their prayer was answered.

The Piper came. With his charming smile and music, Hamelin was free at last. Sam was happy at first, caught in the joyous celebration of the townsfolk, but the novelty wore off. The absence of the rodents felt haunting. The scurrying that used to echo through the walls and streets at night now fell silent. The ghost towns in his storybooks did not seem so distant anymore.

And when the Piper played his music . . . it was horrid. Sam held his tongue when it happened, not wanting to displease his parents, but the sight of thousands of drowning rats still haunted his dreams. The rodents' paws and tails jerked with the wailing tunes. Even when the water was littered with dead bodies, still the Piper played.

Massacre. That was the word that came to Sam's mind. He pulled the word from a thick, old tome he found in the library. The word always came with pictures of men on horses and a field riddled with still bodies.

The Piper was a miracle at first. That was what Sam's mother had called the musician. That was what *everyone* called him. Now, as Sam shivered in this city, far, far away from Hamelin, the Piper was more like a demon. Why else would he take Sam and all the other children away? Was it because his parents were hypocrites, turning back on the very lessons they parroted to all their children?

Don't be greedy. Never lie.

In the end, it was the adults who broke this promise, and here the children were, left in this hostile, new town. Everyone talked and spoke differently. The air was humid and dry. Sand swirled in the breeze, stinging his eyes. Even the sun seemed to have betrayed Sam, beating down on his head twice as hard.

The biggest difference was perhaps the rats in Sunmu. Unlike the rodents in Hamelin, who were plump and comfortable with human presence, the rats in Sunmu were skinny, short-tempered, and cunning. They stole meals from the children. Food that had taken a whole day to earn was snatched away.

When night fell, Sam and the fellow children had to hide their bloody toes under worn blankets to stop the rodents from nibbling at them.

And unlike the rats in Hamelin, these were ferocious. They knew how to fight. Jack had told him of the time he'd seen a rat tussle with a stray dog and win. The rats cleared out the bloody carcass of the canine in a matter of minutes.

Every night, the group of children huddled together. The desert city, while sweltering during the day, was cold enough at night to freeze. Warmth was prioritized over the stench of unwashed bodies. When the sun rose, they forced their tired bodies to get up. If they didn't find enough treasures by lunchtime, they would not get fed.

Sam hated this new life. It was hard and tiring. Every day, he daydreamed of his cozy bed back home. His breakfast was always ready when he woke up, the table piled with toasts, fruits, and bacon. Here, he would be lucky if he got a strip of bread for breakfast. The soup resembled a muddy puddle and tasted as much.

Sam was not alone in this sentiment. The other children, when they woke up from the Piper's musical stupor, were scared. They cried and demanded their parents back. Everyone quickly learned that Hager's temper was bad. He did not tolerate any tears. When punishment came, and it always did, nothing ever stopped at a small reprimand.

Hager was their new "dad," or so he called it. He bought them from the Piper, so they now belonged to him. He paid for them, and now it was their duty to be good kids and repay his kindness. They were to bring him scrap coins from the streets, precious jewelry dropped between pavement cracks, or anything that looked valuable or out of place. What qualified as "valuable" to Hager was always unpredictable. Sometimes a shiny jewel was tossed aside with a swift dismissal from Hager.

"Useless," he would grumble and toss the children's lunch to the rats instead.

Sometimes a blunt kitchen knife would be looked upon with interest. Hager would grunt his approvals, and the lucky kid would be rewarded with a rare slice of ham. The others would stare in envy with salivating mouths.

So when Sam picked up the little wooden flute, he had not done so out of curiosity—he was following his stomach's primal urges. Music had brought him into this situation. Maybe music could at least give him his lunch for the day.

BASMALA ZYADA

YEARS AS MENTEE: 2

GRADE: Senior

BORN: Cairo, Egypt

LIVES: Brooklyn, NY

MENTEE'S ANECDOTE:

One of the first things I told Megan about myself was that I never get things done. I come up with a great idea for a story and spend weeks thinking about it, only to have my attention span give out on me. That became my goal for this year, to start and commit to a story all the way through. And so, for a giggly, wonderful hour every Monday morning, Megan and I sat together, honing my daydream of a ghost story into something I love and am going to see through to the end. (Hopefully. Fingers crossed.)

MEGAN REID

YEARS AS MENTOR: 1

OCCUPATION: Vice President of Series Development at FX

BORN: Sacramento, CA

LIVES: Brooklyn, NY

PUBLICATIONS & RECOGNITIONS: *Who Did It First?, Maryam's Magic: The Story of Mathematician Maryam Mirzakhani, Bustle*

MENTOR'S ANECDOTE:

Basmala and I bonded over being trapped in our apartments: her with her family (who I'm sure are lovely), and me with my yappy dog (who's often not). As unavoidably irritating as both situations could be, I was excited to read Basmala's work and be transported into a story that felt otherworldly. Haunted lovers, a moody graveyard, a vengeful twist: it was in the vein of stories I love, from Jane Eyre to Madeline Miller's *Circe* (when you read it, you'll get it). Working together to expand her narrative and play with the chapters was a fantastic Monday-morning escape.

molasses to drown in

BASMALA ZYADA

This is an excerpt from a novel I've been working on called To the Grave. *It follows Isolde, a woman haunted by the ghost of the boy she killed, and Helena, the silent observer.*

It was a strange thing to belong to something, and for you to belong to it in return. It felt to Helena both like suffocating and like floating, free-falling and drowning. She held on to it tightly, uncertain of the reliability of this newfound feeling.

They'd left her room empty for Helena to decorate how she wanted, her foster mother Mrs. Smith explained, a sunshine grin on her lips as Helena stood dumbfounded in the doorway. After so many years, a clean slate: just over this threshold. Fists clenched, Helena vowed she wouldn't squander this new chance she'd been given.

So she tried. She tried her hardest. She spent nights hunched over her desk until her assignments came back with perfect scores. She dialed back everything that could've made her strange among her peers, a smiling image of carefully crafted perfection. Gradually, with a "hello" here and a familiar "morning!" there, she slowly became another familiar face in her high school's backdrop, no longer the new girl who flinched a little too quickly at loud noises and sudden gestures.

The pieces of an ordinary life were all falling into place. But a niggling worry still sat at the back of Helena's mind. All her life, she'd known what to expect. Torment and abandonment were nothing if not reliable. But *this*, what was this? Would this belonging, this contradictory feeling, prove fleeting? What if it slipped between her fingers like water, and beyond her grasp?

She didn't know. But she supposed the only thing left to do was cling to it as tightly as she could.

*＊＊＊＊＊

Isolde's eyes were black and shifty. Meeting them felt like staring into molasses.

Helena tried not to be wary of Isolde, her partner for their geography project; she knew better than anyone that looks could be deceiving. But there was something off about Isolde, something she couldn't shake even as she smiled brightly and read over the project sheet. She couldn't shake it: It was those eyes.

Isolde was sharp: tall stature, elegant fingers at the ends of long arms, prominent cupid's bow, carved cheekbones, arched brows enhancing sunken undereyes. Her words were minced, voice low and used sparingly. She could pin you in place with her gaze alone.

But it wasn't just that. Those eyes felt familiar to Helena, like a cold, unwelcome alternate version of her past self had come to say hello.

Helena didn't miss the bruises coloring Isolde's neck either, covered with foundation but still visible to Helena's knowing eye. She averted her gaze and pretended she saw nothing.

On the way home from school, the sun shone pleasantly, the air smelling of the last breath of spring before summer began in earnest, and so Helena took the long way home on her bike to savor the warm breeze. Out of the corner of her eye, she recognized long, black hair and a hurried, loping gait; it was Isolde.

Helena could never explain to herself why she did what she did next. Maybe it was simple curiosity, maybe pity. But she hopped off her bike and followed Isolde.

Isolde came to a stop behind the old McGregor house, locked up by relatives after the old man died. She hopped over a broken section of the fence, disappearing out of view. Helena leaned her bike against the side of the house, tiptoed forward, and peeked over.

Isolde was crouched down, her hair obscuring her face. At her feet was a cardboard box, half covered with a dirty blanket; from inside the box came increasingly agitated mews. Isolde reached into her bag, pulled out a little plastic box that she set inside. Next, she filled the rounded lid of the box with water from her own bottle and set that inside too. The mews died out as the cats inside became occupied with their food and a small smile softened the sharp edges of Isolde's face.

Suddenly, Helena felt foolish and small, like she was watching over something not meant for her eyes. She retreated quickly, only to bump loudly—conspicuously—into her bike.

"Well, screw you too," she whispered to the traitorous bike. She slowly turned to see Isolde coming to investigate the crash, and met those fierce eyes as anger burned in them.

At that moment, Isolde was a wild predator baring its teeth, fury in her clenched jaw as she stepped closer to Helena, making her back up instinctively. Before she could think it through, Helena righted her bike and ran with it, hopping back on and biking back home, far from Isolde and the fear those disquieting eyes awakened in her.

But as she biked farther and farther from McGregor's house, she remembered the desperation in Isolde's molasses eyes, the tremble in her hands. It made Helena wonder which of them was really the cornered prey.

GIRLS WRITE NOW CURRICULUM

Unmute and Unplug:
The Year of Reality and Escape

In this unusual year of upheaval—quarantine and activism, illness and insurrection, change and stagnation, rage and sorrow—we sought balance by framing our curriculum around the themes of Escape and Reality. Sometimes we just needed to unplug, take a break from it all, flee to the shores of our imagination. Other times, we needed to be more present than ever, digging down deep into the movement for racial justice and the issues of inequity that COVID revealed, penning intersectional environmental memoirs, filming documentaries of a life confined, or recording audio diaries of our days in seclusion.

As a tonic for isolation, we invited collaboration. We tripled our virtual programming, letting our fingers do the commuting on Zoom, from Wellness Wednesdays, to Community Chats on Thursdays, to Friday Night Salons, to Saturday 360 Workshops, to weekly pair sessions. Mentees hunkered down midwinter in breakout rooms with thriller authors to create chilly thrilly stories of their own. Our community traversed miles on our keyboards, pounding out songs of heartbreak, stories of romance, articles exploring grief, essays to make us laugh, animations of alien conventions, and . . . tales told by fish. Always, there was poetry— poetry about where we come from, where we're going, how we live, and who we love. We were joined by students in India and Peru, teaching artists and authors from California, to Canada, to Spain. Even the employees of our corporate partners needed time to process all that was going on, and together mentees and their "mentors for the day" wrote their way to wellness, sifting through thoughts and feelings in mutual letters of personal and professional advice and encouragement.

Our lives may have been confined, but our passion and our words were not. The clickety-clack of fingertips on keys paused only to listen to one another, our guests, and our playlists, and to applaud essential workers for keeping this world spinning. With the following selection of multigenre prompts, we invite you to unmute yourself: Make a record of the world you know—or compose a new world of your own. The choice is yours!

—Erica Silberman, *Girls Write Now Director of Curriculum & Engagement*

MEMOIR:
YOUR ENVIRONMENTAL STORY

Inspired by Girls Write Now Saturday 360 Workshop teaching artist Kristy Drutman, an environmental media host of Brown Girl Green, speaker, activist, and digital media strategist.

OPENING LINES. . . .

Make sure your feet are firmly planted on the ground and you're sitting up tall (if possible). Close your eyes and take three deep breaths. On your last breath, begin to imagine a warm yellow light floating down through your head to the center of your heart. Then, once that light disperses across your body, imagine you are in a place in nature where you felt safe as a child. Most of the time, an image will instantly appear—this could be a beach, a forest, even your local park or backyard. Just think of what that space is right now—what do you see, smell, or hear? What about this place provides you a feeling of comfort or safety? Really get deep and specific with the details—the colors, the textures, the temperature of this place. Now slowly come back, wiggle your arms and legs, and open your eyes when you're ready.

Now write as much as possible about what you saw during the meditation—brain-dump, list out anything and everything you remember about that experience—treat this as the first free-write and soon-to-be foundation for your memoir.

Exercise

An environmental memoir specifically details an individual's relationship with the natural world and/or their surrounding environment. The surroundings that the author is located within are the focal point of the narrative.

Pick your memoir "moment" and write out key elements of the plotline, characters, and setting.

Questions to consider when picking your memoir "moment":

- What is a moment that made you feel connected to nature?
- How did the environment you grew up in influence your actions/views on the world? (For example, if your family had a garden, do you cook more often? Do you think about your relationship to the food you eat?)
- Was there someone in your life who taught you about air, water, or land? What was a lesson you took away from their teachings?
- Does climate change concern you? Was there any moment in your life that this became more apparent and you felt inspired to explore that?

DISCOVER THE MAGIC OF ROMANCE FICTION

Inspired by Girls Write Now Saturday 360 workshop teaching artist Donna Hill, a Girls Write Now mentor and author of more than one hundred novels.

OPENING LINES

Choose a time period for your romance story. Does it take place in the past, present, or future?

Exercise

Use this exercise to create the plot for your romance novel. Pick *two* identities from the following list of characters. Don't overthink it, just go with your initial instinct:

Priest, Nanny, Dog Walker, Nurse, Architect, Truck Driver, Lawyer, Artist, Store Clerk, Gardener, Assassin, Secretary, Rising Star, Dancer, CEO

Now choose *one* of the following:

Beach, Office Building, Starbucks, Gym, Classroom, Concert, Subway, Restaurant, Alley, Apartment Lobby, Tropical Island, Cemetery, Nightclub, Bar, Wedding

Finally, choose *one* of these challenges your characters will face:

Loss, Betrayal, Second Chances, Family Secret, Sibling Rivalry, Engagement, Car Accident, Secret Baby, Marriage, Scandal, Lottery, Snowstorm, Flood

This is the foundation for crafting your romance. Begin by writing a scene between your main characters. Challenge yourself by adding one of the common tropes of romance:

Love Triangle, Secret Billionaire, Friends to Lovers, Stuck Together, Enemies to Lovers, Forbidden Love, Second Chance, Soul Mates, Fake Relationship

DOCUMENTARY FILMMAKING:
TELLING STORIES ON A SMARTPHONE

Inspired by Girls Write Now Saturday 360 workshop teaching artist Olivia Abtahi, a documentary filmmaker.

No camera? No problem. Your smartphone is a perfect tool to film, edit, and create documentary films!

OPENING LINES

Think of a point in history or the future that you wish you knew more about. If you could actually go there, who would you interview and where would you visit to learn more about that point in time?

Exercise

Make a one-minute documentary about another person. It could be a friend, family member, pet—your choice! Be sure to answer questions like: Who are they? Where do they live? What are their hobbies and interests?

A great resource for editing your documentary is KineMaster (you can download it online!).

Now that you've got the basics down, try creating a new video that investigates something. Find a part of your neighborhood to look at further, ask your parents about your family history, make a film about your favorite mug—anything that you feel tells a story.

NO GOOD DEED . . . WRITING THRILLERS

Inspired by Girls Write Now Friday Night Salon guest author Megan Giddings's thriller Lakewood.

OPENING LINES

Thrillers often include different experiments that characters take part in. Write your own outlandish research experiment. Try to make it as detailed as possible, and think about what readers could learn from the experiment.

Exercise

In *Lakewood*, Giddings's main character, Lena, writes several letters to her best friend, Tanya, to talk about what's happening in the novel. Begin a story by having a character write a letter to another character. Think about how your letter can establish voice, give your audience a glimpse of your world, and establish a connection between characters and your readers.

Think about how objects can help create characters. Look around you and choose a small object (a bag, a T-shirt, a pen, etc.). Imagine this object belongs to the character you created. Write three paragraphs about three important moments in your character's life when this object is present.

IT'S FINE TO FEEL STRANGE!
WRITING HUMOR AND FUNNY PERSONAL ESSAYS

Inspired by Girls Write Now Friday Night Salon guest author Mia Mercado's collection of essays Weird but Normal.

OPENING LINES

Try writing a satire piece by starting with a very boring or serious question and then answering it in ways that are absurd, angry, stupid, or brutally honest. Start by writing answers to the question "How are you doing?"

Exercise

You can also use humor to find absurdity in the ordinary. Think of a memory or otherwise regular event that, on second glance, felt strange or weird. Now write a story about it. It could be a childhood memory, something that happened to you yesterday, a new story, or anything else that felt "off" to you.

MAKING ART OUT OF HEARTACHE: SONGWRITING

Inspired by the songs of Anna Witiuk, mentor, mentee alum, and Girls Write Now Friday Night Salon guest artist.

OPENING LINES

Write a letter addressed to a person who "broke your heart," hurt your feelings, or lied to you in some way.

Exercise

Now go back and circle the key word or words that stand out in your letter. Can you find a theme? These key words are a great way to find a hook or a chorus for your song.

Using these words, write the chorus or refrain to your song. This should be two to four rhyming lines that hold the motivation of the song. In your song, these lines will be repeated or returned to. Be sure to think about what type of heartbreak song this is—pleading? angry? resolute?

EXPLORE YOUR FEELINGS: WRITE IN OUR WARM BRAVE SPACE

Inspired by Girls Write Now Community Chat guest speaker Brittany Barker, a spoken-word artist and Girls Write Now mentee alum.

What do you enjoy most about whoever you are today? What draft of yourself were you in the beginning of 2020? What draft were you in the summer and fall? What draft are you now?

Exercise

When it comes to the world, what are we in control of? What are we unable to control?

Reflect on who you were in the weeks leading up to the election cycle. How did the 2020 election climate make you feel? Did it inform the way you showed up in private and public? What can you take from this experience?

SPEAK YOUR TRUTH:
FINDING HONESTY THROUGH WRITING POETRY

Inspired by Girls Write Now Friday Night Salon guest author Jasmin Kaur's poetry and prose story "When You Ask Me Where I'm Going."

OPENING LINES

What's a boundary that you maintain for your well-being?

Exercise

When do you feel free? Use the following prompt: *I am free when . . .*

Write whatever comes to your brain, in prose or poetry, like a stream of consciousness. Try to incorporate metaphor and simile. *Bonus! Use these words in your poem: Water, Roots, Replenish, Bloom.*

Now pick one line from your self-reflection and write an entirely new piece that tells us a truth about you that you would like to share with the world.

SECRETS AND SISTERHOOD: WRITING FICTION

Inspired by Girls Write Now Friday Night Salon guest author Brit Bennett's novel The Vanishing Half.

OPENING LINES

Sometimes we fantasize about escaping our lives and becoming someone else. If you were to vanish and become your fictional half, *the "shadow you," your evil twin, your better half,* where would you go, and what would you leave behind? Give yourself a new name and write a few sentences in the third person about leaving.

Based on what you wrote for your opening prompt, write the scene in which your fictional identity has been uncovered and your secret has been exposed. Who exposes you, and what is their relationship to you?

MEMORY, METAPHOR, AND MAGIC: WRITING POETIC MEMOIR

Inspired by Girls Write Now Friday Night Salon guest author Arisa White's poetic memoir Who's Your Daddy.

OPENING LINES

Identify where light comes in. You can interpret this literally or figuratively.

Exercise

Bring attention to someone whose absence has affected you. Where do you feel it in your body? Write down the part of your body where you feel the absence. Describe the feeling as a series of colors and objects. Ask your absence a question. Write this question down.

Take these colors and objects and think of a memory. Write about the memory, describing the colors you see. Give us the who, what, where, and when of the memory. Then write about the memory, starting with touch or texture. Allow yourself to be transformed.

Return to the question you asked your absence. How does your writing respond to the question? What patterns do you notice: word usage, image, sentence structure, and rhythm? What ideas or new questions arise?

(UN)SPOKEN RULES OF GROWING UP GIRL: WRITING POETRY FOR YOUNG ADULTS

Inspired by Girls Write Now Friday Night Salon guest author Mahogany L. Browne's young adult novel in verse, Woke: A Young Poet's Call to Justice.

OPENING LINES

What is your purpose? And what are you going to do with that purpose?

Exercise

Use writing to unpack the rules. Think back to your childhood. What instructions do you remember being told? What expectations were placed on you? Did any of these rules or expectations contradict themselves? Do you feel like you still follow these rules?

Write an "instruction manual" poem about the rules you have been taught to follow in society. How can poetry help you to recognize and break free from these rules?

UNDER THE (MICRO)SCOPE: AMPLIFYING OUR TRUTH BY WRITING MICRONARRATIVES!

Inspired by Girls Write Now Friday Night Salon guest author Darien Hsu Gee's book of micronarratives Other Small Histories.

A note from Darien: Micronarratives are short, intense bursts of lyric storytelling and evocative writing, usually three hundred words or less. You can use micronarratives in a number of ways: as a caption to a photograph or piece of artwork, as backstory for a character you're struggling with, gathered into a collection of poems or essays, or simply as a single piece of distilled writing that captures a pivotal moment in your life. Learning how to write micro will help you discern what's most essential in a piece of writing, and what feels most urgent or relevant to you. It's also easy to write micro on the go, to help you establish a daily writing practice, and to easily build a small body of work.

OPENING LINES

What would be the first line of a poem or essay about your family history (by blood or by choice or by inspiration) or your artistic lineage?

Once you have your first line, finish your poem, or aim to write your essay in three hundred words or less.

What are your connections to this person—the emotional truth? That's what we are going for here, a small revealing of yourself or somebody in your life, real or imagined, or an intense moment that may have changed you or triggered a significant or pivotal moment.

As with all prompts, follow where it leads and don't worry if you stray or go down a rabbit hole. Explore whatever shows up on the page.

Exercise

If you wrote a poem, take a few minutes to revise it into an essay of three hundred words or less. If you wrote a micro-essay, take a few minutes to revise it into a poem. Which version do you like better?

Title the piece when you are done.

SAVE THE LAST WORD: A SPACE FOR HEALING

Inspired by Girls Write Now Community Chat guest speaker and Girls Write Now mentor Shanice Anderson Tchamambe.

OPENING LINES

Healing begins by connecting and exploring the stories we tell ourselves. Respond to one of the prompts below:

Mind: What limiting beliefs are holding you back?

Body: Have you picked up unhealthy habit(s) and what are they?

Soul: Which emotions are negatively impacting your life and how?

Exercise

Look back at your response and identify one or two negative words that stand out in your writing.

Write a healing message to yourself.

WRITING OUR WAY TO WELLNESS:
LETTERS BETWEEN WRITERS

OPENING LINES

Take a step back and respond to *one* of the following prompts:

- Everyone comes from something and somewhere. How are you feeling today? Really feeling? How have you been feeling this year?
- Think of a piece of writing—a book, lyrics, a quote, a letter, a speech—that you turn to for inspiration. What about it inspires you?
- This past year has been a roller coaster. Think of your recent life as a theme-park ride. What would it be called? What snack do you (or do you not) eat before getting on?
- Think of your recent life *as a book*. What is the title? What is the genre?
- Think of your recent life as *a TV show*. What would it be called? What is the genre (sitcom, drama, news, late-night variety, or cartoon)?

Exercise

Writing has the power to move, heal, and inspire.

Try writing a letter you can exchange with a friend, family member, classmate, mentor, or mentee. Or write a letter to the past or future you! When writing your letter, think about some challenges you have experienced or are experiencing. How did you get through them? Write from your own perspective. Your life experience can help someone else make sense of the world.

Choose a subject for your letter, such as:

- A discovery you made this past year about yourself or the world
- A battle you've overcome (large or small) and the strength you gained from it

- Traditions from your life: What makes them unique or special? Is there a recipe from your family or friends you grew up with that brings you comfort or sparks joy?
- A recipe for wellness
- A recipe for success

—Girls Write Now curriculum exercises compiled and curated by Director of Curriculum & Engagement Erica Silberman and Special Initiatives Assistant and Teaching Artist Spencer George

ABOUT GIRLS WRITE NOW

For twenty-three years, Girls Write Now has been a nationally respected leader in arts education as the first writing and mentoring organization for girls and gender-expansive youth of color. Built on the pillars of writing, mentoring, equity, and wellness, Girls Write Now breaks down the barriers of gender, race, age, and poverty, preparing young adults to be skilled communicators and competitive candidates, amplifying diverse voices, and creating a pipeline into the schools and industries most in need of their talents.

Girls Write Now matches underserved teens—over 90 percent of color, 90 percent high need, 75 percent immigrant or first generation, and 25 percent LGBTQ/gender nonconforming—with professional writers and digital media makers as their personal mentors. Mentees' multi-genre, multimedia work is published in outlets including *Teen Vogue*, *LitHub*, and *The New York Times*, is performed at Lincoln Center and the United Nations, and wins hundreds of writing awards.

Girls Write Now ranks as one of the top programs nationwide for outstanding performance driving social-emotional growth for youth, and 100 percent of seniors are accepted to college—equipped with confidence, portfolios, and lifelong bonds.

Girls Write Now has been distinguished three times by the White House as one of the nation's top youth programs, twice by the Nonprofit Excellence Awards as one of New York's top ten nonprofits, by NBC-Universal's 21st Century Solutions for Social Innovation, by Youth INC for Youth Innovation, and as a DVF People's Voice nominee. Reaching more than thirty thousand youth, Girls Write Now is a founding partner of the STARS Citywide Girls Initiative.

With features in *People*, *Newsweek*, *Bustle*, *LitHub*, and more, Girls Write Now's annual anthology has received numerous awards and recognitions.

GIRLS WRITE NOW 2021

TEAM

Andrea Ambam, *Community Coordinator*

Elizabeth Baribeau, *Senior Grant Writer*

Ariah Dow, *Community Manager*

Spencer George, *Special Initiatives Assistant*

Kelsey LePage, *Development & Operations Associate*

Molly MacDermot, *Director of Special Initiatives*

Natalie McGuire, *Controller*

Tatiana Mena Ramos, *Fellow*

Teresa Mettela, *Intern*

Maya Nussbaum, *Founder & Executive Director*

Lisbett Rodriguez, *Community Coordinator*

Erica Silberman, *Director of Curriculum & Engagement*

Richelle Szypulski, *Public Events & Content Manager*

BOARD OF DIRECTORS

Ellen Archer, *Board Chair*

Cate Ambrose

Judith Curr

Bruce Morrow

Maya Nussbaum

Mustafa Topiwalla

HONORARY BOARD

Cazzie David

Abbi Jacobson

Tayari Jones

Rupi Kaur

Emma Straub

Cleo Wade

TEACHING ARTISTS & SPEAKERS

Olivia Abtahi

Esme Addison

Raquel Almazan
Cynthia Amoah
Carolina Audley
Brittany Barker
Natalie Baszile
Brit Bennett
Romaissaa Benzizoune
Dr. Joy Harden Bradford
Mahogany L. Browne
Lindsay Burstedt
Keisha Bush
Marjorie Cader
Sande Chen
Maya Contreras
Brooke David
Naomi G. Davis
Kristy Drutman
Tori Eldridge
Janelle Finch
Jessica Friedman
Priscila Garcia-Jacquier
Lisa Gardner
Megan Giddings
Susan Golomb
Sarah Gruen
Wendi Gu
Natalie Guerrero
Christina Ham
Cheryl Head
Haydil Henriquez
Ruthie Herztberg
Donna Hill
Cate Holohan
Susanna Horng

Kimberly Howe
Darien Hsu Gee
Anna Humphrey
Andrea J. Johnson
Djassi DaCosta
　Johnson
Julia Kardon
Jasmin Kaur
Jisu Kim
Maria Konnikova
Lisa LaBracio
Sammi LaBue
Toasca Lee
Sherese Lee Robinson
Alexandra Levick
Laurie Liss
Jasmine Mans
Bernice L. McFadden
Lynn Melnick
Mia Mercado
Sheena D. Miller
Sepideh Moafi
Andrea Morrison
Therese Nelson
Janice Nimura
Christina Olivares
Nikki Palumbo
Momo Pixel
Andrea Plasko
Angelica Puzio
Tom Rabbitt
Megan Reid
Tracy Sherrod
Jenny Stephens

Shanice Anderson
   Tchamambé
Michele Thomas
Eliza Van Cort
Elizabeth Van Dyke
A. J. Verdelle
Arriel Vinson
Samantha Wekstein

Abby West
Arisa White
Samantha White
Diana Whitney
Britton Williams
Anna J Witiuk
Noelle Yasso
Amy Zhang

HONOREES

Masuma Ahuja
Thembi Banks
Dr. Joy Harden Bradford
Naima Coster
Edwidge Danticat
Abi Daré
Cazzie David
Dominique Fishback
Ashley C. Ford
Hannah Gadsby

Kaitlyn Greenidge
Rupi Kaur
Georgina Lawton
Jenifer Lewis
Laurie Liss
Imbolo Mbue
Lauren Ashley Smith
Solome Tibebu
Cleo Wade

GIRLS WRITE NOW CIRCLE

Honorary Chairs

Ann and Bob Hammer
Abbi Jacobson
Maja Kristin

Susan and Charles Sawyers
James M. and Margaret V.
   Stine
Brent and Ann Wilson

Co-Chairs

Cate Ambrose
Ellen Archer and Jeffrey
   Gracer

Lisa Baumgartner
Amy Berkower

Erin Collier

Judith Curr and Ken
Kennedy

Rebecca Gradinger

Agnes Gund

Kate Levin and Robin
Shapiro

Suzanne Levine

Amy Morrill

Bruce Morrow

Maya Nussbaum and Todd
Pulerwitz

Lynda Pak

Mustafa Topiwalla and
Melissa Connor

Vice Chairs

Marci Alboher and Jay
Goldberg

Rachel Bloom

Rachel Cohen

Catherine Greenman

Hope Pordy and Bob
Osmond

Alina Roytberg

Elaine Stuart-Shah and
Nirav Shah

Lisa and Frank Wohl

Patrons

Nisha Aoyama

Jillian Berman

Daniel Brodnitz

Marie Capasso

Veronica Chambers

Jill Cohen

Deborah Coonts

Brian DeFiore

Melissa Febos

Elizabeth Frankel

Anne B. Fritz

Josh Getzler

Forsyth Harmon

Janice Horowitz

Laurie Liss and Julie
Shigekuni

Molly Meloy and Jeff Fitts

Erica Mui

Caroline Preston

Linda Rose

Liane Roseman

Alanna Schubach and Scott
Kilpatrick

Emma Straub

Gail Stuart

Roni Teson

Suzanne Williams

Members

Christine Ambrose

Mona Anand

Stuart S. Applebaum

Claudia Ballard

Steven Baum

Carolyn Brouillard

Lynn and Seth Cohen

Marya Cohn

Cathy Deckelbaum

Margit Detweiler

Ritik Dholakia

Sarah Edwards

Joan Fleischman

Roswita Fragomeni

Merle Froschl

Carrie Frye

Laura Geringer Bass

Megan Giddings

Keli Goff

Karl Hampe

Courtney Hartman

Peregrine Heard

Claire Karwowski

Robin Keegan

Kelly and Chris Koenig

Megan Kohler Griffin

Lois Kohn-Claar and Gary Claar

Robert and Suzanne Koroshetz

William Koster

Myung Jin Lee

Meghan Louttit

Erica Lubetkin

Natalie Nussbaum

Carol Paik

Christina Prestia

Molly Pulda and Gary Sernovitz

Lilli Ross

Lisa Schwartz

Katy Staples

Samuel Stoloff

Nicole Summer

Charlotte Van Doren

Renée Watson

Anne Weisberg

Paul Weiss, LLP

Crystal Zerrenner

AGENTS OF CHANGE CORPORATE PARTNERS

Visionary

Kickstarter

News Corp

Innovator

Adobe

Amazon Literary
  Partnership

Comcast NBCUniversal

Estée Lauder

HarperCollins

Houghton Mifflin Harcourt

RBC Capital Markets

WarnerMedia

Champion

Bloomberg

GFP Real Estate

Spivak Lipton, LLP

Creator

Europa Editions

Nike

Scholastic, Inc.

Wells Fargo

Supporter

Audible

Forbes

Fresh

Jane Rotrosen Agency

Oracle

Piccolina

Spotify

Sterling Lord Literistic, Inc.

FOUNDATION AND GOVERNMENT SUPPORTERS

$90K-$125K+

New York City Council
  STARS Citywide Girls
  Initiative

New York Community
  Trust

New York State Council on
  the Arts Regional
  Economic Development
  Council

Upswing Fund, seeded by
  Pivotal Ventures, a
  Melinda Gates company

$75K

Ford Foundation

The Pinkerton Foundation

$40K-$50K

Blanchette Hooker
    Rockefeller Fund

Harman Family Foundation

National Endowment for the
    Arts

New York City Department
    of Cultural Affairs

$15K-$25K

Cornelia T. Bailey
    Foundation

Costas Family Foundation

The Rona Jaffe Foundation

Youth INC

$10K

Charles Lawrence Keith &
    Clara S. Miller
    Foundation

The Hyde & Watson
    Foundation

Literary Arts Emergency
    Fund

Malka Fund of Jewish
    Communal Fund

New York State Council on
    the Arts

$5K-$8K

Berger Family Foundation

Blue Hill Road Foundation

French-American Aid for
    Children

JANX Foundation

The Lotos Foundation

National Philanthropic
    Trust

$1K-$3K

Blumenthal and Feasley
    Family Fund

DuBose Family Foundation

Fondation Femme Debut

The W.I.L.D. Foundation

ANTHOLOGY SPONSORS

We are grateful to the countless institutions and individuals who have supported our work through their generous contributions. Visit our website at girlswritenow.org to view the extended list.

Girls Write Now would like to thank Dutton, including Christine Ball, Maya Ziv, Lexy Cassola, Susan Schwartz, Dora Mak, Claire Sullivan, Sabrina Bowers, and Kaitlin Kall for their help producing this year's anthology, and Amazon Literary Partnership, which provided the charitable contribution that made this book possible.